Energy Sources—

The Wealth of the World

This photograph of the solar corona was taken on September 22, 1922, with a camera of 40-foot focal length at Wallal, Australia. (*Lick Observatory.*)

Energy Sources—
The Wealth of the World

EUGENE AYRES
Technical Assistant to the Executive Vice-President
Gulf Research & Development Company

CHARLES A. SCARLOTT
Editor, *Westinghouse Engineer*

FIRST EDITION

McGraw-Hill Book Company, Inc.
New York Toronto London
1952

ENERGY SOURCES—THE WEALTH OF THE WORLD

Library of Congress Catalog Card Number: 51-12558

SECOND PRINTING

THE MAPLE PRESS COMPANY, YORK, PA.

WHY!

On April 12, 1948, the Program Committee of the American Petroleum Institute met to plan the agenda for its fall meeting. Energy sources kept coming up as a topic for discussion. The members were in unanimous agreement that with an energy-costly war behind us a reevaluation of the world's and the nation's energy resources was timely. But the task of such an analysis was recognized as formidable. The question was, "Who would bell the cat?" Considerable discussion brought forth no suggestion of an author who might be willing to undertake to collect the enormous mass of data necessary if the survey were to be a real contribution. Finally Eugene Ayres volunteered: "I'll tackle it." Ayres had long had a general interest in the subject, had spent many years in the petroleum phase of the fuel business, and visualized here an opportunity to widen his knowledge of the subject. Besides the job needed doing.

The result was the very long paper, "Major Sources of Energy," presented to the Institute at its meeting in Chicago, November 9, 1948.

That, Ayres thought, was that. But it wasn't! It seems that people wanted reprints. After three batches of reprints had been run off and 6000 copies sent out, the strain on stenographic talent and the financial drain on an indulgent employer and the American Petroleum Institute indicated that that practice could no longer be followed. Furthermore, the interest manifested and the inquiries suggested the desirability of expanding the text and making it available in book form. The response indicated the fundamental and widespread interest in this subject.

Presentation of this material as a book has given opportunity to include much material of necessity omitted from the original Institute paper. It has allowed the inclusion of more critical analyses of resources, descriptions of many of the energy-conversion processes, enumeration of the chief sources of waste of energy, detailed explanations for the conclusions reached, and the substitution of the latest statistical and interpretative data. Some of the chapters of this book have been based upon articles by Ayres in *Scientific American*, *Nucleonics*, and *Proceedings of the American Petroleum Institute*, and our thanks are extended to these journals for permission to reproduce in part.

A treatise of this sort is obviously an interpretation of a large mass of information from many sources. The bibliography at the end of the book suggests how large. For this painstaking compilation and organizing of pertinent source material the authors are indebted to Mr. Sidney E. Winn.

One major objective in the preparation of this discussion is that the text, although founded on figures, be readable. But to give solidity to such treatment requires a final accounting, down to the "penny" (in so far as available data will allow). Such is included in the Energy Balance Sheet (Chapter 21). For these extremely concentrated nuggets of energy information we bow to Mr. Rolande C. Widgery.

Many persons and firms have made signal contributions of data, suggestions, and criticisms. And—we might add—sympathy. A detailed listing of these would be impossible. But it is only fair that a more than passing nod be given our respective employers—the Gulf Research & Development Company and Westinghouse Electric Corporation. While these two organizations in no way officially sponsor this treatise, their share in it is probably much greater than our managements or our immediate superiors have knowledge.

And while we are in the business of giving thanks we would like to extend some in advance. By this we mean to express our appreciation to those readers who will favor us with comments, constructive criticisms, and—above all—additional data by which the picture of our energy resources can be made both more accurate and complete.

The matter of the world's energy is of more than passing interest. It is not a story that can be concluded. On that April afternoon three years ago the subject was important. But with the probability of long-continued international strain—or worse—and fiercer international competition for energy, the subject can be counted on to command increasing attention from everyone.

THE AUTHORS

PITTSBURGH, PA.
September, 1951

CONTENTS

1

Energy—Our Priceless Heritage

Atomic energy is considered something new—predicted by Einstein, and first publicly realized at Hiroshima. That is not so. Essentially all energy that man has contrived to convert to useful work is of atomic origin. Furthermore, it seems that nearly all future supplies of energy will come—in various ways—from this ultimate source. This is because the sun has been and is the earth's one energy source of any consequence. Our converted energy—whether from fossil coal, crude oil, natural gas, or a waterfall—originated in the sun, where the transmutation of hydrogen to helium is believed to provide energy in the form of radiation, mostly visible, but with minor supplements of infrared and ultraviolet. The only important exception is our own attempt to create energy-releasing nuclear reactions. The sun, in short, resembles a colossal and, fortunately, continuous hydrogen bomb. This accounts for all of our energy except for microscopic amounts that come from radioactive transformations in the earth itself.

The present convenient and economic sources of energy used on a large scale are four in number—three nonrenewable and one renewable. The first group is of ancient arrival from the sun. It comprises petroleum, natural gas, and coal, which are often called "stored sunlight" because they were formed from carbon dioxide and water in living organisms by the influence of solar radiation. Hydroelectric power represents more recent contributions from the sun as it comes from the precipitation on our land areas of the water evaporated (and elevated) by sunlight from the earth surface. Sources of energy less convenient or currently uneconomic are: vegetation that can be burned to produce nearly as much energy as the amount of solar energy absorbed in its growth, or which can be converted to such liquid fuels as gasoline or alcohol with a considerable loss of energy; wind, which is an erratic consequence of solar radiation; and the direct conversion of sunlight into forms of energy that can be controlled, intensified, or stored. No doubt some of these secondary sources of solar energy will become exceedingly important in the rather near future.

Much if not most of the heat of the earth itself is believed to come from the radioactive decay of a few elements. A minuscule portion of this earth heat is being utilized now for power generation. Atomic scientists are beginning to separate the elements from the inert materials with which they are associated in the earth in order that the effects of atomic degradation may be concentrated and controlled. These earthly sources of atomic energy may become important in the more distant future by virtue of nuclear and engineering research.

Possibly the only earth energy that is not of atomic origin is that energy of momentum and heat with which the earth was endowed at the time of its cosmic birth. A little of the energy of rotation appears in the tides of our oceans, and a very little can be, and ultimately will be, harnessed.

The energy available to us is vast; but we require machines, processes, and projects for converting it from the forms in which we find it into useful forms. A host of technologists is working constantly on the problems associated with power production, transmission, and utilization. While technology is progressing with enormous strides the demand for power is accelerating even more rapidly. Under such circumstances it is natural to expect that power research, in its almost numberless ramifications, will be still further intensified.

An enormous mass of data has appeared on the subject. This book is an attempt to bring together a few interesting statistics, and "orders of magnitude," and to point up some of the more obvious problems. More and more we will be required to live on our energy income and be less dependent on our energy principal within the next few decades. All petroleum products could be made (at a price) in almost unlimited quantities for the indefinite future from air and water without depleting any natural resource. All of our present production of gasoline could be made from the forests of the earth, but such dependence on vegetation would be unwise. Such things could be done now without any new knowledge, but some of them will become rapidly more plausible as progress is made in the many pertinent branches of technology. So-called "atomic energy" is unlikely to become important except for the limited uses demanding the highest energy potential or those having special requirements that make the characteristics of a nuclear-power plant attractive.

The energy requirements of the world are of several different kinds. By far the largest single requirement is just to keep people warm. At present this is accomplished for the most part by fuels (solid, liquid, and gaseous), and to a minor extent by electricity, by volcanic steam (in Finland and Iceland), and by solar heating (in Florida and California). In this country, about one-quarter of our fuel production is used for space heating, and in less mechanized countries the fraction is even greater. In China, for example, probably more than nine-tenths of the consumed energy is for heating.

A rapidly growing requirement is for power to drive machines or to conduct industrial processes. Power energy is derived from portable fuels, from transmissible electricity, and from waterfalls. Fuels are used for steam and for internal-combustion engines. Internal combustion and steam are used largely for mechanical power or for the generation of electricity. Electric power is derived from fuels or from waterfalls. These examples are given merely to emphasize the fact that, when we talk about the total energy requirement of this country or of the world, we are grouping together several very different things.

The only way to summate these diverse elements so as to arrive at a figure for total energy requirement is to express all elements in the same terms. Energy balance sheets have been drawn up. One such attempt is included in Chap. 21.

Although mathematical conversion factors are precise and easy to use, actual conversion in a physical sense is beset with uncertainties, losses, economic pitfalls, and complex relationships between widely separated technologies. This point must not be overlooked. To locate a large body of energy is not enough. It must be made accessible and in usable form. For example, the conversion factors for tons of coal, barrels of petroleum, and kilowatts of electricity to horsepower are reasonably definite if we assume 100-percent conversion, average specifications, and interchangeability. But we know that the conversion to power of these energy sources varies all the way from 10 to 95 percent, depending upon the nature of the power plant. We know that much of the energy is used for heating rather than for power. And we know that we cannot use coal to operate a conventional motor car, or petroleum to operate an electric motor, without physical operations through which variable and sizable amounts of energy are lost. The different forms of power are not interchangeable in their major applications. To add them together seems almost like adding foods to fuels merely because each can be expressed in calories.

In spite of these difficulties, if we keep in mind what the total means, there is no reason why we should not express the magnitude of sources of energy in common terms. Chapter 21 shows this total to be around 14 trillion hphr per annum. Also it is well to remember how different the total would be if our economy required the preparation of all of our liquid fuel by the conversion of coal, or if we had no hydroelectric power, or if our requirements of electric power should become a much larger proportion of the total (as it probably will). We shall discuss the effects of taking into account the average efficiencies and load factors of major applications and the peculiar figures on rated horsepower of machines in service. And we shall see what ideas with regard to the future can be gained by a study of the trends of the past.

If we take 14 trillion hphr per annum for the United States, it is reasonable to take a figure of 40 trillion hphr per annum as the present energy requirement of the entire world. (This is in spite of the fact that the United States has only 7 percent of the world's population.) This increment is derived from world estimates on consumption of petroleum, coal, and wood.

With these units of measurement, we may proceed to look at the order of magnitude of our sources of energy. Observe that the unit is a *rate* instead of a quantity. Also, when the measurement is applied to a process that is essentially unrenewable, such as the combustion of fossil fuels or the accelerated nuclear fission of elements, the answer is related to the number of years during which that source could be relied upon if our requirement remained constant and if the present conversion and utilization efficiencies remained unchanged. On the contrary, if the source is relatively continuous, like water power or vegetation, the answer is the rate at which power might be obtained for the almost indefinite future. The two kinds of figures are not comparable.

2

The Last Few Minutes

The earth is believed to be about two billion years old, but it is still young. Most of its life is in the unknown future. The past, also, is largely unknown, but geologists, archeologists, paleontologists, and other scientific specialists have fashioned an outline of the past, which, however shadowy, is full of significance for those who now briefly inhabit the earth.

No matter how accustomed we may become to thinking in terms of geologic time, our intuitive yardstick of time must inevitably be in terms of our own span of life. It is always useful, therefore, to translate the incomprehensible thousands, and hundreds of thousands, and millions of years into measures of more familiar size. So let us personify the earth as a robust man who has just reached maturity. A lot of interesting things have happened to this young man during his early years. But a series of peculiar events begin to take place on his "sixteenth" birthday. He begins to store up an excessive amount of energy. This corresponds to the formation of deposits of coal, petroleum, oil shale, natural gas, and other forms of fossil fuel. The period of accumulation takes about "five years" of the young man's life. During the last "year" of this period there occurs a mysterious transformation corresponding to the complete evolution of man from (perhaps) the rat-sized tarsiers to the present complex Homo sapiens. When he is "twenty-one" these two related events have been completed. Then something happens to use up the excess energy stored during the preceding "five years." This corresponds to the initial stages of our machine age, in which we are burning up our fossil fuels. In the case of the young man the complete dissipation of excess energy requires only "*five minutes*." (You and I are now living in the midst of these "five

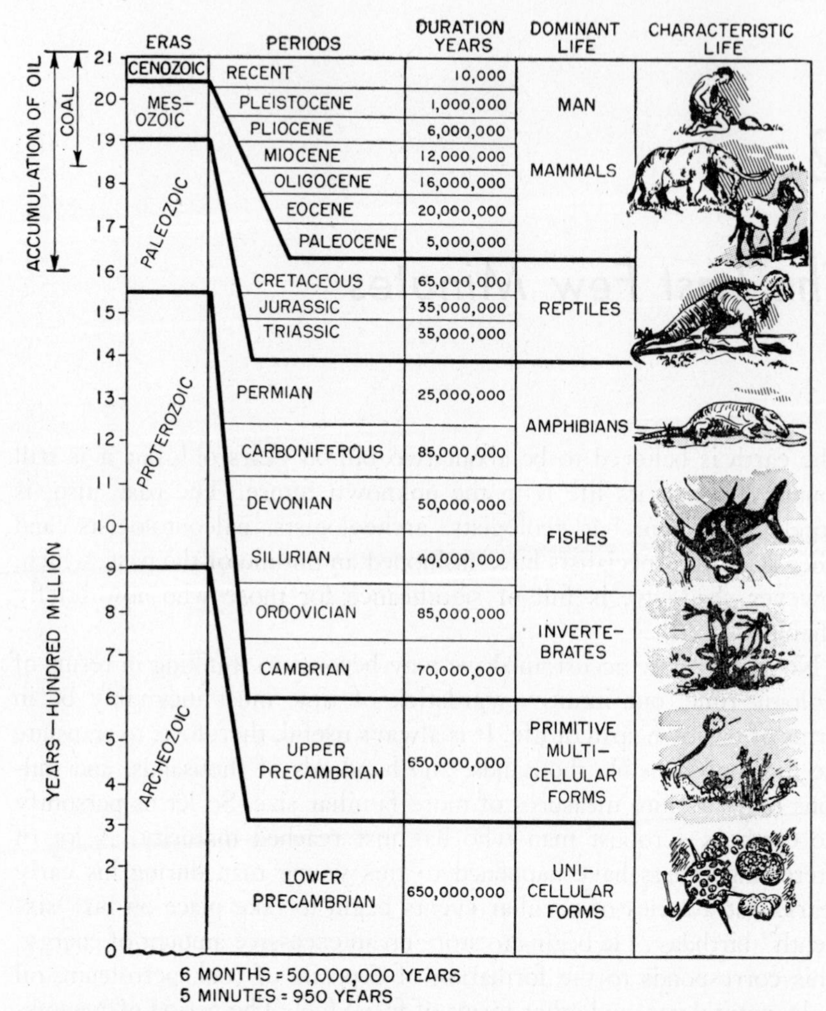

FIG. 1. On a scale in which the earth is now twenty-one years old, a few seconds ago man began to use the stored fossil fuels. These fuels had their beginning when he was but sixteen. (*Adapted from geologic time chart prepared by the Sinclair Oil Company.*)

minutes.") So about the time that the young man reaches his majority, he will be right back where he started, energywise, but through the irreversible process of the evolution of man, there are immense potentialities for the future. The machine age will not end with the exhaustion of fossil fuels. The really significant parts of the machine age are bound to come much later.

After the exciting period through which this young man has passed, who can say what eventful "years" lie ahead before he reaches his "three score and ten." The personification of the earth in this way helps us to understand the time relationships of some of the events that particularly concern us. But now we shall proceed to examine more closely the most recent "few days" of the young man's life and more particularly the last "few minutes." Or, in terms of the age of the earth, the last million years and finally the period of recorded history.

The accumulation of some petroleum deposits began before such prehistoric animals appeared on the earth. The Tyrannosaurus, shown on the right, was carnivorous. (*Sinclair Refining Co.*)

With all the changes that have taken place on the earth during the past million years, there is one thing that has been unchanging. This is the fact of man's dependence upon the sun. Through the only partially understood process of photosynthesis—the sunlight-absorbing reaction between the carbon dioxide and the water of the atmosphere to generate oxygen and the substance of plant growth—in the past as now, man has been provided with his food to eat and his oxygen to breathe, vitamins for health, and clothing and materials of construction for protection. In addition the sunshine has provided directly a substantial part of what he has required of warmth for comfort. The only difference between "then" and "now" is that we have become even more dependent upon the sun, for now most of our power has an indirect solar origin. Man has not been altogether satisfied with all these direct benefactions. Even our "near-human" ancestors who populated the Eurasian continent a million years ago found a way to concentrate and control the generous supply of solar energy by means of fire. The combustion of fuel is, of course, merely the liberation of the solar energy which was stored in the fuel during the period of growth.

Before man had learned to make use of cotton, linen, and wool—products of photosynthesis—he used vegetable fibers of cruder form and the skins of animals. He built habitations of wood, and he burned wood to provide warmth. Fire was essential to survival particularly during the long glacial periods. He used fire also to roast his food, and, by enlarging the diet, this had an important bearing on the evolution to a more complex form of life. But at that time heat for cooking was the only process-energy required for his primitive way of life. He depended upon his own muscles for power. In most of the populated areas of the earth wood was abundant and there were no inhibitions against extravagance; the population was small and the total consumption of energy materials must have been negligible compared with the supply.

As his pattern of living became more complex and his numbers multiplied, man's energy demands gradually approached equality with the renewable supply of wood. In a few cases the demand finally exceeded the known supply. This was conspicuous in the case of the Eskimos, who were left behind in the arctic regions when men trekked from the cradle of civilization in Eurasia over the Bering Straits to America about twenty thousand years ago. The Eskimos had to depend largely upon fish oil for fuel and probably used this scant commodity for space heating (as they do today) more efficiently than our best modern space-heating installations. The various American Indian races were founded at this time. Later some of these races were to use wood with disastrous extravagance.

Since our information about prehistoric times is limited by archeological and paleontological research, to construct any sort of picture of the period before 6000 B.C. it is necessary to make a liberal use of imagination and to interpret many apparently unrelated clues. The able scholars who have been interested in the anthropological implications of energy supplies have done an outstanding job of detective work. These disciplines are in their infancy. As time goes on we may expect a wealth of new information. But even now we may safely assume that during the past twenty thousand years in various parts of the earth man found it desirable to use fuel for an increasing number of purposes. Several important technologies are of prehistoric origin. No one can say how long ago the combustion of fuel was applied to the preparation of fertilizer and of durable materials of construction, the recovery of metals from their ores, and the manufacture of tools, utensils, and other artifacts. It seems that even a half million years ago the evolution of man depended more upon the stage of his technology than upon anything else. And while nearly all the peoples of the earth in those early years had an abundance of fuel and were familiar with the control of fire, they naturally showed various degrees of ingenuity in the utilization of heat.

There is evidence that burnt brick was made and used as early as 10 000 B.C. This, in itself, constituted a miniature fuel revolution. Brick was to provide a superior substitute for wood for the construction of buildings, but more wood was required to burn the brick than the brick displaced as a material of construction. The less efficient modern brick kilns (burning gas or oil) require the expenditure of about 2 million Btu per cubic foot of burnt brick. The more efficient semicontinuous kilns require only about 100 000 Btu. The average for the United States in 1947 was about 750 000 Btu. The ancient kilns are not likely to have been more efficient than modern ones. It must, therefore, have required at least 150 cubic feet of wood (as fuel) to make 1 cubic foot of burnt brick. The ancient peoples took advantage of the superior strength of brick to build more massive structures. Thus the substitution of brick multiplied the consumption of wood for construction purposes manyfold wherever brick was used, except, of course, to the extent that the brick kilns may have been fired with fossil fuels instead of wood.

This should not be regarded as extravagance because there was (and is) a distinct economic justification for brick. But as the peoples of the earth became "agriculturalists" instead of "gatherers" of food, a truly extravagant waste of fuel emerged. In river valleys the fertility of the cultivated fields was maintained by periodic flooding. But in tropical countries with too heavy rainfall the fertility of the land was low. Adequate crops could not be grown without enrichment of the soil. Ancient peoples, such as the Mayas, discovered that this enrichment could be provided by wood ashes, and they invented the "slash-and-burn" method of agriculture. When corn was planted in a newly burned-over area, the yield was good for the first season, moderate for the second, and poor for the third. As a result, the destruction of the forest land was progressive and the waste of wood was stupendous. This procedure has persisted up to the present time in many parts of the world; the claim has been made that even now in certain regions there is no economically acceptable substitute. Thoreau has described the practice of this sort of agriculture near Concord, Mass., around 1850. It would be interesting to know what proportion of the world's agriculture today is maintained by "slash-and-burn." Judging from modern data it probably required about 200 acres of forest land to maintain one person. The populations would increase to the limit of accessible forest land, and then, finally, the growth of vegetation would fall behind demand, crops would fail, and cultures would vanish from the earth. The energy requirements per capita in such cases doubtless exceeded by manyfold the energy requirements per capita today in highly industrialized communities.

Lighting, which requires a substantial proportion of the energy utilized today, was a negligible factor in prehistoric times. However, one of man's earliest dissatisfactions with the world about him was the length of the day, and lightmaking was one of man's first attempts to alter his environment.

Probably the first lamp was a burning stick snatched from a wood fire. The wood torch was long the only artificial light, although it was soon learned that the pine knot burned much better and longer than an ordinary stick. Somewhere ahead of all records it was discovered that sticks on which animal fats had been spilled made excellent torches. This set the stage for the candle. Sticks of wood were purposely soaked in animal fat after the hunt and held or mounted as lights. The next step came with the invention of the rush candle. A large rush would be stripped of most of the outer sheath, leaving one segment to support the pith, which would be repeatedly dipped in melted animal fat. A well-made rush candle two or three feet long would burn for an hour. There have been many versions of these crude candles. Even now some Malay islanders make light by igniting bundles of palm leaves dipped in resinous gums. The candle thus began a long period of development that will be touched upon in later paragraphs.

Man Turns to Fossil Fuels

From 6000 B.C. the findings of archeology are supplemented by ancient literature, from which it is necessary to filter out bits of reality from legend. Unfortunately, various ancient cultures differed widely in their historians. For example, we know too little of China and India and the Americas of those early days. We know more about Egypt and still more about the Near and Middle East, where it happens that most of our petroleum is found today—Irak, Iran, Arabia, and Kuwait. This is Biblical territory and historical references are abundant. It is also dry territory, where archeological exploration can be especially fruitful.

Scattered over this country between the Nile and Indus rivers there were (and still are) various deposits of asphalt, seepages of crude

Engraving on ancient coins shows the flaring of natural gas at Baku thousands of years before the birth of Christ. (*Bettmann Archive.*)

petroleum, and flares of natural gas. There are evidences of similar ancient showings of fossil fuels in many other parts of the earth—particularly where vast underground stores of petroleum have been subsequently discovered. As far as we know, the first fossil material to be used as a fuel was asphalt, which was apparently an article of commerce about 6000 B.C. About that time the Sumerians, who are said to have been using asphalt from a deposit near Ararat, came to the country between the Euphrates and Tigris rivers—the supposed site of the

Garden of Eden. Here they found similar deposits, which they mined. The asphalt or pitch was first used primarily for its plastic and waterproofing properties and became an important commodity.

It is not known to what extent the fossil fuels were used in these very early days as fuel, but there may be some significance in the fact that burnt brick was manufactured more abundantly at that time in areas where fossil fuels were accessible than in areas where such fuels were unknown. Terra-cotta vessels of the Near East (requiring hot fires) date back to 5000 B.C. Iron and various other metals cannot be produced from their ores without fuel. Wood charcoal (or its equivalent) was required then as now not only to produce the heat but also to react with the ore to free the metal. Evidences of a copper age (between stone and bronze) at about 4000 B.C. have been found only in places where fossil fuels were known and used. The Chaldeans then had already become skillful metalworkers. Silver, gold, copper, tin, lead, and iron were known to them.

Another important use of process fuel appeared before 3000 B.C. (about "fifteen minutes" ago). This was the calcining of limestone to make lime. The modern Mayan Indians burn ten times as much wood as the quantity of limestone to be calcined. The ancient Mayas, the Egyptians, and the Babylonians must have been even more extravagant. Before 3000 B.C. lime was produced in relative abundance. Lime was used not only to make mortar but also lime cement which covered many ancient buildings and was employed for paving.

Before 3000 B.C. flares of natural gas (probably ignited by lightning) were focal points for temples of worship. These flares, which burned for centuries, are illustrated on ancient coins. Apparently it was not until somewhat later that gas was used as an industrial or domestic fuel.

About 3000 B.C. the Egyptians began the construction of the pyramids and the sphinx, for which asphalt was one of the materials employed. Egypt imported much of its asphalt from the Near East countries, and, because asphalt was relatively expensive to them, probably used wood charcoal for their extensive metallurgical operations. This importation of asphalt was carried on for thousands of years.

By 3000 B.C. man was manufacturing glazed and enameled pottery, porcelain, and glass. The beautiful turquoise-blue cupriferous glaze of the Persians at this time has never been surpassed. All of these operations require hot fires and all seem to have been most highly developed in fossil-fuel areas.

The lighting in these early days was done largely with lamps provided with liquid fuels. Archeological finds all over the world have produced a great variety of lamps beginning with simple bowls made from burnt clay, terra cotta, hollowed stone, shells, or even human skulls. These employed some form of wick dipping into an oil reservoir. Some fuels for early lamps were of animal origin—fish, fowl, and mammals—but most of it was vegetable—from nuts, seeds, cocoanuts, olives, peanuts, etc.

The time of the Babylonian Empire (from 2500 to 538 B.C.) was the first world-wide "fossil-fuel age." Babylonia was in what is now known as Irak. Burnt brick was commonly used for the construction of buildings, walls, bridges, and tunnels. The mortar contained not only lime but asphalt, and asphalt was also used as a waterproofing agent. The walls of Jericho (2500 B.C) and of Babylon itself were made in this way, and also Solomon's Temple and the Tower of Babel. Nebuchadnezzar built roads of flat stones set in asphalt—an invention that was not used again until the nineteenth century A.D. Another invention of the Babylonians, which was lost until the nineteenth century, was the treatment of wooden piles with asphalt to protect them against decay when used for the support of buildings over water or in swampy terrain. These things were done with pure bitumen, which was recovered from asphalt by a crude refining operation. Max W. Ball estimates that in 2000 B.C. this bitumen sold for something like the modern equivalent of $30 a ton, which happens to be about the price of good paving asphalt today.

In Babylonia, asphalt and crude petroleum were used as fuels in preference to wood. Asphalt was preferred to crude petroleum because the latter is too easily inflammable. Asphalt was available in more than adequate quantities for domestic and export trade, and it was easily manageable. It could be burned but was not volatile. It required only moderate labor for production.

Coal was quite a different matter. Mining was a laborious task which could be undertaken only if the rewards were great, as in the case of the Egyptian emerald mine, which was operated for two thousand years. Outcroppings of coal were undoubtedly in existence in many parts of the earth, but as far as we know it was mined and used in this first fossil-fuel age only by the patient Chinese (1100 B.C). Before this time the Chinese had made enormous technological progress. They had produced niter, borax, alum, corrosive sublimate, arsenic, mercury, vegetable and essential oils, paper, and sugar. They were engaged in printing. They were making gunpowder. Many of these processes require fuel. Wood was doubtless their mainstay but they also used coal and natural gas.

Before 1000 B.C. the Chinese were deliberately drilling wells to produce natural gas for space heating, for lighting (apparently the first use of gas for light), and for the manufacture of articles of commerce. The gas was transported for considerable distances in bamboo pipe lines. The churn-drilling process by the spring-pole method used by the Chinese was still standard practice up to the time Drake drilled his famous well in Pennsylvania in the nineteenth century A.D. The ancient Chinese drilled many wells. The deepest is said to have been about 3000 feet.

While the Chinese were using natural gas for lighting, the Phoenicians are believed to have been using the first candles made of some sort of wax. These were luxuries for the wealthy. At the same time the Phoenicians were using the energy of the wind to propel their sailing vessels.

This first "fossil-fuel era" is distinguished by the fact that fossil fuel for the first time played a significant part in supplying energy, but wood, after all, was much more important. In India, for example, the demand for fuel was so great in those early years that she denuded her forests and made the country into desert. In recent centuries the principal fuel has been the dried dung of domestic animals, which has resulted in the loss of fertility in the soil. She has great deposits of coal, but this was not known until relatively modern times. China also has used too much of her wood and has suffered accordingly. This is in spite of the fact that the legitimate per capita demand for fuel in both India and China has been minor compared with industrial communities.

Many parts of the world came near to disaster as the forests were destroyed in later centuries. In a sense it was fortunate that a series of apparently unrelated events served to slow down technological progress to a snail's pace. In the case of Babylon it was in 538 B.C., when Cyrus conquered Belshazzar. This was the occasion of the celebrated handwriting on the wall, and signified the end of the Babylonian Empire and the beginning of a long era of industrial stagnation. In China the end of industrial progress was coincident with the crystallization of Confucianist philosophy. In India the caste system stifled progress for centuries because it called for the withdrawal of the intellectual community from active participation in the crafts. Greek industrial progress ended in the fourth century B.C., when Alexander the Great completed his conquest of the Persian Empire. The Greeks had no word for *scientists* but called them *philosophers*. The philosophers scorned those who attempted to turn technical theory to practical advantage. It is strange that these diverse and widely separated obstacles to technological progress should have occurred so close together in the long

Animal power was used thousands of years ago by the Egyptians to grind corn. (*Bettmann Archive.*)

period of recorded history. But if these obstacles had not existed the world might have become an eroded desert. For the demand for fuel was far outstripping the technology of fossil-fuel procurement, and two thousand years were to elapse before man could conceive of ways to solve the energy problem without wood fuel.

While 500 B.C. may be considered the beginning of a long period of industrial stagnation, it marks, paradoxically, the beginning of a slow germination of abstract ideas that were to culminate in modern science. The Greeks, in particular, were laying the foundation for industrial progress that was to come more than two thousand years later.

While progress slowed down after these events it did not entirely stop. Fuel continued to be increasingly important to generate heat for comfort and for industrial processes, but it was not to be used for power until many centuries after the birth of Christ. And yet the demand for power energy was growing steadily with the complexity of social organization. In the absence of the machine, power had to come from muscle. Man could no longer depend upon his own strength to accomplish the things that he felt must be done. He solved the problem by domesticating the ox, horse, camel, and yak, and then by the institution

Wind power and slave labor were used to operate Phoenician merchant galleys on the Red Sea in the seventh century B.C. (*Bettmann Archive.*)

of slavery. No census figures are available for the ancient states, but it is clear that there was a high ratio of slaves to free men—of men who supplied power energy to men who enjoyed the fruits of such labor. Slavery was an inevitable partner of progress until the machine could take over. Power was needed for the construction of housing and roads, for agriculture, for mining, for industry, and for the acquisition of fuel. States like Babylon and Egypt, when at the peak of their political power, had an almost unlimited supply of slave labor. The gas wells of China must have demanded incredible patience and manual effort. One of the spoils of ancient warfare was power energy in the form of subject peoples, just as some modern wars are fought to acquire power energy in the form of fuels to feed machines.

The Greek and Roman civilizations added little of importance to fuel technology. The Greek republic, as described by Aristotle, was a so-called "democracy" in which the few enjoyed the labors of the

Until a recent earthquake the island of Cos in the archipelago of the Dodecanese (Greece) was dotted with ancient windmills. Only one has survived. (*Bettmann Archive.*)

many, and the Roman Empire was characterized by the same abundance of human power energy. It is of interest to note, however, that prior to 640 B.C. there was the beginning of attempts to utilize solar energy by optical concentration. Concave mirrors of bronze lined with silver foil were used to focus the rays of the sun. Later the Romans employed this device at times to reignite their "eternal fire." The same sort of thing is being studied by engineers today with the idea of using solar energy as a primary source of power.

There may be some significance in the fact that the Romans installed waterwheels for power. Except for the use of wind for propelling ships, this is the first historical example of power derived from anything except muscle. The levers, which had been used for several thousand years by the Egyptians, were merely instruments for the concentration of muscular effort. The Romans had many slaves but they may have sensed the social advantage of inanimate power. Or perhaps the incentive was purely economic. In any case this was a small beginning of the movement that was to culminate in the machine age.

The Mayas had no metallurgy but in various other ways wood was essential to them, and when this resource was finally exhausted through extravagance in their areas of living, the empire came to an abrupt end. And yet the Mayan contemporaries of the Romans developed in some ways a superior civilization. They have been acclaimed as the most brilliant people of their age not only for their material achievements but also for abstract intellectual accomplishments. For example, they developed man's first positional arithmetical system with the concept of zero. It is a pity that such a people should have been lost to posterity for the lack of a continuing supply of energy. Unlike the people in certain other parts of the world they were not endowed with natural fertilization of the land, they had no accessible supplies of fossil fuels, and their technology did not keep pace with their needs.

There were some noteworthy developments during the few centuries before the birth of Christ. In 400 B.C. the first coal outside of China for industrial purposes was produced near Mount Olympus in Greece. (This may have been gilsonite rather than coal.) In the same year, according to Herodotus, an oil well was completed on the island of Zante in the Ionian Sea. (There are still bituminous wells and oil springs on Zante.) According to Pliny, this oil was distilled by stretching a hide over a cauldron of boiling oil and wringing out the condensed liquid. The condensate was used as a fuel for lamps—the first recorded substitution of petroleum for vegetable and animal oils for lighting. But it appears that the attitude of man during this period was one of curiosity and interest rather than of economic utilization.

It is told that Alexander the Great, before 300 B.C., when traveling through Mesopotamia, was amazed when the "barbarians" poured liquid naphtha in the street leading to his quarters and ignited it. The flames promptly ran the whole length of the street. The Dead Sea was the source of much of the ancient asphalt. At one time Mark Antony conquered the Dead Sea area and gave it to Cleopatra for its asphalt, but Cleopatra is said to have been unimpressed. About 200 B.C. the Carthaginian general Hannibal used asphalt in compounding the so-called "Greek fire." From then on petroleum was of some military importance. Well before the birth of Christ oil was used by sailors to

In Athanasius Kircher's travel book on China (1677), he expressed his amazement at the use of burning wells for cooking. (*Bettmann Archive.*)

calm "troubled waters," and the Greeks are said to have destroyed a hostile Scythian fleet by pouring oil on the sea and igniting it.

Affairs deteriorated rapidly in the Near East after 500 B.C. The Persian successors to the Babylonians abandoned the use of asphalt in their mortars, and finally abandoned lime. The final step of retrogression was to use unburnt brick. And all this was in spite of an abundance of fuel and a knowledge of its use. This world-wide period of technological apathy continued for centuries after the birth of Christ. Engineering languished. Practical methods of distillation were invented in the second century A.D., but were not applied to petroleum until four hundred years later. Tallow candles came about the second century A.D. But somewhat before A.D. 1000 the Arabs had made important intellectual contributions to culture and the Burmese to fuel engineering.

The Arabs seem to have been uninterested in fuels, but they proceeded to develop the use of the waterwheel and the windmill. These were, in fact, the primary sources of power in Persia, Afghanistan, and the Near East—areas which are known today to be particularly rich in petroleum reserves, and in which naturally outcropping petroleum had been used extensively a thousand years before.

The Burmese by A.D. 1000 were drilling primitive wells and producing commercial quantities of petroleum, which were to grow until, about a thousand years later, Burma was to become the world's principal source of oil. (In 1950 Burmese oil was being shipped to the West Coast of the United States.) Similar hand-dug wells were being drilled near Oil Creek, Pa., by a mysterious race of Indians who preceded the Algonquins. Nearly two thousand years later the United States was to become the world's principal source of oil.

In Central and South America the Indians used petroleum long before the Spaniards conquered them. There were asphalt seepages in Mexico used by the Toltecs (predecessors of the Aztecs), and there were "fountains of pitch" in Peru. The Digger tribes of California, who had forgotten how to make fire, used asphalt for a variety of purposes.

For the next eight hundred years the growth of petroleum production was negligible. Coal resources were developed somewhat more rapidly. Coal had been rather widely used in Britain at the time of the Roman conquest. Production grew slowly, but it was not until the thirteenth century (about "four minutes" ago) that British trade in coal became really active. Strangely, it was in the same century, two hundred years before Columbus came to America, that coal became an important natural resource for the Hopi Indians in what is now Arizona. Their production and use per capita was astonishingly high considering the primitive character of their mining and the simplicity of their social organization. There must have been a local shortage of wood in that region. In the same century Marco Polo witnessed a producing oil well at Baku. Nothing had changed very much there in a thousand years.

In Britain and on the continent of Europe the promising new coal industry was strangled at the outset by ignorance and prejudice. In 1306 King Edward I made it a capital offense to burn coal because it had been found that the gases of combustion were poisonous. At least one man was executed for burning coal. The penalties were finally abolished but the prejudice remained. As late as the seventeenth century many cities objected to the use of coal (preferring wood), somewhat paralleling the "smoke-control" movements of modern times. In France smiths were fined if they were caught using coal without a license.

In spite of commercial bans technologists made some progress. The coking of coal was a special subject for study. In 1587, when Mary Queen of Scots was beheaded by Queen Elizabeth, coke was coming into use for house heating, and in 1620, when the Pilgrims made their historic voyage on the Mayflower, British patent 15 was issued for the coking of coal.

In the meantime, the demand for fuel, which had remained nearly dormant for centuries, was again looking up—not only to warm the growing population but to support the operation of blast furnaces to make iron. And, of course, there was a steady increase in many other industrial and military directions where fuel was required. In the early part of the seventeenth century the demand of the British navy for wood for space heating and cooking was so great that industries that had used wood for centuries were forced to coal. (An interesting by-product of this circumstance was that the glass industry with hotter coal fires was able for the first time to work with the more refractory flint glass.) This renewed demand was not serious for parts of the earth that were thinly populated (like the Americas) or industrially backward (like much of Europe and Asia). However, the forests of England were almost destroyed by the prolific use of wood fuel. The discovery that coke could be substituted for charcoal for blast-furnace operation came just in time to prevent the reduction of England and parts of France to barren desert. By 1709 the commercial use of coke for this purpose was firmly established, and coal itself was tolerated in spite of its smoke and odor. But the power energy required for the mining of coal was still the muscle of men and the transportation of coal was still accomplished by the muscle of horses.

When coke is made from coal there are two major by-products—coal tar and gas. The former was described in British patent 214 in 1681, and the illuminating value of coal gas was demonstrated in Ireland in 1691. However, a full century was to pass before either of these products achieved commercial importance. The reason for this delay was that man had not yet learned how to generate power from fuel to use in the procurement and transportation of fuel. The substantial growth of fossil-fuel production had to wait until the steam engine initiated the industrial revolution.

While these interesting things were happening to coal technology, equally interesting and scarcely less important things were happening in other directions. An "oil spring" was discovered in 1627 near Cuba, N.Y. An oil well was completed at Modena, Italy, in 1640 which flowed moderately for nearly two hundred years. (Kerosene from this oil was used to light the streets of Genoa and Parma in 1803.) In 1650 Roumanian oil production was started. In 1692, the Spaniards were granting oil concessions in Peru. And in 1694 oil was manufactured in Britain by the retorting of oil shale and cannel coal. In these early days the advantages of liquid and gaseous fuels were already beginning to be recognized. Coal was valued first for its use directly as fuel; later for its coke; and still later for its tar (regarded at first simply as a liquid fuel) and for its gas. Oil shale contained too much inorganic matter to be useful as a fuel, but it could, and finally did, form a starting point for the manufacture of liquid fuel.

In 1750, while Roumanian oil was being used for lighting and lubrication, oil production was started in Galicia, and Galician kerosene lighted the streets of Prague about seventy years later. It was about this time that the whaling industry introduced two new fuels—spermaceti, a fatty substance that provided an excellent candle, and sperm oil, which proved to be an excellent fuel for lamps. Spermaceti became the international measure of light. The world standard light source until recently was a candle burning 120 grams of spermaceti per hour. These two fuels led to the fabulous whaling industry, which prospered for about a hundred years—until wax and kerosene from fossil fuels became sufficiently available and barely averted the extinction of the whale.

The first commercial mining of bituminous coal in North America (after the Hopi Indians) was in Virginia in 1730. This was sixty years before the commercialization of the steam engine and was, therefore, necessarily on a small scale.

Curiously, in several thousand years of use the oil-burning lamp had improved but little. It appeared in different forms, but designers were absorbed with making lamps objects of art or improving their convenience—not with increasing their light productivity. Through the centuries, down to two hundred years ago, lamp flames were feeble, flickering, smoky, and vile as to odor. The break came in 1784 when

Argand introduced the lamp chimney, truly a great invention. Then in 1792 William Murdoch fathered coal-gas lighting when he used it to produce a feeble glow in workshops in Cornwall. In the same year gas was used to light a foundry in Soho.

The Machine Age Begins

James Watt in England began his experiments with the steam engine in 1760 but commercial realization came about 1790 (less than "one minute" ago)—and this is regarded as the beginning of the industrial revolution. The mutual dependence of fuel and machine is not always correctly explained. It is true that the development of machinery created a demand for fuel, but it is even more significant that the need for more fuel created a demand for machinery. The early machines used wood and charcoal as fuel. Many years elapsed before the application of machine power to fuel procurement could bring production of fossil fuels up to a high enough point to displace wood.

The first steam locomotive was built in 1803. It was built for the specific purpose of transporting fuel. The first practical steam engines were used in the mining of coal, and, soon after, machine power gave the first real improvement in oil-well drilling since the days of the ancient Chinese.

With machine power it was possible to produce fuel and to transport it at an enormously accelerated rate. By 1812, the year of Napoleon's retreat from Moscow, more than 120 miles of coal-gas pipe line had been laid in London. London Bridge was gas-lighted in 1813, Westminster Abbey in 1814, and by 1817 some 300 000 cubic feet of coal gas was being produced daily in London. This was sufficient to operate 76 000 Argand burners of 6 candle power each.

In the New World the fuel industry was then somewhat backward. During 1814 only 22 tons of anthracite coal were mined. This was not much more than the average annual production of the handful of Hopi Indians in the thirteenth century. During 1820 only 300 tons of bituminous coal were mined. (These happen to be our earliest production records.) Twenty years later each grade of coal had passed the million-ton mark, and now combined production is at the rate of around half a billion tons per annum.

But we are ahead of our story.

In 1815 (the battle of Waterloo)—about 120 years after the initial invention of the process—commercial oil-shale retorting was started in New Brunswick, Canada. There was then a definite demand in the United States for liquid fuel, and shale oil was made to satisfy this demand. We had almost no petroleum production and only a little natural gas. However, in 1821 houses in Fredonia, N.Y., were heated with natural gas—a small beginning of the immense use of natural gas today. Between 1850 and 1860 more than 50 commercial plants came into operation in the eastern United States to distill oil from shale imported from Canada and from cannel coal imported from Scotland.

In the meantime, oil-well drilling methods were being improved. Wells were being drilled here and there (usually for the purpose of producing brine), and some petroleum was being produced. In 1829 a well in Kentucky was brought in at a thousand barrels a day. In 1845 a petroleum lubricant was being manufactured at Tarentum, Pa., for use in a Pittsburgh factory, and a few years later Tarentum kerosene was sold for use in lamps. The small petroleum production was supplemented by shale oil. The Lucesco shale-oil plant near Pittsburgh could turn out about a thousand barrels a day, which it sold for thirty to forty dollars a barrel.

For a century whale oil had been the principal oil for lamps. By 1850 the whale population had declined dangerously, rapeseed oil was used for a time as a substitute, and finally kerosene from petroleum and from shale oil became sufficiently abundant.

The first large-scale use of natural gas occurred in Pittsburgh in 1884. The gas was piped from the Murraysville field, about fourteen miles away, and was used both for lighting and for industrial heat. Then in 1886 Karl Auer von Welsbach produced his famous mantles consisting of fabric impregnated with cerium, thorium, or magnesium. The Welsbach mantle tripled the light output of both kerosene lamps and gas burners and had the effect of increasing the demand for lighting. Instead of cutting the consumption of fuel to a third, the Welsbach mantle, by providing more adequate light, increased the demand for fuel manyfold.

However, it was about 1880 that the shadow of the electric industry began to fall across the liquid- and gas-lighting applications. The electric industry was founded to provide light. Motors came later—did not really arrive until the introduction of the polyphase system toward the end of the century. Again, electric lighting, by providing more light, created an increased demand for light until about a third of the electric power produced in the United States in 1950 was consumed by lamps. Whale oil had lasted a century; kerosene lasted only a half century (as a principal light source); who can predict the successor to the electric current?

The temporary exhaustion of forest land during the early part of the nineteenth century, when there was a premature drift toward industrialism, resulted in major shifts of population. Thriving communities dependent upon manufacturing operations suddenly found themselves without fuel for manufacture or for the homes of the people. There were no more trees to be cut down near at hand, transportation had not developed to the point where wood could be brought in from distant points, and the production of coal and oil was still on a tiny scale. Cape Cod is an interesting example. At one time Cape Cod was heavily forested. A dozen important industries flourished there in 1800. By 1900 the forests had virtually disappeared, factories were shut down, and people migrated to the places where they could find employment. Towns of 12 000 became villages of 1000 or less. In 1951 the population of the Cape is again growing but is well below the 1800 figure. The land is again becoming forested because wood is not used for manufacture and is used for only about one-half of the space heating, but there is not yet as much timber as in 1800.

The stage of market demand in 1859 was all set for the Drake well, which deserves mention not because it was a technical or economic achievement but because it was drilled at a critical time (about "thirty seconds" ago). It has been said that Drake did not make use of the advances in the drilling art that had been made since 1800, and that the Chinese of 1000 B.C. could have done quite as well. The Chinese drilled deep wells through hard formations. The Drake well was shallow and the earth was soft. But the Drake well has been accepted as a symbol. From then on liquid fuel was produced in adequate quantity. The first petroleum era, which lasted nearly two thousand years, was to be overwhelmed by the second (and last) petroleum era, which started less than a hundred years ago.

During this century technological advancement in the recovery and transportation of coal, petroleum, and natural gas has been phenomenal. In spite of the exponentially rising curve of demand, fuel production has kept pace. It will probably continue to keep pace for a century or perhaps for even two centuries, but then we shall enter an entirely new era of energy supply which will feature other more lasting methods of deriving usable energy from nature.

The harnessing of waterfalls for power could not grow rapidly until the beginning of this century, when practical means had been developed for the generation and use of electric power. So for two thousand years after the first use of water power by the Romans, waterwheels were used only for local purposes such as the grinding of wheat. Many mills were built in all progressive communities of the world, but the total output of industrial power was perhaps no greater than the little bit obtained from the competitive windmills. As soon as a way was found to transmit power to distant points, hydroelectric development was rapid. It will continue until all of the practicable sites are in service. The contribution of water power is now substantial, for in this country it about equals the supply of energy from the wood we burn. In 1900 the energy utilized from waterfalls was probably no more than one percent of the energy from wood.

While water power was coming into its own, the major use of wind power was on its way out. Since the dawn of history ships were equipped with sails. At first they were clumsily arranged and had to be supplemented with oars, but for thousands of years wind had been made to do a large part of the work of marine transportation. By 1900 sailing vessels had been largely supplanted by vessels powered with steam.

The startling newness of our fossil-fuel era can be well illustrated by comparing the consumption of fossil fuel during the first half of the twentieth century with the consumption during all of the prior history of the earth. Reverting again for a moment to the personification of the earth as a young man twenty-one years old, we shall be comparing the last "fifteen seconds" of his life with all that has gone before. The records of production of the various fuels do not go back very far, but the curves rise so sharply that all production prior to recorded data can be ignored with a probable error of less than 1 percent. We find that of all the fossil fuel recovered since the earth was created two billion years ago, more than 86 percent has been produced and used since 1900.

This extraordinary record of fossil-fuel production, made possible by the machine, gives the earth at least a temporary reprieve from sudden and disastrous deforestation, but the danger has not been completely averted. Man started out with dependence upon wood. Man is still largely dependent upon wood. In Canada today more than 80 percent of the fuel used in agricultural areas is wood. In Brazil today wood provides about 85 percent of *all* energy used. And this does not include the wood destroyed by "slash-and-burn." The same situation is believed to exist in many other parts of the world where forests are still in existence. And yet statisticians continue to make the serious error of ignoring the importance of wood.

A recent statement was made that "up to 1850, man and animals furnished nearly all the useful energy." This is obviously wrong. At the present time, even with our high generation of power and process energy, space heating constitutes about a fourth of the energy demand of the United States. Outside of the United States the proportion is probably more nearly one-half. Before 1850 the proportion must have been higher because relatively less power and process energy was employed. Before 1850 nearly all space heating and process heating was done with wood—none of it with man and animals. Furthermore, most of the machine energy up to 1850 was derived from wood. There are few dependable data on wood fuels today and none at all for 1850. There is no way of making a quantitative estimate (which is perhaps why the statisticians like to forget about it), but it is clear that up to 1850 wood, not man and animals, furnished most of the useful energy. A hundred years ago about sixteen times as much work was done by man and beast as by *fossil fuels*, whereas today it happens that the relationship is almost exactly reversed. The comparison here is limited to power energy and excludes wood.

The curve for combined production shows that all of the fossil fuel produced in the world up to 1900 would satisfy the present world economy only about five years. The consumption of fossil fuel per capita is high but there is serious doubt that the per capita consumption of total energy materials is higher today in our most advanced countries than it was in the most advanced aboriginal civilizations. An important difference is that we are wasting only about 30 percent of the fuel used whereas the ancient peoples probably wasted 90 percent in some cases or even more.

The distribution of technology among the peoples of ancient times was uneven. Present distribution is still more uneven, for while some present cultures closely resemble the aboriginal, our most highly industrialized cultures are beyond comparison. So while some of us are using up the fossil-fuel resources of the world at an appalling rate, the great majority of the population of the earth are faring today much as they fared a thousand years ago. During the past decades, with almost inconceivable rapidity, the minority of the cultures of the earth have substituted machine power for muscle power. Now, in the United States, each of us has available for his use the energy equivalent of the labor of about 200 slaves. This may be a higher ratio than the actual slave ratio in any ancient civilization, but, even if it were not, the fact remains that electric power, the internal-combustion engine, the turbine, and the jet can do things for us that human slaves could never do.

The political and sociological consequences of this fuel revolution have been profound. The consequences are both international and domestic. Increasing disparity among peoples means world instability. More mechanical power is available to some of us than we can properly use. Too many of us are fit for little else than the exercise of our muscles. Manual labor is not yet a thing of the past, but we require less of it than our present social organization could tolerate to advantage. We are out of equilibrium internally and externally and becoming more so every year. Accordingly, we are confronted with new and perplexing problems that will require our keenest minds to solve.

3

How Much Petroleum

There is no way to measure the volume of ultimate reserves of petroleum in the United States or in the world. The so-called "proved reserve" is quite definite. This is merely an estimate of the quantity of

The land of the United States is dotted with oil wells. Nearly half a million wells were producing as of January 1, 1950. (*Gulf Oil Corp.*)

petroleum which we can reasonably expect to produce *based on present data*. The proved reserve of liquid hydrocarbons of the United States as of Jan. 1, 1950, was about 29 billion barrels; that of the world was about 80 billion barrels. These figures are not obscured by policies of taxation as in the case of iron-ore reserves, which are sometimes taxed as soon as discovery is announced and hence such policies act as a deterrent to exploration. Also, the figures do not reflect the considered judgment of geologists. For a long time proved reserves have represented *minimum* expected recoveries. Thus, in spite of a rapidly increasing rate of production of oil, the estimates of what remains to be pro-

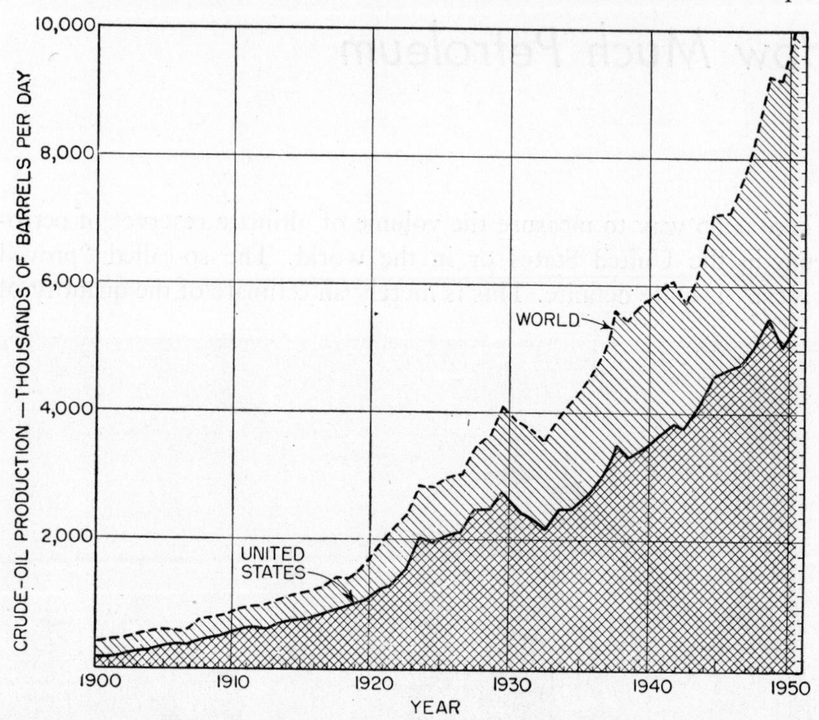

FIG. 1. The saw-tooth but ever-rising production curve of crude oil in the world and the United States.

duced have continued to rise, year by year (Fig. 1). The production of the United States in 1950 was almost as much as the entire proved reserve of the country in 1900. This means, of course, that oil has continued to be discovered more rapidly than it has been consumed.

Recent figures for proved reserves of the world show the most prolific region to be the Middle East, where petroleum was first used many thousands of years ago. Table 1 shows cumulative production of oil, proved reserves, and estimated ultimate production. Liquid hydrocarbon associated with natural gas is not included. In the United States such liquid hydrocarbon raises the reserve figure by about three billion

TABLE 1. World Oil Production, Proved Reserves, and Resources
In Billions of Barrels

Country or Region	Cum. Production to Jan. 1, 1950	Proved Reserves Jan. 1, 1950	Estimated Ultimate Production
United States	38.9	24.7	110.0
Bal. North America	2.6	3.0	40.0
Total North America	41.5	27.7	150.0
Venezuela	5.0	9.5	} 80.0
Bal. South America	1.7	1.0	
Total South America	6.7	10.5	80.0
Total Western Hemisphere	48.2	38.2	230.0
Europe, excl. Russia	1.7	0.8	13.0
Middle East, incl, Egypt	3.5	33.0	155.0
Bal. Asia, excl. Russia	1.9	0.4	24.0
Indonesia	0.6	1.1	30.0
Africa, excl. Egypt	...	...	8.0
Total Eastern Hemisphere, excl. Russia	7.7	35.3	230.0
Russia	6.3	5.0	150.0
Total Eastern Hemisphere	14.0	40.3	380.0
Total World	62.2	78.4	610.0

Source: Data after L. G. Weeks, published 1948, modified by G. F. Moulton in 1950.

TABLE 2. World Crude Petroleum Production and Demand
Rate for May, 1950; In Thousands of Barrels Daily

Area	Production	Imports	Exports
North America	5 397	703	137
South America and Caribbean	1 520	767	1 200
Western Europe	39	692	0
Middle East	1 789	136	1 071
Other Asia	16	33	0
Other Africa	1	19	0
Oceania	228	7	22
U.S.S.R. and Eastern Europe (?)	820	3	0
Total	9 810	2 360	2 430

Source: U.S. Bureau of Mines, *World Petroleum Statistics.*

barrels, but in other areas of the earth liquid other than crude oil is not substantial. Production figures in 1950 are shown in Table 2.

The reserves of the Middle East are divided fairly equally between Iran, Irak, Saudi Arabia, and Kuwait. The United States is in second place and Russia is now a poor fourth. Some geologists believe that

Russia may eventually prove to have most of the oil to be found in the future. Asiatic Russia and China together now have less than 1 percent of the world's proved oil reserves. Discovery of oil in the Soviet Union has been seriously hampered by the psychology of communism, which has a tendency to punish a man for an unsuccessful gamble. Petroleum exploration has always been a gamble and will remain so. In 1950 a total of 5290 new-field wildcat (rank wildcat) wells

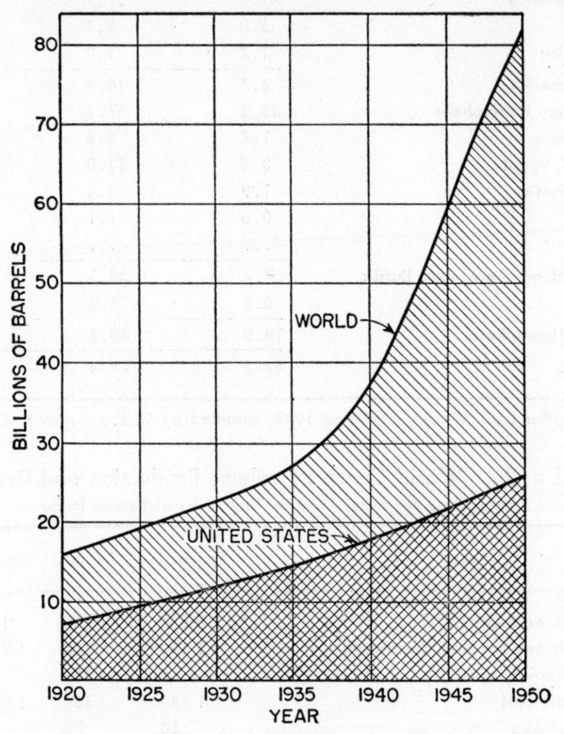

FIG. 2. Estimated reserves of crude petroleum for the world and the United States.

were drilled in the United States. Only one in nine, or 592 of these wells, was successful. The rest were dry holes. Even the new-field wildcats whose locations were determined by the best of modern technology averaged 5 failures for each success. But no one here was "purged."

Estimates of ultimate producible reserves are guesses (Fig. 2). Pessimists believe that the United States may eventually produce about 20 billion barrels more than the 1950 "proved reserve." Optimists believe the figure should be nearer 60 billion barrels. A century hence we may know who was more nearly correct. A recent guess for the world is 530 billion barrels more than the 1950 proved reserves of the world.

Fortunately, the fact of greatest importance to our economy is not "how much petroleum is in the earth," or even "how much petroleum can be ultimately recovered," but rather "how fast can we produce it." To know whether we have much or little, or whether we are likely to be producing petroleum for the next hundred or ten thousand years, would be of minor interest if the rate of production in any case were to supply only a fraction of what we need.

In the case of coal, there are no limiting factors to great increases in rate of production except the sociological and economic ones. Several limiting physical factors, however, are imposed on petroleum production. In the first place, we cannot produce today oil that will be discovered tomorrow. In the second place, a limit to the rate of production is imposed by (1) the rate of accumulation of oil in the well; (2) the bore of the well; (3) the pressure in the oil reservoir; (4) the number of wells tapping the reservoir. Circumstances vary widely in different oil fields, but on the average around 12 percent per annum probably represents the highest practicable rate of withdrawal. In the third place, an additional limitation is imposed by considerations of conservation. In recent years the annual production has not exceeded 9 percent of proved reserves, and this is believed to be somewhere near the optimum rate for maximum long-term recovery. Occasionally production has been cut back still further by legal regulatory action when production threatened to exceed market demand.

Table 3 shows the relative status of some of the oil fields of the world as of 1950. The figures for "relative depletion" show a striking difference between the new fields of the Middle East and the older fields of the world.

Sometime in the future our reserves will begin to go down instead of up. It has occasionally been assumed that we can then maintain a high rate of production by increasing the ratio of production to reserve. This would be economically and politically unwise if it were possible, but beyond certain limits it would not be physically possible. We must accept the fact that to maintain the rate of production of crude in this country, it will be necessary to maintain our reserve by finding new oil at least as fast as we produce. As a matter of practical fact, the ratio of reserves to production must increase, because, as fields age, the proportion of the fields that are in the stripper class becomes larger.

Since the relationship between rate of production and size of proved reserve is fairly definite, there would appear to be no particular reason to prefer one to the other as an historical indicator. The difficulty with proved reserve will be outlined in later paragraphs.

TABLE 3. Relative Depletion of Oil Reserves, 1950

Country	Current Production, Percent of Reserves	Relative Depletion,* Percent
Kuwait	1.2	2
Irak	0.6	5
Saudi Arabia	2.2	6
Iran	2.0	20
Venezuela	6.4	38
Indonesia	5.8	54
Columbia	8.3	55
United States	7.5	61
Mexico	5.5	65

* Relative depletion is the cumulative production expressed as a percentage of the sum of cumulative production and proved reserves.

Reservoir engineers are constantly studying production data in order that they may predict the course of production of oil fields. Since 1935 the science of interpretation of such data has advanced to the point where predictions are surprisingly good. With few exceptions, all important oil fields of the United States found before 1940 have passed their peaks of production. The pattern has been qualitatively the same. Production rises rapidly until a peak is reached, then descends rapidly from the peak, and then gradually melts away. Two typical cases are shown in Fig 3.

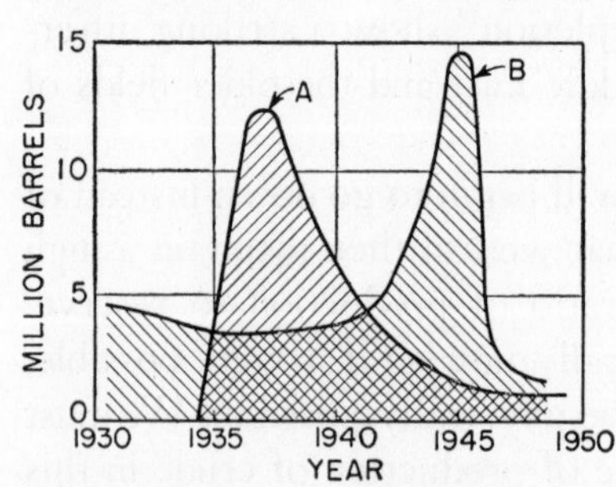

FIG. 3. Annual production of petroleum of (A) Rodessa, Tex., and (B) Elk Hills, Cal.

The production pattern of some modern fields that have been under strict conservational control is somewhat different (Fig. 4). In the case of the great East Texas field, production has been kept on a relatively level basis for a considerable period. The "peak" is flattened out. Other future Texas fields will probably be made to follow similar patterns, but less drastic control is now exercised in other states.

Production history of some older fields is complicated by advances in production technology. The Bradford, Pa., field is the sixth largest in cumulative production that has been found in the United States. Its history has been unique in that it reached a high peak in 1881, and then, through waterflooding, achieved a new, although more moderate, peak in 1947 (Fig. 5). In other cases secondary peaks have been reached by drilling wells to lower horizons. A good example is Spindletop, Tex., which reached its first peak in 1902 and its second still higher peak in 1927 (Fig. 6).

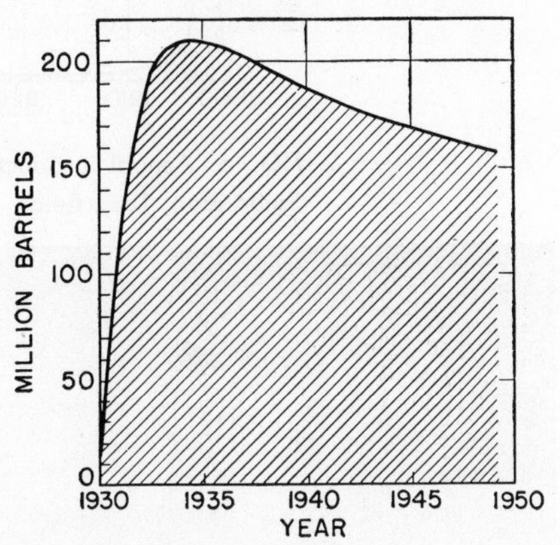

FIG. 4. Annual production of petroleum of the giant East Texas field.

Perhaps this kind of thing could happen in the case of some states or countries where production is petering out, but the probabilities of such technological reversal do not seem high. And such rejuvenation, although economically important, merely postpones a little the day of scarcity—it does not change the fundamental fact of ultimate depletion.

At Bradford, all of the additional petroleum gained by waterflooding was sufficient for only 30 days of 1950 United States consumption. In the case of Spindletop the additional oil gained by deep drilling was sufficient for 12 days. The rejuvenation of oil fields will apply to a number of other older fields but not (as far as we know now) to modern fields already operated with the advantage of modern technology.

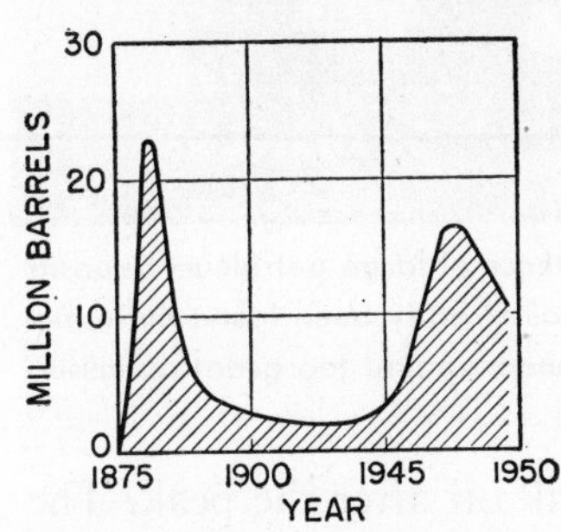

FIG. 5. Annual production of petroleum of the Bradford, Pa., field.

The problem of prediction in a geographical area like a state or a country is much more complicated because there is no way to know how many new fields will be discovered or how large they will be. The peak of production of a country depends, of course, upon the summation of many fields, some of which are on the way up while others are on the way down. While we know the general shape of the production curve, we do not know the year in which the peak will occur, the height of

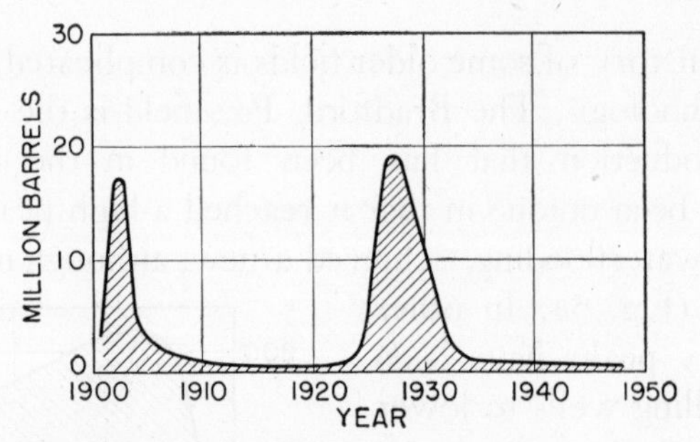

FIG. 6. Annual production of petroleum of the Spindletop, Tex., field.

Geologists say that conditions are favorable for the existence of large petroleum deposits off the shores of the land masses of the earth. Some oil has already been found there, but the engineering difficulties are great and we are cautioned against too great optimism. (*Gulf Oil Corp.*)

the peak, and how rapidly production will fall off after the peak. The shadow of this coming event will obviously not be "cast before" by trends of production rates. Instead we shall have to keep our eyes on the "rate of discovery," the peak of which should come some years before the peak of production. Petroleum geologists are constantly studying the statistics of discovery in order that they may detect the first reliable signs of approach to the historical peak of production. It is generally believed that the United States is somewhere near the peak of discovery (a very different thing), but the figures are not easy to interpret.

The figure for United States proved reserves as of a given date is the sum of the amounts of oil believed, at that time, to have been ultimately recoverable from each producing field. The belief is always based on the best technical evidence available when the estimate is made. As additional data accrue, estimates are revised. It is convenient to leave the original estimates as they were, and to add differences between new and old estimates to the reserve figures as of the time of the new estimates. This is probably as good a method of accounting as any other, but we must realize that an estimate, for example, of proved reserves for the beginning of 1940, if made in 1940, would be quite different from an estimate for the same date made in 1950, because in the intervening ten years we would have accumulated more information. It happens that ever since the beginning of the petroleum industry, the net revisions for the United States have been upward rather than downward. While some fields have not fulfilled their earlier promise, many more fields prove to be better than expected. This accounts for the fact that when we look at the annual estimates for proved reserves we find them ever larger as time goes on—thus far at least.

This does not mean, of course, that our total reserves are actually larger than they were. On the contrary, they are becoming smaller. Whatever the reserves may have been at the start, they must now be about 40 billion barrels smaller, because that is the amount of oil that has been produced, and new oil is not being formed at an appreciable rate. The increase in figures for proved reserves from about 19 billion barrels in 1940 to about 29 billion barrels (liquid) in 1950 means two things: (1) we have found more of the oil that remains in the earth; and (2) we have changed our opinion (because of new technical evidence) as to the magnitude of some of the prior discoveries. What is the relative importance of the two factors?

Since 1940, additions to reserves from discoveries of new fields and new pools in old fields have varied from 25 to 10 percent of total additions. There is no clear trend. The other 75 to 90 percent of additions comes from the discovery that some of the old fields are larger than we thought they were. In other words, the additions are made up primarily from matured reestimates of old pools, and secondarily from initial estimates of new pools. It is rather interesting to calculate what our 1950 proved reserves would be if we had found no new pools during the preceding ten years. The answer is about 23 billion barrels instead of 29. Only about 6 billion barrels of reserves (less than three years of production at the 1950 rate) have come from pools discovered in this decade.

The 1940 proved reserves, refigured on 1950 data, would have been nearly 40 instead of 19 billion barrels. But in 1960 we might be able to say that the 1940 figure should have been 50 or 60.

Because of the nature of the statistical data it is not possible now to decide whether the rate of discovery of new reserves has been keeping well ahead of production or falling far behind. All we know is that the *initial* estimates of new reserves found each year during this period have been very much smaller than our annual production (Fig. 7).

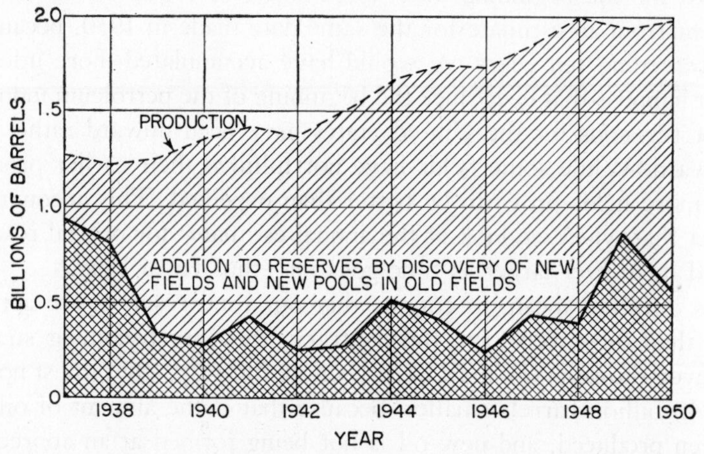

FIG. 7. Trends in United States oil production and additions to reserves. (From *World Oil*, April, 1949.)

This is without special significance as long as we have a relative abundance of oil in the older fields. (The numbers after 1946 in Fig. 7 are not quite comparable with the rest because the basis for estimates of proved reserves was changed at the end of 1945.)

A clue of possible significance lies in the figures assembled each year by a committee of the American Association of Petroleum Geologists. Since 1940 the total number of new fields found each year has been fairly constant, but the number of fields estimated to have an ultimate reserve over 10 million barrels has markedly decreased. Also the number of fields with less than one million barrels has increased. We are finding more fields but most of them are much smaller. This trend may be seen in Fig. 8. H. J. Struth, petroleum economist, has attempted to revise the original estimates by crediting extensions and revisions to years of

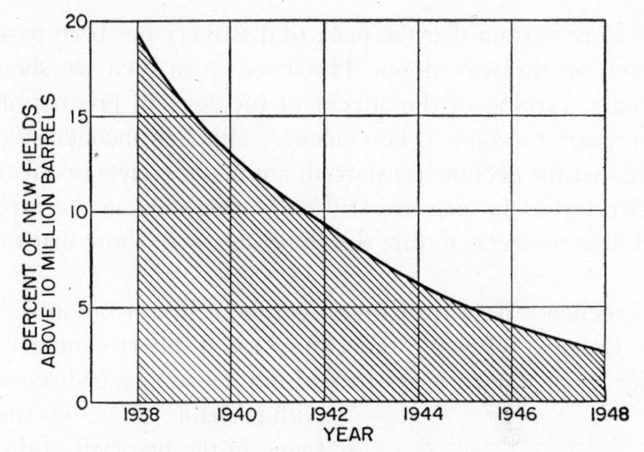

FIG. 8. In the discovery of new oil fields the proportion of large ones is declining markedly. (*From Bull. Am. Assoc. Petroleum Geol., June,* 1949, *p.* 798.)

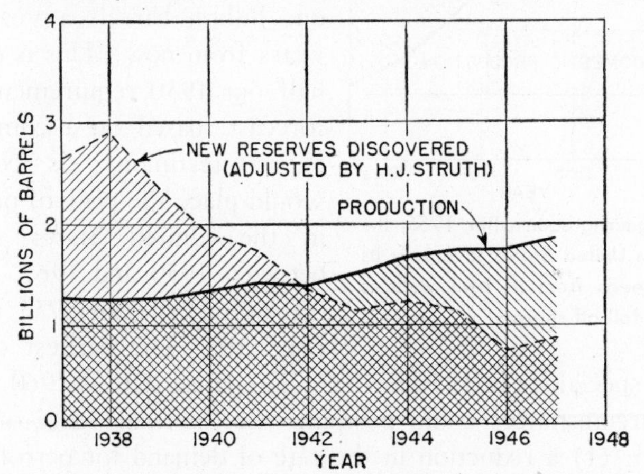

FIG. 9. Oil production rate is steadily climbing while the discovery of new reserves is declining. (*From H. J. Struth, "The Petroleum Data Book,"* 1948, *p.* C-31.)

original discovery. Some of his conclusions are shown in Fig. 9, where new reserves are compared with annual production. The alarming trends cannot be taken too seriously for the simple reason that while the earlier years have the benefit of substantial additions from modern production data, the later years have not yet had the benefit of additions that presumably will be indicated by future production data. A reestimate of this period made in 1958 might show a different picture.

All of this seems complicated. It is set forth here to emphasize the point that in spite of the most thoughtful analysis of statistics we are not likely to be certain that the peak of discovery has been passed until we are well on the way down. However, even then we should have several years warning of the advent of the peak of production and of the leaner years to come. The evidence, although inconclusive, seems to indicate that the decline has started, not in our conventional estimates of proved reserves (which are still increasing) but in the rate of discovery of new reserves. Future developments may show that this is not the case.

In the excellent "Report of Investigation of Petroleum in Relation to National Defense (1947)" the Hon. Dewey Short concludes that it "may take about ninety years to find our remaining undiscovered oil, with probably some two-thirds of it found in the first half of the period, or forty-five years." He infers from this a production of not more than one billion barrels a year twenty years from now. This is only one-half our 1950 requirement. If this forecast, based on a composite of expert testimony, is correct, it would place the peak of production in the United States sometime between 1950 and 1967, or, more plausibly, between 1955 and 1960 (Fig. 10). The earliest date estimated by specialists in 1950 is 1955. The latest date is 1960.

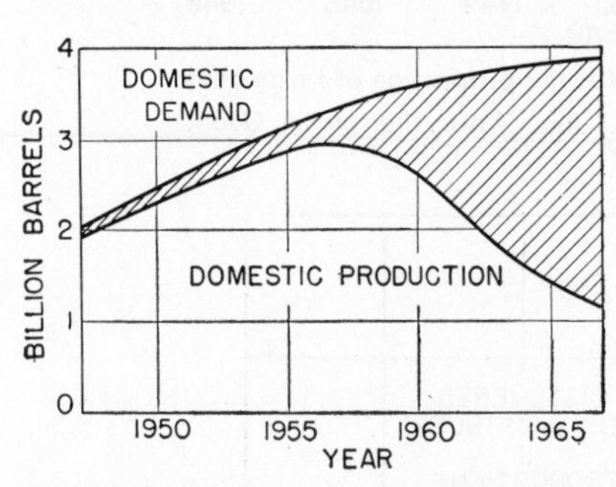

FIG. 10. Beginning soon after 1955, the ability of the United States to supply its liquid-fuel needs from its own wells is expected to fall off sharply.

Two circumstances could postpone the "normal" date of peak of production: (1) a reduction in the rate of demand for petroleum (extremely unlikely); and (2) a substantial increase in the rate of importation. Our net imports are increasing, but still constitute an almost negligible fraction of our supply. The peak could be postponed for a few years by abandonment of regulation of the rate of production. If the valves were opened wide, declining production would be postponed, but we would pay for it by a somewhat lower ultimate recovery and by a much more rapid decline in production a few years later. This would seem to be opposed to national interest.

The largest oil field in our petroleum history has been the East Texas field, which through 1950 has produced about 2.5 billion barrels. This cumulative production in twenty years is only slightly more than the 1950 United States production. Thus, if another field of this size were found, it could not delay the peak of production more than a few months.

One development might postpone the United States peak of production for several years. This would be a prolific production of petroleum from the Continental Shelf. Geologists feel that conditions are favorable for large petroleum deposits off the shores of the land masses of the earth. Some oil has already been found there but the engineering difficulties are great and we are cautioned against too great optimism.

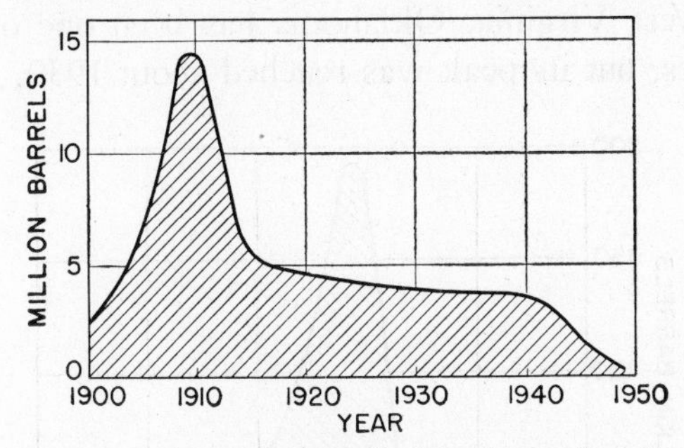

FIG. 11. The annual production of petroleum in Poland suggests the pattern that can be expected in the United States.

There may be vast quantities of oil that will never become economically recoverable.

The idea of "peak of production" in the United States should not seem strange. When each year finds production higher than the year before, and when it becomes necessary, as it has many times in the past, to hold back production to avoid glutting the markets, we are inclined to forget the inevitable shape of things to come. And yet the peak of production of petroleum has been passed long ago in some other countries.

In Poland, for example, the peak was reached about 1910 (Fig. 11) and in Mexico about 1921 (Fig. 12). In each case after the peak was passed there was a sharp descent. This catastrophe has occurred also in Roumania, Peru, Germany, Trinidad, Burma, and Indonesia. In some cases, the shape of the production curve has been affected more by political, economic, or military events than by natural exhaustion of the reserve of petroleum. This is especially true of Indonesia, which was devastated by World War II. It is possible that a still higher peak may be reached there at a later date if reconstruction of facilities can go forward. In Mexico and Germany new higher peaks of production may be reached.

More valid examples of past peaks of production may be found in the states of the United States where the political and economic climate has been fairly uniform and where artificial factors have been at a minimum. In nine of our states the peak of production has been passed. These are Ohio, West Virginia, Indiana, Arkansas, Oklahoma, Pennsylvania, New York, Michigan, and Illinois. In Ohio the peak came before 1900 and the trend has been downward ever since. This is true also of West Virginia. Oklahoma has been one of our great oil producing states, but its peak was reached about 1930.

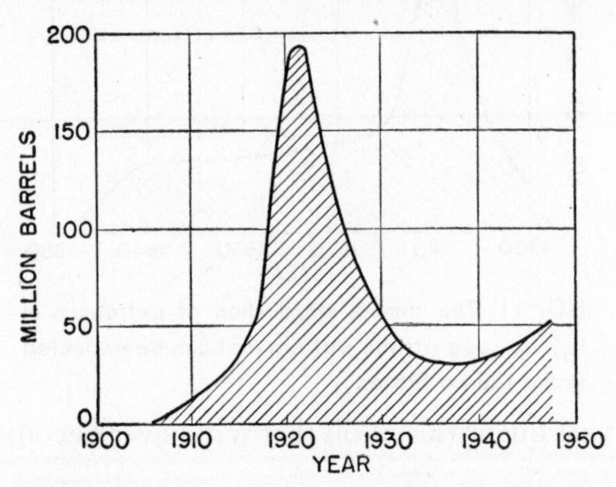

FIG. 12. The rate of petroleum production in Mexico passed its major peak in the early 1920's.

The fact that Venezuelan production has not yet reached its peak is important to us in a military sense. The rising curve of Canadian production is even more important because Canadian imports cannot be cut off by submarine activity. But the proved reserves of Canada are not yet sufficiently great to provide one year of United States consumption, and this will be gradually produced over a period of several decades, with a peak of production perhaps between 1970 and 1980. This is a wild guess because the rate of discovery is still going up and the rate of production must now be artificially regulated to markets. This naturally postpones the peak of production.

At the turn of the century the natural-gas reserves of the Appalachian area were about 25 trillion cubic feet. The remaining reserves as of 1950 are only 4 trillion. The peak of production of gas from this area was reached many years ago. The exact year cannot be determined because production records are inadequate. But we seem to have consumed more than 20 trillion cubic feet of this gas since 1900.

The rate of petroleum production in the Middle East is expected to be high long after the rate in the United States has declined, and the peak of production in Russia may not come until the end of this century, or possibly even later.

Some oil is found almost 3 miles below the surface of the earth. To drill deep wells requires massive and expensive equipment. (*Gulf Oil Corp.*)

The crude petroleum picture is quite similar to that of coal, in that the present annual production of petroleum in the United States depletes about 150 square miles of petroleum-producing territory. The figure can have almost less than casual interest because we have no way of guessing the total area of this territory. Also, like coal, we leave considerable fuel in the ground. The usual maximum recovery with water drive is 75 percent, although occasionally (as in East Texas) we reach

85 percent. For gas drive, 25 to 30 percent is normal. The adoption of better producing practices has led to an improvement during the past decade of around 50 percent in average recovery. This represents a marked difference from coal-mining technology, where modern practice is inclining toward lower average recovery.

The petroleum industry is interested in the development of "mopping-up" techniques to recover oil that has been left in the ground. The so-called "secondary-recovery" operations involve, for the most part, the application to old fields of the effective principles that are now used for primary production in new fields. Whether secondary recovery can yield a worth-while increment of production from modern fields depends upon the future advance in "reservoir engineering," but from the older fields of the United States it is estimated that we might obtain, perhaps, 10 billion barrels—enough to satisfy the 1950 demand for five years. The production of this 10 billion barrels would be spread out over several decades.

Estimates of petroleum keep going upward—perhaps because there is little basis for realism in petroleum predictions that go beyond proved reserves. Optimism and imagination can be completely unfettered. Inasmuch as there is no possible way of showing that some of the higher estimates are wrong, there is no reason why we should not add a few hundred billion barrels to the ultimate reserves of the world now and then—if we feel like it.

Some technologists look at crude-petroleum reserves in this fashion: This country has produced, so far, about 40 billion barrels. If we produce this much more in the future, we shall probably be doing well. In recent years we have been pleasantly excited by the discovery of an occasional 100-million-barrel field. There have been only about 110 fields as large as this discovered in the past (although many of these have, of course, been much larger). Only four domestic fields of this magnitude have been found since 1936. If we are to get 50 billion barrels in the future (or, say, 10 billions of new oil more than our present proved reserve plus another 10 billions from secondary recovery), we shall have to locate the equivalent of 100 more fields of this size. This does not appear probable.

Some other technologists are more optimistic. For example, the figure of 120 billion barrels (including past production, proved reserves, and new discoveries) would mean that we would have to find a lot more producible oil in the future than we have produced in the past. Dr.

Wallace E. Pratt, petroleum economist, has estimated our ultimate petroleum resources (excluding the Continental Shelf) at 100 billion barrels. There is no possible way to know whether we shall add a total of 20 or a total of 60 billion barrels to our present proved reserve. Perhaps these two figures could be regarded as limits corresponding to six and eighteen times the present total annual United States energy requirement. These figures will be used later in a discussion of years of supply.

The Natural-gas Situation

Little is known of the gas reserves of the world. It has been claimed that Russia has the largest reserve, and a figure of 35 trillion cubic feet has been claimed. This is about a tenth of the reserve that is believed to be ultimately recoverable in the United States. The following discussion is limited to the domestic reserves.

We have seen that the problem with oil is to continue to produce as rapidly as we consume. The problem with natural gas is to develop useful ways to consume as rapidly as we produce. For more than a third of the gas production is from oil wells rather than gas wells, and nearly a third of the proved reserve of natural gas is now associated with oil. It is this third that is the most difficult to conserve because some of it must be produced in order to produce oil. The problem may gradually become more serious through the years because it is expected that most of the natural gas of the future will come from oil wells.

More than half of our known reserves are in Texas, and when adjacent counties of other states are added, we can account for 85 percent of our reserves. The other 15 percent is mostly in Oklahoma, New Mexico, and California.

The net production of gas is being held back to conform as closely as possible with demand, and the demand is limited largely by pipe-line facilities for transportation. So there is no significant relationship between gas production and gas reserves. We could probably double or triple the rate of production of "nonassociated" gas without harming ultimate recovery, but if it were economically feasible we would prefer to limit still further the production of gas for long distance pipe-line transmission. The proved reserve in 1950 was about 180 trillion cubic feet, about fifty times the rate of use in 1950.

Expert predictions have been made that by 1960 the volume of natural gas transmitted through pipe lines will have doubled. To handle this larger volume will require about 50 000 miles of additional pipe line and nearly ten million additional horsepower for pumping the gas. In 1950 the transmission pipe lines of the United States were about 108 000 miles, and the installed horsepower for pumping was about three and a half million.

The trend of production figures since 1938 is shown in Fig. 13. The curve happens to be rather smooth, and one is tempted to round it off at the top to make an early peak. It will be better to wait and see what happens during the next few years. But geologists appear to feel that the major part of reserves in the United States of "nonassociated" gas has already been found. The future growth of reserves of total gas will apparently depend upon the discovery of new oil in deeper horizons.

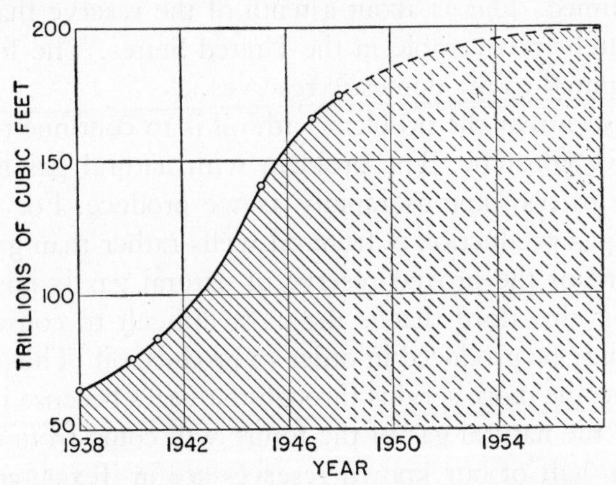

FIG. 13. The production of natural gas in the United States is still on the increase.

There is no way, of course, to know the ultimate reserve of natural gas, except that we can be sure it is larger than the proved reserves. The geologist E. DeGolyer has made a conservative estimate of 200 trillion cubic feet, which could bring the reserves peak between 1955 and 1960 if we feel like making a smooth extrapolation of the curve in Fig. 13. On the other hand, DeGolyer expects the ratio of gas to oil to increase in the future. If this expectation turns out to be correct, and if large new reserves of oil are discovered, an estimate of 400 trillion cubic feet would seem to have at least the same validity as some of the estimates of ultimate crude-petroleum reserves. We are probably justified in assuming 200 and 400 trillion cubic feet as minimum and maximum estimates of ultimate natural-gas reserves, which would correspond to six and twelve times the 1947 total annual United States energy requirement. Crude petroleum and natural-gas reserves appear to have roughly about the same order of magnitude.

The total amount of natural gas produced in any year is not definitely known. In 1949, for example, about 41 percent of the presumed production was marketed by utilities. Additional amounts were marketed direct to large users such as chemical companies and carbon-black manufacturers. Some was pumped back into the oil formations to effect pressure maintenance. This is called "repressuring" and accomplishes a dual purpose of improving the ultimate recovery of oil and postponing the production of the gas for use. The practice of repressuring has grown rapidly over the past few years, as shown in Fig. 14. In 1948

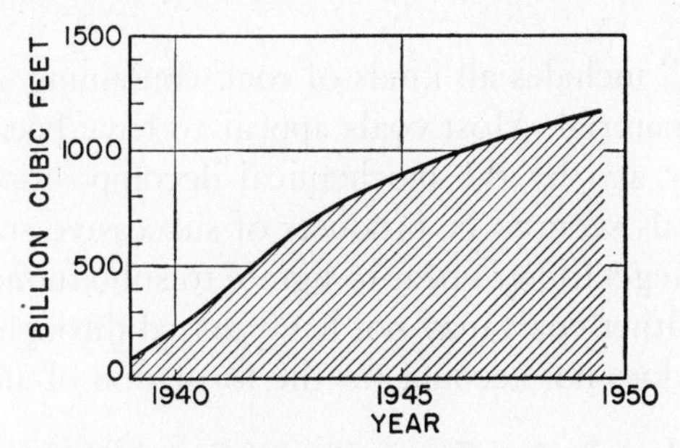

FIG. 14. The amount of gas used for repressuring is increasing steadily.

repressuring accounted for about 15 percent of the presumed production of natural gas. Much natural gas is used to generate power for the production of both oil and gas. This amounts to about 20 percent of presumed production. Then, of course, there is venting to the atmosphere (flaring) and general waste, much of which is not reported. Losses are therefore indeterminate.

The total amount of gas produced since 1900 is probably of the order of magnitude of 115 trillion cubic feet, of which about 8 trillion have been used for repressuring and will therefore be available for recovery for later use. The balance has been used or lost. The total corresponds to about 45 trillion hphr—nearly four times the 1947 total annual energy consumption of the United States.

4

How Much Coal

The word "coal" includes all kinds of rock containing a predominance of combustible material. Most coals appear to have been formed many millions of years ago by the biochemical decomposition of vegetable matter. Some coals seem to be products of successive stages of decomposition—from vegetation to peat to lignite to subbituminous to anthracite (Table 1). Other coals may not have passed through this sequence. A single theory does not account for the formation of all coal deposits.

TABLE 1. Typical Composition of Certain Hydrocarbons
In Percent

	Carbon	Hydrogen	Oxygen
Wood	51	6	43
Peat	60	6	34
Lignite	66	6	28
Subbituminous coal	75	5	20
Bituminous coal	91	4	5
Anthracite coal	96	3	1

Coals vary not only in composition of combustible material but also in the proportion of associated substances such as water, sulfur, and ash. Lignites contain from 6 to 23 percent water and from 2 to 10 percent ash. Bituminous coals contain from 0.5 to 15 percent water and 1 to 9 percent ash. Thus some lignites are dryer than some bituminous coals and contain less ash, but usually the reverse is true.

Coal varies in composition in any given seam. The variations are both vertical and lateral. For example, bituminous coal from the same bed may vary in fixed carbon from 60 to 75 percent. The heating value of coal also varies within wide limits, depending not only upon composition of combustibles but also upon ash, moisture, sulfur, and other components. Any simple statistical data must depend upon averages of available samples. Weighted averages are not possible because over-all sampling is impracticable. However, a general idea is conveyed by the figures in Table 2, which are often used.

TABLE 2. Heat Value of Coals

Kind of Coal	Btu per lb
Anthracite	12 700
Low-volatile bituminous	14 000
High-volatile bituminous	13 500
Subbituminous	9 500
Lignite	6 700

Coal is by far the most abundant fossil fuel. The magnitude of coal reserves is, therefore, of the greatest importance. Several estimates have been made for the world, but these estimates are little more than informed guesses. Table 3 shows two sets of figures which are, perhaps,

TABLE 3. Estimated Coal Reserves of the World
In Trillions of Tons

	1913	1938
North and South America	5.1	4.3
Asia	1.3	2.0
Europe	0.8	0.8
The rest of the world	0.2	0.2
Total	7.4	7.3

equally unreliable. The totals are about the same, but the later estimate shows North and South America revised sharply downward and Asia revised sharply upward. Most of the American coal is in the United States. Most of the Asiatic coal is in China. Both sets of figures are based on the assumption that coal can be recovered with little loss from depths of several thousand feet. The 1938 estimate assumes 3.2 trillion tons in the United States, but it will be seen that this figure must be considerably discounted. Similar reductions may have to be made for Asiatic coal, but no evidence on this point is available now and will probably not be forthcoming for a long time. Fuel production, essentially all coal, in the Soviet Union has been doubling approximately once in five years, an increase of about 15 percent per year except in the early part of World War II. If this growth curve should continue, energy production would equal that of the United States within seven or eight years. It is possible, though improbable, that the Soviet will achieve this goal before 1960 unless another war intervenes.

Coals vary in their usefulness. The most generally useful coal is bituminous because some of it is the only source of metallurgical coke, it is good for steam boilers, and it is a preferred coal for conversion to liquid fuel. It happens that more than half of the bituminous coal of the earth is in the United States. More than 80 percent of the anthracite coal is in Asia. America has about 93 percent of the subbituminous and lignite. Of the total world reserves, 53 percent is bituminous, 40 percent is subbituminous and lignite, and 7 percent is anthracite. In the United States most of the bituminous and all of the anthracite are east of the Mississippi River, and most of the subbituminous and lignite is in the West.

Unlike petroleum there is no reason to expect a natural limitation to the rate of production of coal in the United States within this century. The limitations will be those imposed by labor relations, transportation, consumer demand, and supplies of labor, water, and capital. The first three of these factors have been controlling influences in the past. The last three will be more influential in the future.

The drastic effects of work stoppages on coal production are obvious, and the uncertain supply has had its effect both upon cost and upon demand. Coal must be transported in railroad cars, and the supply of cars has often been a problem. When production is low, investment in idle cars is troublesome. On the other hand, the limited number of cars has frequently been a bottleneck in times of high production. The demand for coal has been affected not only by its relatively high cost and by its uncertain supply but also by a shift of preference from solid to liquid and gaseous fuels and by the development of the internal-combustion engine with its appetite for motor fuel and diesel fuel—the latter because of higher efficiency and the former because of popular demand.

Future large-scale production of coal in the United States will be in Western areas, to which labor will have to be attracted. Homes and amenities will have to be provided. The primary reason for large coal production may be for conversion to liquid fuel. This will require great supplies of water, which are not presently available, and the investment of far more capital per barrel of fuel than has been required in the past.

Because of these complicating factors it is scarcely possible to recognize natural peaks of production of coal anywhere. There are a few possible exceptions. Michigan and Texas, both small coal-producing states, seem to have passed their peaks before 1920, as shown in Fig. 1. Great Britain may already have passed its natural peak of production, but it is more probable that the peak lies somewhere in the future. If there were a substantially increased economic demand for British coal

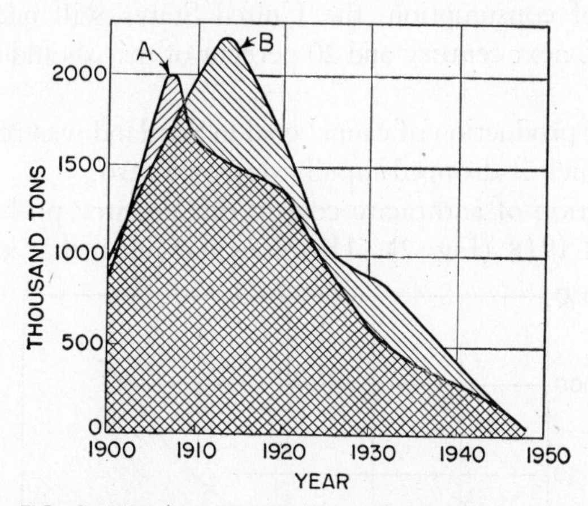

FIG. 1. The annual rates of production of coal in (A) Michigan and (B) Texas.

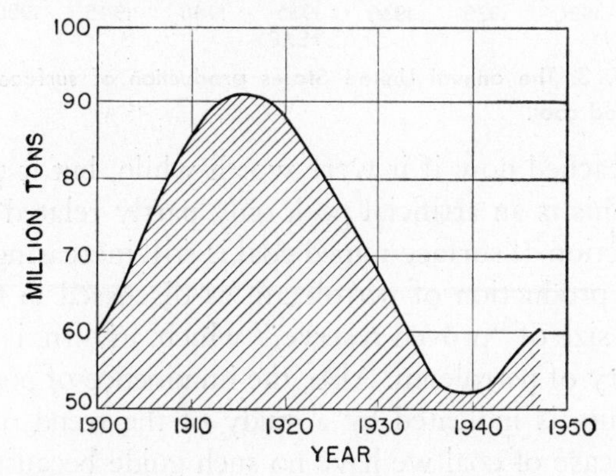

FIG. 2. The annual United States production of anthracite.

in 1960 or 1970 and if there were no sociologically impeding factors, British production might double or triple for a few years. This would be accomplished, of course, by mining the most accessible coal. When this is exhausted, the production rate will necessarily drop.

At the First World Power Conference (1924) the coal reserves of Great Britain were given as about 150 billion tons. This has recently been pared to 48 billion tons for the portion of the reserve likely to be produced. The Ministry of Fuel and Power of Great Britain estimates that within the next century British production can be made about 24 billion tons, and of this only about 6 percent would be suitable for metallurgical coke (for making steel). By way of orientation, at the present rate of consumption, the United States will need 50 billion tons during the next century and 20 percent of that should be for metallurgical coke.

The peak of production of cannel coal in Scotland was reached before 1860, after which it dropped rapidly down to zero.

The production of anthracite coal in this country probably reached its peak about 1918 (Fig. 2). This does not mean that a higher peak

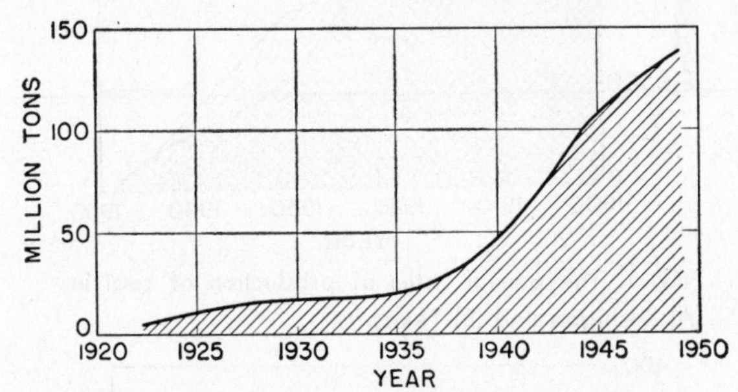

FIG. 3. The annual United States production of surface-mined coal.

could not be reached now if it were worth while, but it probably will not happen. This is an artificial peak only partly related to accessible reserve. Production of surface-mined coal is still increasing (Fig. 3.)

The rate of production of petroleum, as discussed in Chap. 3, is a function of the size of "proved reserve," which, in turn, is a function of rate of discovery of petroleum. Also, the imminence of peak of production of petroleum is indicated by a study of the trend of rate of discovery. In the case of coal we have no such guide because about all of the coal has presumably been already "discovered," and there is no limiting ratio between production and reserve. Exploration (in this country) does not add to our geologically inferred reserve—it is more likely to subtract from our practically recoverable reserve. The only way to predict the approximate date of peak of production of our lower rank coals (the grades in greatest abundance) is to project into the future—demand for energy, availability of domestic petroleum and natural gas, policy with regard to imports of crude petroleum, trends of preference for electricity (which involves a loss of energy) and for liquid and gaseous fuels (the synthesis of which also involves a loss of energy), the substitution of continuous sources of energy, and the efficiencies of energy utilization. This is indeed a formidable job. So many faulty assumptions are possible. But assumptions that seem reasonable at this time indicate that the peak for all coal may be reached by the middle of the next century or almost certainly not later than the middle of the century after that.

Great blocks of bituminous coal can be recovered from seams of unusual homogeneity. (*Pittsburgh Consolidation Coal Co.*)

About all we really know about coal reserves is that there appears to be lots of coal in the world; that the United States has a substantial proportion (perhaps almost one-half); that North America probably has somewhat more than one-half of the world's supplies. Instead of 7 trillion tons there may be double that. On the other hand there may be less than half that.

The reasons for such uncertainty with regard to coal resources are many. The so-called "geologically inferred" estimates for the areas that have been explored are neither "fish nor fowl" They do not express the total accumulations of coal deposits regardless of recoverability, nor do they express the amount of coal that can be practically recovered. They are somewhere in between. When we dig where geological maps show coal, we sometimes find no coal because of faulting or the pinching out of coal seams. An immense amount of coal can never be recovered because the seams are too thin or because they slope too much or are otherwise located badly. Dr. A. C. Fieldner, U.S. Bureau of Mines, believes that "further investigation of our coal reserves by core drilling methods may cut down the geologically inferred reserves as much as 50 percent." Estimation of any resource underground is not an exact science; and coal, in some localities, is erratic in its conformations. Widely quoted figures from U.S. Geological Surveys have been wrongly construed as proved reserves. Instead, they have been geological estimates of coal deposits having a minimum bed thickness of 14 inches for bituminous and anthracite coals, 2 feet for subbituminous coal, and 3 feet for lignite. Beds have been included to a depth of 3000 feet below the surface.

In 1907, 1936, and then in 1944, geological surveys indicated that the United States reserves (prior to the start of mining) had been about 3 trillion tons. But the reserve figures include deposits that must now be regarded as unrecoverable in a practical sense. The U.S. Geological Survey is now making a careful study, in cooperation with industry, to determine present practically recoverable reserves. Net figures will be obtained by subtracting production and losses, and the figures for reserves before mining will be reexamined in the light of more modern geological and mining data. Until this study is completed, we shall have no realistic picture of the present recoverable coal reserve—the reserve upon which we shall have to depend in the future for economical fuel.

Pending the completion of this study, it is interesting to consider a few random factors. For example, Federal estimates of original reserves made in 1907 and 1936 show marked differences for some of the states, although the national totals were about the same (Table 4). These differences for single states—sometimes up and sometimes down—were many times as great as the total of all United States coal mined to date. In the more important coal-producing areas, state surveys, made by subtracting production and losses, have shown surprisingly large contractions from Federal estimates of original reserves. The combined contraction for Pennsylvania, West Virginia, and Ohio is six times the

TABLE 4. Federal Surveys of Coal Reserves
In Billions of Tons

	1907	1936
Illinois	204	198
Michigan	12	2
New Mexico	164	21
Montana	303	381
North Dakota	500	600
Wyoming	424	620

total United States production to date (Table 5). Between 1907 and 1936 the geological estimate for Michigan dropped 10 billion tons, but the total amount of coal produced there in that interval was about 30 million tons—0.3 percent of the difference in estimates. A competent

TABLE 5. Coal Reserves of Three Eastern Province States
In Billions of Tons

	Federal Survey, 1936	Corrected for Production and Losses
Pennsylvania	118	44
Ohio	92	10
West Virginia	148	116

mining engineer believes that the coal economically recoverable in Utah is about 1 percent of the first Federal estimate of original reserve (Table 6). The National Coal Association has put United States reserves at 1.6 trillion tons. Andrew B. Crichton, mining engineer,

TABLE 6. Coal Reserves in Utah

	Billions of Tons
1907 Federal survey	196
1936	93
1945 National Coal Association	46
Opinion of coal operator	2

thinks the present reserves of coal that are economically recoverable may not exceed 0.224 trillion tons. In view of such conflicting estimates the new Federal survey will be awaited with interest.

We cannot say yet whether the present United States coal reserve is equivalent to 1700 times the present total annual United States energy requirement, or one-tenth this amount. It may well be somewhere in between. Later on we shall see what this means in terms of years of supply when the uses to which coal may be put are taken into account. What we can be sure of at this time is that coal will soon become both more costly to produce and more costly to use. In other words, when it costs more, it will be worth less. It will contain more sulfur and more ash. It will have fewer Btu per ton. It will have to be recovered from thinner seams, and these seams will be harder to reach. It will come

Seams of coal more than 5 feet thick are not too common in the Eastern Province. Most seams are much thinner and more costly to mine. West of the Mississippi some coal seams are as much as 100 feet thick. (*Pittsburgh Consolidation Coal* Co.)

from areas more remote from major points of use, and transportation costs will be higher. Even now, almost half the cost of bituminous coal on the Middle Atlantic coast is for transportation.

R. W. Roley, Illinois state geologist, has stated that it cannot be assumed that coal supplies, necessary for large-scale production of liquid fuels, are immediately, conveniently, or economically available. In fact, he makes the surprising assertion that during the past few years the coal industry has become increasingly cognizant of the fact that no large coal reserves are commercially producible at the present time at present costs.

The optimum coal-seam thickness for economical deep mining is said to be between 5 and 10 feet. Costs go up for either thinner or thicker seams. The weighted average thickness of coal seams now being worked in the United States, both in deep mines and in strip mines, has been estimated at about 5.3 feet—just within the optimum range. The country still has plenty of seams of this sort. The thinner seams in most localities are not being mined, and many never will be mined because of damage done to them by present selective mining operations. On the basis of present mining practice, it can be figured that one year's production of coal "exhausts" about 120 square miles of coal field.

More and more of the coal of the future will come from thinner and thinner seams. Because the difficulty of recovery and cost increases in thin seams, the amount of coal seams that can be counted as reserves is indefinite. (*Pittsburgh Consolidation Coal Co.*)

About 85 percent of the coal so far produced in the United States has come from the so-called "Eastern Province." The U.S. Geological Survey shows the area of coal land in this province to be 70 000 square miles. This is believed to be an excessive figure, because it includes in some cases the entire area of counties where coal is found. Almost 10 percent of the area has been worked out, leaving as a maximum an area of 64 000 square miles. In Pennsylvania, bituminous-coal seams more than 5 feet thick constituted less than 10 percent of the bituminous reserve in that state. In Ohio and West Virginia, 70 percent of the seams were less than 4 feet thick. These data apply to conditions prior to the start of mining; but almost all the mining has been done on the thicker seams, which are fast running out. The weighted average seam thickness of present bituminous reserves in the Eastern Province is probably not over 4 feet now, and may gradually approach 14 inches as mining proceeds. For purposes of rough calculation, assume an arithmetic average of 17 inches as the average mineable thickness for the future. This corresponds to 420 square miles of coal land per annum at 1950 production rates. The maximum area of 64000 divided by 420 gives 150 years as the probable *maximum* life of the coal reserve of the Eastern Province.

This is a rough way of calculating life, and Mr. Crichton's estimate of ninety years may be more realistic. It is certainly true that, long before bituminous coal is gone, it will be too costly to mine in competition with more abundant coal from other provinces. Both in deep mines and in strip mines we have been taking the "cream" of the coal. As easily mined coal deposits become partly depleted, centers of coal production will move to more profitable areas, and may eventually return to the Eastern Province to get the "skimmed milk."

At that time the idea of underground gasification of coal may come into its own. If residual coal deposits are uneconomic to mine, it may be desirable to produce the gas that now appears possible from combustion *in situ*. Because of its low Btu concent this gas could not be piped long distances, but it could certainly be used locally for the generation of electric power or for industrial plants. It might be suitable for making synthetic fuels if processes are developed for the economical conversion of synthesis gas that is variable in composition and highly diluted with nitrogen. Such a development is by no means improbable.

The cheapest coal to mine, other things being equal, has been that which is not too deep and not too shallow. Until the modern development of economical "strip mining," it has not been safe to mine coal with less than 75 feet of earthen overburden. On the other hand, it costs more to dig deeper. The deepest vertical shaft in the United States is less than 1000 feet while the *average* depth of shaft in Great Britain is more than 1000 feet. This contributes to the high cost of coal mining in England. Another factor is the steeper slope of the coal seams. The average slope of seams now *being mined* in the United States is about 2 degrees. But we are coming closer to the time when we shall have to tackle the more difficult seams like those in Great Britain, which have steep and variable slopes.

Exhaustion of the seams of intermediate depth in some localities has forced a trend toward deeper mining. This trend is particularly apparent in Pennsylvania, West Virginia, Ohio, Kentucky, and Utah—nearly all of the major coal-producing states—and some minor ones.

At the same time there has been a marked increase in strip-mining operations, in which the overburden of the earth is removed with power shovels and the coal seam is exposed. This is a short-lived trend for

In strip-mining operations as much as 100 feet of the overburden of earth can be removed to expose the coal seam. Huge power scoops can take up to 50 cubic yards at one time—almost enough to fill a railway gondola. (*Pittsburgh Consolidation Coal* Co.)

the Eastern Province because the coal within 100 feet of the surface is strictly limited. Most of the areas now being strip-mined will be exhausted within a few years, and the peak of surface production east of the Mississippi is likely to come before 1970. But the technology of strip mining will be applicable on a very large scale to some Western deposits. For this reason the marked advance in mechanized surface mining since 1930 is of great interest.

When the Panama Canal was built (1907 to 1910) the largest power scoop for removing earth had a capacity of about 8 cubic yards. Now such scoops are used merely for loading trucks with coal. The overburden itself is removed with power scoops that take up to 50 cubic yards at one time—enough to almost fill a railway gondola. Such a machine can economically uncover up to 100 feet of overburden from a coal seam.

It is nice to know that nearly all of the exposed coal can be recovered, but, of course, the only part of the seam exposed is that lying within a practicable depth—say, 100 feet for the best machines. Whether the extensions of the seams at greater depths will ever be recovered by underground technique depends upon how much coal is there and how

Machines are replacing men's muscles in the coal mine. Here is a continuous-mining machine operating in a thin-seam coal mine. (*Joy Manufacturing Co.*)

it is physically disposed. It is safe to say that most of the coal left behind in surface-mining areas will never be recovered. In fact, recovery is considered so improbable that the great surface-mining trenches are sometimes reinstated into the landscape by partially filling in, formation of lakes, and development of pasture and forest land. The elimination of the unsightly "spoil banks," as practiced in Ohio, is excellent from aesthetic and agricultural standpoints, but it is idle to assume that the marginal coal (which in some cases represents ten or even a hundred times the coal recovered by surface mining) will ever be sought by underground-mining technique. So, in an overall sense, the highly mechanized surface mining may prove to have been wasteful.

Mechanization is being applied not only to surface mining but also to underground operations. This has caused a change in emphasis from beds of moderate thickness (5 to 10 feet) to beds of greater thickness. Mobile loaders are now able to operate on beds as thin as 30 inches, but this is a long way from the 14 inches used in estimates of bituminous-coal reserve. The loaders are also limited in the degrees of bed slope in which they can operate. Conveyors are being adapted to use on thin beds and have permitted the recovery of some coal otherwise too expensive to mine.

The most marked advance in mechanization has been the development of coal-cutting machines that cut and load in one operation.

Ingenious machines are being developed for coal mining. Mobile loaders are able to operate on beds as thin as 30 inches. (*Joy Manufacturing* Co.)

Drilling and blasting are eliminated. Under favorable conditions, these machines can produce 100 tons per man per shift with advance of 100 feet per shift. Their designed capacity is even greater. But most of the coal deposits east of the Mississippi are not such as to allow the full benefits from such extreme mechanization. A location might be favorable for a few days of high production, but labor and capital charges on the equipment during the delay in moving to another location sometimes make the average cost of mining higher than with more mobile and smaller equipment. Coal-cutting machines are expected to be especially suitable in some Western areas.

Because of the general mechanization of mining, interest is now centering on thicker beds lying under less than 100 feet of overburden. On this basis it is believed by the Bureau of Mines and the U.S. Geological Survey that the assured, immediately accessible reserves of recoverable coal probably represent only a small fraction of the total estimated in accordance with earlier official formulas.

Mining losses are believed to be as high as 50 percent of the coal originally in the ground. A large part of this loss is technically avoidable, but probably not economically so. When coal finally becomes so

Vast quantities of lignite lie under the prairies of our North Central States. Recovery of much of it is fairly simple by the use of large efficient earth-stripping draglines and coal-mining shovels. (*Truax-Tracer Coal Company.*)

valuable that it would pay to recover what is now being lost, the improved recovery will apply only to the then current operations. In general, what is left behind now is forever gone.

Much coal is irretrievably lost because of the waterflooding of mines. The Bureau of Mines is studying this problem for the anthracite mines from which it is estimated that enough water is being pumped from the collieries each year "to cover an area the size of Rhode Island a foot deep." The rising cost of pumping has forced some collieries to close down. They are not likely ever to be reopened.

About 20 percent of the bituminous coal produced is used to make coke. F. M. Becker, of the United States Steel Corporation, has made a thoughtful analysis of our reserves of good coking coal, and he points out a number of interesting things. "Coking-quality coals are found only in the semibituminous or bituminous rank. These groups also include a variety of other coals that do not produce a homogeneous mass on heating and, therefore, are noncoking." The depletion of coking coals has progressed three times as rapidly as the depletion of noncoking coals, although coking coals originally constituted far less than a fifth of our total coal reserves. The quantity of high-quality coal (low ash and low sulfur) is only a small fraction of the reserve of coking coal. ". . . It is generally agreed that a high percentage of exhaustion (of good coking coal) has been achieved . . . it is evident that future coals will be higher in average sulfur than those formerly available." Fortunately, "acceptable pig iron can be made with coke higher in sulfur than indicated by presently established standards." It is possible to desulfurize iron; and, when low-sulfur coal is no longer available, this will have to be done.

In 1950, the Bureau of Mines completed a survey of coking-coal reserves in Cambria County, Pa. It was estimated that less than half of the coal in beds of 28 inches or more thickness is recoverable by present mining methods. The average recovery in Cambria County has been only about 48 percent, and this applies to beds not less than 28 inches thick. At least 500 million tons of coal are believed to exist in this county in beds between 14 and 28 inches, but beds that are thin are not being mined because costs of recovery are too high. This is symptomatic of the coal-mining situation everywhere. The Bureau of Mines is studying the coking properties of coals not now widely used for making metallurgical coke, and also the possibilities of upgrading marginal coals by the use of suitable preparation steps. This work was stimulated by the concern over shortages of high-grade coking coal that impeded steel production during World War II.

The steel industry is nearing the time when it must adapt its manufacturing process to inferior coal (85 percent of its coal is for metallurgical coke), and the time is not too far away when it may have to make really fundamental changes in its ore-reduction practice. It is unfortunate that we should continue to speed this day by burning good coking coal in our domestic furnaces and industrial steam plants. Low-cost abundant steel is so vital for all of us that the time may come when we may prefer to see our remaining coking coal used for metallurgy rather than for heat or power or conversion.

5

How Much of Other Fossil Fuels

Of the fossil fuels, liquid petroleum is the most convenient for production and use, and coal is by far the most abundant. Several other materials are either less desirable as fuel sources or less accessible or in smaller supply. But they are not unimportant. These minor fuels include oil shale, peat, and tar deposits.

Oil Shale

The coals of the earth have many different qualities. The only things they have in common are that they are solid, they are usually black, and they can be burned. But coal is not the only form of solid fuel. A substantial portion of the fossil-fuel reserve is rock that contains bitumen and yields oil when heated. Such rock varies over wide limits in quality and ranges in color from tan through gray, brown, and blue to almost black. So, oil shales do not have even color in common. Very few oil shales can be burned.

The gradations in bitumen content as we pass from oil shales through bituminous rocks to coals are imperceptible. The character of the bitumen may vary in these solids, which may have quite different geological origins. However, it is convenient to class as oil shales those solid materials that are largely inorganic (*i.e.*, mostly rock) as opposed to coals, which are largely organic.

Oil shales to be burnable, even in thin slices, must be abnormally rich in bitumen. Also because of the high ash content (usually above 90 percent) most oil shale is not likely to become a practicable fuel, per se. To provide energy, oil shale must be heated. This partially decomposes the bitumen with the formation of a liquid resembling petroleum. In effect this processing separates the oil shale into two parts: (1) a spent shale nearly free from combustible material, and (2) crude shale oil that can either be used, itself, as a fuel or subjected to more or less conventional refinery processes to obtain typical petroleum products.

Coal is a fossil fuel usable with little or no processing. Oil shale is a raw product from which a usable fuel can be obtained only by destructive distillation. Hence the reserves of the two cannot be directly com-

The oil-shale formation at Rifle, Col., is several hundred feet thick and covers many square miles. An outcrop is shown near the top of the plateau. (*U.S. Bureau of Mines.*)

pared. About 7 trillion tons of coal of various grades are believed to exist in the earth. About 1.25 trillion tons of oil-shale have been reported. This does not mean that we can obtain a fifth as much energy from oil shale as from coal, because the combustible product from the total oil-shale reserve is less than 10 percent of the oil shale itself. Thus the potential energy from oil-shale reserves is less than one-fiftieth of the potential energy from coal. How much less we cannot be sure because of the meager data on oil yields of world-wide oil-shale deposits. Even in the United States, where extensive exploration has been under way for several decades, we still do not have a definite picture. It is satisfactory to assume that the one is about 1 percent of the other for the world, and perhaps about 3 percent for the United States. In spite of this unfavorable relationship, oil-shale reserves probably rank as second in magnitude of all fossil fuels.

The experimental oil-shale mining at Rifle, Col., has led to marked advances in mining technology and economics. Columns 60 feet in diameter are left to support the roof. Holes are drilled in the rock for explosives. (*U.S. Bureau of Mines.*)

Oil shales are widely distributed throughout the world, but nearly 55 percent of the known reserve is in the United States and nearly 43 percent in Brazil. This leaves only a tiny proportion for all of the remaining countries of the world. Most of this little is in Sweden, with minor amounts in Estonia, Manchuria, Australia, France, Scotland, Canada, and Tasmania. Abundant oil shale may some day be found elsewhere.

To evaluate even the potential value of oil-shale reserves it is necessary to consider the yield of oil from the different deposits (Table 1). This yield varies from 60 gallons per ton down to 10 gallons per ton. Some rare oil shales run up to 100 gallons per ton, and there are countless billions of tons with traces of 3 to 4 gallons per ton. Such lean shale cannot be regarded as an energy reserve.

TABLE 1. Potential Oil-shale Reserves of the World

Country	Billions of Tons of Oil Shale	Billions of Barrels of Recoverable Oil
United States	700	365
Brazil	550	300
Sweden	5	1
Estonia	1.5	1.5
Manchuria	0.5	0.1
France	0.06	0.03
Australia	0.04	0.06
Tasmania	0.009	0.002
Approximate total	1 257	668

In the case of coal, the portion of the potential reserve that can be regarded as recoverable depends primarily on mining factors. If coal can be gotten from the ground it can be burned. But with oil shale there are other complicating factors. After the oil shale is mined it must be "retorted" to produce oil. It costs about as much to retort a ton of lean shale as a ton of rich shale. There is a practical limit, therefore, to the bitumen content of shale that can be regarded as retortable under a given set of economic conditions. When costs of mining, retorting, and transportation are taken into account, the "economically recoverable reserve" is found to vary in size with the cost of other available fossil fuels. Regarded from this viewpoint, the present economically recoverable reserve of fuel from oil shale is zero for the simple reason that such fuel would cost somewhat more than coal or oil. When petroleum residuals become more expensive than shale oil at the points of use, the changed economic relationship will immediately create an oil-shale reserve of some magnitude. Still higher prices will justify the exploitation of leaner and less accessible oil shale, which will then expand the reserve to still greater proportions. This story is represented, in a qualitative sense, in Fig. 1, which is based upon far too little information to have any quantitative significance. A similar generalized curve could be prepared for coal as related to petroleum.

Oil shale varies over wide limits in the composition of its ash or "impurities." Among these are silicon, calcium, aluminum, iron, magnesium, sodium, potassium, water, sulfur, vanadium, and uranium. Sweden has been especially interested in the possibility of recovery of uranium, which sometimes runs higher than 0.1 percent of the shale. But most of the shale there and elsewhere shows uranium concentrations of 0.03 percent or less and would not be considered workable today.

The bitumen content of oil shale is sometimes called "kerogen." This varies widely in its content of nitrogen, sulfur, oxygen, and

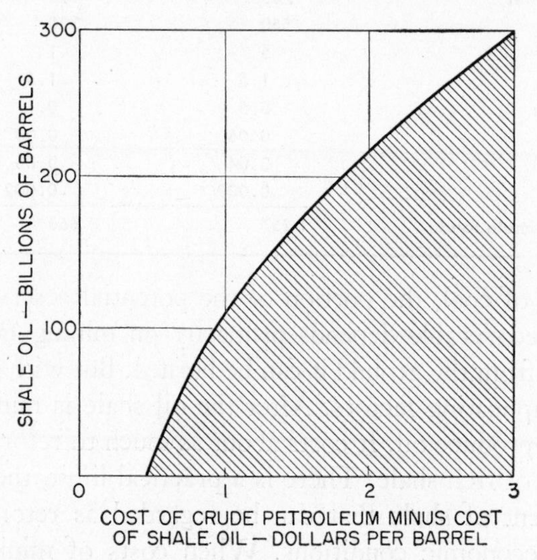

FIG. 1. The amount of shale oil we can count as reserves depends in part on the price of petroleum.

hydrocarbon types. The variability of shale-oil quality is well illustrated by the difference between the two major oil-shale regions of Brazil. The oil from Iraty shale is low-gravity asphaltic material, high in unsaturated hydrocarbons and high in sulfur compounds and phenols. The Paraiba Valley shales yield oil of high-gravity paraffinic quality with less sulfur and oxygen. The Colorado shales yield oil of intermediate quality.

In general, shale oils, although satisfactorily burnable, would have a somewhat lower market value than petroleum residual fuel oils because of their objectional odor. Also, as a charging stock to a refinery to convert to motor fuel and other conventional petroleum products, their worth would be lower because shale oil, containing more impurities, would be more expensive to refine.

Oil shales vary widely in their mineability. The deposit in Colorado is relatively inexpensive to mine because much of it lies in thick horizontal seams, and mines can be highly mechanized. Some deposits can be mined by surface operations. On the other hand, some deposits have

After oil shale has been mined, it must be crushed and retorted to yield its oil. The crude shale oil is somewhat similar to residual oil from the distillation of high-sulfur petroleum. The sheer cliffs of oil shale in the background form a part of the United States naval oil-shale reserves. (*U.S. Bureau of Mines.*)

sharply sloping or undulating seams, which would be difficult to adapt to mechanized operations. A few seams are thin and located under deep overburden. Much of the shale is located far from principal points of use.

Chief among the general problems still to be solved in the commercial production of shale oil is the aridity of some regions in which oil shale is found. While production of crude shale oil requires only about a tenth as much water as coal-conversion processes, the problem will still be formidable for operations on a large scale. In the western part of the United States, where we find the bulk of our reserves of oil shale (and coal), there is a startling contrast between the robust grandeur of the land masses and the pathetic trickle of the rivers. The Brazilian deposits, too, are not in regions of abundant water supply.

Another problem is the disposal of ash. We are accustomed to thinking of ash as a little bit of stuff that is left over. In the case of shale we shall have on the average well over a ton of ash for every barrel of oil. And this ash is material without fertility. It contains salts that can be leached out by rain waters of flash floods. It contains "fines" that could be carried by erosion into river beds. And it is not a matter of dumping it in some unused valley. If all of the rich oil shales of Colorado were retorted, enough ash would be left to cover the entire state of Colorado to a depth of ten feet. Much of the ash could be dumped into the huge canyons of the oil-shale regions, and it would seem that the first billion tons might not be impossible to manage. The disposal of 500 billion tons will require extraordinary ingenuity.

Retorting of oil shale is relatively simple. Shale is ground to a fineness that depends upon the nature of the retorting equipment. But the term "shale" implies a softness not borne out by the fact. Grinding is not easy because of the toughness of the rock, and the cost of grinding to small mesh is very much higher than a coarser operation. The ground material is passed continuously through a chamber with a countercurrent passage of hot air or gas. The heat decomposes the bitumen to form a petroleum-like vapor that is condensed to liquid from the effluent gas.

Commercial recovery of shale oil was carried out during the nineteenth century in Canada, France, the United States, Scotland, and Australia. The project was discontinued in all of these pioneer countries except in Scotland, where it has been subsidized by the government because Great Britain has no oil. The mining of oil shale in Scotland has always been laborious and expensive. Much of the shale is 300 feet below the surface, and Scottish mining has never become highly mechanized. Retorting of the shale there has improved only slowly—at first because the retorting was profitable with crude technology, and later because the industry was subsidized as a move toward nationalistic self-sufficiency. Ordinarily there is little incentive for research and development in a subsidized industry where profits are nominal and fixed by governmental fiat. In the early days, however, James Young became sufficiently wealthy from the recovery of oil from shale to finance the last African expedition of the Scottish missionary and explorer, David Livingstone.

In Australia, shale-oil recovery was resumed during World War II after a lapse of many years to produce a total of about 4 million gallons of motor fuel. The largest modern operations have been in Manchuria, where low average oil yield (16 gallons per ton) has been offset to some extent by low-cost, open-pit mining. In Estonia, also, mining costs are

The recovery of shale oil in Scotland is serious business. Costs are relatively high because of the nature of the oil-shale deposits. The operation is subsidized by the government. (*Anglo-Iranian Oil Co.*)

low, but oil yields are high (up to 60 gallons per ton). During World War II Germany obtained nearly 2 million barrels of oil in one year from Estonian shale. The Estonians actually use some of their richer shales as fuel.

Brazil is petroleum and coal poor. Although Brazil is larger than the United States, production of coal is only 0.3 percent of that of the United States and production of petroleum only about 0.02 percent. The known coal reserves of Brazil are about as large as one year's consumption of coal in the United States, while her estimated total oil reserves would last us but three days. However, in spite of the comparative poverty of the population, the per capita consumption of energy in Brazil is more than one-third that of the United States. This is, of course, because of the extensive burning of wood. Brazil is faced with continued use of large quantities of wood, the development of her high water-power potential, importation of coal and oil, or utilization of native oil shale. Several attempts have been made to commercialize oil-shale retorting there, and new efforts are under way now in the Paraiba River Valley.

The sulfur essential to our industrial economy is a by-product of fuel procurement. The mountains of easily recovered sulfur will soon be inadequate, and more will have to come from crude petroleum and perhaps from oil shale. (*Texas Gulf Sulphur* Co.)

Sulfur is an important part of the oil-shale story. The production of sulfur from natural deposits in the United States may decline within fifteen years. Sulfur is so essential to our industrial economy that this prospect is even more serious than depletion of oil reserves. Significant amounts of sulfur are now being won from crude petroleum and natural gas, and even a slight rise in the price of sulfur would bring in additional recovery plants. However, the sulfur now being wasted by the petroleum industry amounts to only about one-fifth of the sulfur consumption of the United States.

When oil shale is processed, the amount of sulfur produced will be sharply increased. Possibly need for sulfur will turn out to be the predominant factor in the fixing of the national time table for shale-oil production.

Also large-scale production of shale oil could yield as a by-product more ammonia than is consumed in present world markets. We may be thankful some day for such a generous source of supply of these materials, both of which are essential to our way of life, but the possible effects of such production upon present industrial chemical projects cannot be ignored.

The processes of refining petroleum are undergoing a gradual evolution. It is becoming more necessary to convert heavy residuals to distillates by methods applicable to shale oil. Shale oil can be refined now at a rather high cost to make acceptable products. By the time the refining problem is acute the processes will be even more thoroughly worked out, and the transition from crude petroleum to shale oil should be painless.

A maximum oil-shale-reserve figure can be arrived at by assuming that all known, accessible oil-shale reserves yielding 10 gallons of oil or more per ton could eventually be processed to recover shale oil. Excluded from this calculation is oil shale, the mining of which would be impeded by 100 feet of overburden. Such maximum figures are shown in Table 2, in which the reserve is expressed in terms of the

TABLE 2. Ultimate Reserves of Energy from Oil-Shale in Terms of the Present Total Annual Requirement

	World	United States
Maximum	30	65
Minimum	6	12

present total energy requirement of the world (40 trillion hphr per annum) and of the United States (13 trillion hphr per annum). Any such utilization would involve fantastic costs. Much of the total reserve will be economically unavailable for an indefinite time because of such local difficulties as mining, water supply, waste disposal, and transportation.

The minimum reserves, listed in Table 2, are based upon (1) oil shale yielding 20 gallons or more per ton, and (2) deposits of optimum accessibility. The average cost of fuel from this part of the reserve would be higher than 1950 costs of petroleum or coal but within the presumed area of practicality.

It seems unlikely that oil-shale development on a major scale will precede some sort of processing of coal (discussed in Chap. 8). The conversion of coal to liquid fuel by any method involves some loss of energy—sometimes a very substantial loss—whereas the production of shale oil simply adds to the total of available liquid fuel. Thus shale-oil production represents true conservation of our over-all energy resources, but the conservational aspects of such production will be just as valid toward the end of the fossil-fuel era as toward the beginning. Therefore, we must regard as significant the fact that while a ton of good oil shale can be retorted to yield 30 gallons of oil plus nearly a ton of ash, coal can be subjected to low-temperature coking to yield 30 gallons of oil (tar) plus nearly a ton of coke. Shale oil and coal tar are almost equivalent as charging stocks for petroleum processes. The ash is a liability while the coke is not only an excellent fuel in itself but also a satisfactory charging stock for the Fischer-Tropsch process (Chap. 8).

About 2 million barrels of shale oil were being produced in 1950—divided fairly equally between Estonia, Scotland, and Manchuria. This is about 0.05 percent of 1950 world petroleum production. Production will doubtless increase within the next decade, but unless the need for sulfur becomes acute, the major part of the world oil-shale reserves can be regarded as an "ace-in-the-hole" for more distant exploitation.

Tar

The tars with which we are most familiar are by-products of such conversion operations as the distillation of coal or petroleum. But similar tars occur naturally in the earth. Many of these substances have been called "asphalts." Some are called "pitches." The terms "tar sands," "oil sand," "bituminous sand," and "asphalt rock" have been used interchangeably. "Bituminous sandstone" is another common term.

Some tars are believed to be residues from natural evaporation of crude petroleum. Geochemists are wondering whether some tars may not represent early stages in the formation of crude petroleum. In the present hazy condition of knowledge of the subject we can be sure of only one thing—that naturally occurring tars differ in many fundamental ways. While some of them are associated with sand, others (like those in Trinidad) contain colloidal clays. Some tars (like the Canadian Athabaska deposits) can be separated from associated sand by treatment with hot water, while others (like those in Venezuela deposits) cannot.

Our ignorance with regard to tar origin and classification is vast, but we know even less about the reserves in the earth. A few deposits have been explored, but most of them are merely presumed to exist. With few exceptions, the only geographic locations recorded are those where tars are revealed by surface exposures. This lack of information is of small consequence at the moment because ways are not known for the economical recovery of usable fuel from any substantial proportion of even the most readily accessible tars. Future technology combined with urgent need may spur exploration of tar reserves.

A basic difference between tar-bearing rocks and oil shale is that the tar can be extracted by ordinary organic solvents, while the bitumen in shale cannot. A liquid fuel can be obtained from either by "retorting" (distillation), but the tar decomposes to give such a high coke yield compared with the kerogen of the oil shale that liquid yields from tar deposits suffer accordingly. With the use of physical methods of separation, such as displacement by water (when possible) or solvent extraction, yields from average tar deposits are about the same as yields from average oil shales—say, from 20 to 40 gallons per ton. The cost of liquid fuel from tar deposits, however, is excessive because both mining and tar separation are much more difficult. Oil shale is tough but dry. Tar deposits are highly abrasive or sticky, or both. Oil shale can be broken up into small pieces for handling and processing, but tar-bearing material is often hopelessly cohesive.

In the case of all supplementary fossil-fuel reserves, there is a marked difference between "potential" reserves (assuming that we could recover all of it) and economically recoverable reserves. In the case of tar the difference is particularly great.

The largest known deposit of tar is in the northern part of Alberta, Canada, extending along and back from the Athabaska River and its tributaries. The highest estimate of the fuel content of this deposit is nearly 500 billion barrels. The highest estimate for tar deposits in the United States is 5 billion barrels. Most of this is in the Uintah Basin of Utah with about 10 percent as much in California. The known tar deposits in the Western Hemisphere can be taken, therefore, as about 500 billion barrels, with perhaps 1 percent of the total in the United States.

Large subterranean deposits of tar are believed to exist in Venezuela and in Mesopotamia. Data are negligible but guesses have been offered of 150 and 50 billion barrels respectively. Additional subterranean deposits of unknown magnitude probably occur in the United States along the fringes of sedimentary basins of petroleum. The amount *could* be 100 billion barrels. Difficulties of exploration are great because when a well is drilled into a tar formation nothing flows. The routine report is "dry hole."

All these guesses combined give a total of 800 billion barrels—a figure of even less usefulness than the figure for ultimate reserves of coal. The great bulk of the largest deposit—the Athabaska formation—is buried beneath 500 to 1800 feet of shale, sandstone, and glacial drift. Under present economic conditions the top economic limit for removal of this sort of overburden is about 1 cubic yard for every ton of tar sand mined. Only about 1 billion barrels of oil could be recovered by open-pit mining. This is less than 1 percent of the Athabaska reserve. No practical means are known for the recovery of *any* tar from the subterranean deposits in Venezuela, Mesopotamia, and the United States.

The maximum energy reserve of the world and of the United States in terms of the present total energy requirement of the world (40 trillion hphr per annum) and of the United States (13 trillion hphr per annum) is presented in Table 3. The minimum figures in this table are

TABLE 3. Ultimate Reserves of Energy from Tar in Terms of the Present Total Annual Requirement

	World	United States
Maximum	50	1
Minimum	< 1	Trace

based on fuel costs at least double the 1950 costs of petroleum and coal. Some day it may be worth while to go after much of this tar that is now considered quite hopeless.

Peat

Coal, oil shale, petroleum, and tar are all fossil fuels in the sense that they have been in the process of formation for many millions of years. Peat is a very young fossil material—so young, in fact, that it is being formed today at a rate that almost removes it from the classification of unrenewable resources. Peat is included in this chapter because it has some resemblance to the lower grades of coal, but it could be discussed with almost as much reason in connection with agricultural energy sources.

Peat is a product of the natural decomposition of such aquatic plants as reeds, rushes, sedges, and mosses. These plants show luxuriant growth under favorable conditions in fairly still but not stagnant water. The growth is above the water while submerged parts of the plants decay, sink to the bottom, and begin to form more or less compact masses.

The rate of accumulation of peat is doubtful. Different observations of the vertical rise of the surface of the peat bed give figures between ½ and 4 inches per year. Accurate determination is difficult because of the heterogeneous character of the surface and the variable water content of the surface peat. If an average water content of 90 percent is assumed and an average rate of bed growth is taken at, say, 1 inch, we have one-tenth of this, or 0.1 inch, as the growth in terms of dry or nearly dry peat. This corresponds to about 7000 tons per square mile per annum. On a dry basis wood can be produced at an average rate of about 2000 tons per square mile per annum. Thus from a fuel standpoint peat may far outstrip the best a forest can do.

A Roman road of about the first century A.D. was found beneath a peat bed. From the age of the road and the depth of the bed, the rate of accumulation is estimated as 0.04 inch per annum. This is about the same rate of growth as timber, if it is assumed that peat formation began soon after the building of the road.

In this discussion the term "peat" is applied only to the vegetation deposits that have fuel value. The word is often used to cover, also, material in a more advanced stage of decomposition. For our purposes, it is better to call such material "muck." The decay of aquatic vegetable matter can proceed in two different directions—to peat or to muck or humus. Humus is an essential part of the cycle of plant growth, but it is not a fuel. In the process of its formation much of the carbon of the vegetation from which it comes is lost as carbon dioxide. On the contrary, peat retains most of the plant carbon while it loses some oxygen and hydrogen (as water). The reactions of decomposition in each case are highly complex and are influenced by bacteria and by temperature.

Peat has been regarded as a cold-weather product, and the observation has been made that there are few peat bogs between latitudes

45°N and 45°S. This is not strictly true. For example, the Dismal Swamp, which is south of 45°N, is making an excellent peat bog. Peat bogs are forming on Andros Island in the Bahamas, in Colombia, which is nearly on the equator, and along the eastern coast of Brazil. Peat bogs are also forming along the southern coast of Australia (35°S) and in the Basrah Province of Mesopotamia (30°N). A glance at the map will show the paucity of good swamp conditions in current geologic time south of 45°N. It might well be, therefore, that peat bogs are abundant above 45°N, not so much because peat forms best where the mean annual temperature is around 45 degrees F, but rather because primary glaciation in the north has provided an abundance of swamps and lakes.

The widely distributed peat reserves of the world could be estimated more successfully than reserves of materials like coal, petroleum, oil shale, and tar, which are either deep in the earth or in deposits of irregular form and extent. The areas of peat bogs can be measured, and the average depth of the peat deposit is easily determined. But many extensive peat bogs have not been explored. For example, Canada has extensive peat bogs for which little data are available. Strangely, so have England and Scotland.

Peat is traditionally recovered from bogs by draining off the water, cutting the wet, sodlike deposit into convenient pieces, and drying them to make them combustible. The drying may be natural or with supplied heat. Cutting of peat sod has been done for thousands of years by manual labor. The Vikings in Greenland depended upon peat for fuel. When Cape Cod lost its timber in the nineteenth century because of excessive use of wood fuel, peat was substituted. In Ireland and in Russia during this twentieth century, peat has been recovered in much the same way. But in more recent years machines have been developed to do the job efficiently on a large scale. Such machines are in operation in Russia, Ireland, Sweden, and Denmark and are being considered for Scotland. The value of peat as a source of energy is just beginning to be appreciated.

In mechanized recovery, the water is first drained off to lower the moisture content to 90 percent or below. This sometimes requires several years. The machines can then excavate this peat material that can be either stored for air drying in stacks under cover or milled (dry-kneading process) to the consistency of a thick mud. The mud can be extruded like brick clays to pieces of suitable size.

When bogs have considerable timber that interferes with machine operation, the "hydropeat" process is used. Here water jets are directed against the peat, and a thin mud containing around 95 percent water is pumped to a drying field where it is spread in a suitable thickness.

The whole idea of mechanization as applied to peat recovery is in its infancy. New machines are being designed and built, and the cost of recovery, which is already competitive with coal in some areas, should become substantially lower.

Peat is not uniform. Toward the bottom of the bed the peat is much more compact than toward the top. In general the color is brown. The bogs are of two kinds—"low bog" in the low lands and "high bog" in the highlands. The ash of the "high-bog" peat is usually minor. "Low-bog" peat sometimes shows high ash and has even been used as a source of iron ore.

Under most favorable conditions highly compacted peat can be air-dried to about 17 percent moisture, but the average figure is nearer 25 percent. In drying peat in stacks there is danger of spontaneous combustion. This is one of the many problems receiving attention from technologists.

Nearly 60 percent of the known peat reserves of the world are in Russia. Peat is probably being produced in Russia at the rate of about 30 million tons per annum. The Btu value of this peat is about one-half that of good coal. Much of the Russian material is utilized for domestic heating, but some of it is distilled to form a fuel gas, a semicoke, liquid fuels, ammonium sulfate, calcium acetate, methanol, and creosote. The products are similar to those from wood distillation. The yield of liquid fuel is about five gallons per air-dried ton of peat—lower than can be obtained by the distillation of coal or oil shale. Russia is said, also, to be using peat as a fuel for the production of electric power. Most of the peat produced in Ireland (around 6 million tons per annum) and in other countries, such as Denmark, Sweden, Norway, the Netherlands, and Argentina, is used for space heating. Some of the peat in Finland is used to operate railway locomotives, although two-thirds of the locomotives use wood.

It is interesting to speculate a little regarding the rate of production of the various peat reserves compared with the probable rate of formation. The depth of peat beds depends upon the character of the subsoil and the contours of the land surrounding the bog. While some beds are more than 50 feet deep, more commonly they are about 10 feet deep. If we assume an average rate of formation of 1 inch per annum (wet basis) and an average depth of 10 feet, we arrive at 120 years as the average time required for the average peat-bed formation. If peat is produced and used each year at the rate of a little less than 1 percent of the reserve, there should be no eventual depletion. This assumes, of course, that the area from which the peat has been removed can be successfully rehabilitated. Technologists are not enthusiastic about research on projects that require many decades for fruition, but the time will come when such research will become important. At present the annual consumption in Russia is not more than 0.05 percent of reserves. The annual rate of consumption in Ireland is about 0.2 percent. But the rate in Denmark has been relatively high. Between 1940 and 1948 Danish consumption was 47 million tons, which represents an average annual rate of 2.1 percent of reserves. This high rate was forced upon Denmark by the German occupation in World War II, and represents undoubted depletion of peat reserves.

There are two ways of looking at peat reserves. The earth has about 136 billion tons of peat, which would correspond to about 68 billion tons of bituminous coal. This is about 1 percent of the coal reserves of the earth. The United States is believed to have about one-tenth of the world's peat (most of it in Minnesota), but because the United States has so much of the world's coal, our peat represents only about 0.25 percent of the optimistic coal estimates and perhaps 2 percent of the more pessimistic estimates. In terms of the present total annual energy requirement of the world, the world's peat reserves amount to 12 years' supply. In terms of the present total annual energy requirement of the United States, the peat reserves of the United States amount to 4 years.

The other way of looking at peat reserves is to assume that peat bogs can be made to form again at a normal rate after the peat has been removed. If the earth now has the peat equivalent of 68 billion tons of coal, we might consider that this could be made to yield somewhat more than half a billion tons of coal equivalent per annum indefinitely. This would correspond to about 5 trillion hphr per annum—one-eighth, of the world's present annual requirement of energy. In the case of the United States our peat reserve might correspond to nearly 4 percent of our present annual requirement. It is up to the agriculturalists and the mechanical engineers to solve this important problem.

Peat has been proposed as a raw product for the manufacture of liquid fuel. The various coal-conversion processes can be applied to peat, but technologically bituminous coal is the best raw product. After this comes subbituminous coal and then lignite. Peat would be less satisfactory than lignite. Almost no research has been done on peat conversion and no reliable economic studies are presently available.

6

How Much All Together

One of the most difficult of intellectual tasks is to maintain a sense of proportion. When we hear a very large number or a superlative adjective, we cannot help being vaguely impressed. Trillions of tons of coal, hundreds of billions of barrels of oil and tar, mountains of oil shale, many tens of thousands of square miles of peat bogs—what does it all mean? Can we sit back comfortably with a sense of abundance of natural resources? Can we regard seriously the optimistic pronouncements of all the energy we shall need for thousands of years? With the background of knowledge of processes by which one form of energy producing material can be converted to another, can we assume that as one fuel is exhausted we can turn to another? Can we be reasonably certain that when fuels are gone we can depend upon nuclear energy?

The answer to most of these questions is no. As for conversion, the answer is yes, at a price. The possibilities and penalties of conversion processes will be discussed in Chap. 8. But in the meantime let us look at the whole fossil-energy picture.

The tables in preceding chapters have been based upon present total energy requirements (excluding animate energy). Tables 1 and 2 summarize the data from preceding chapters. Our present requirement is made up of various fossil fuels, wood fuel, and hydroelectric power. The total amounts divided by our annual consumption of energy would seem to represent the number of years that each reserve would last if we used that material alone to fill all of our energy needs. But it is not as simple as this. The requirements of the United States for energy are going up year by year. Even on a per capita basis the demand for Btu is increasing. World requirements will go up even more rapidly because most of the world is starting from a much lower point. The world as a

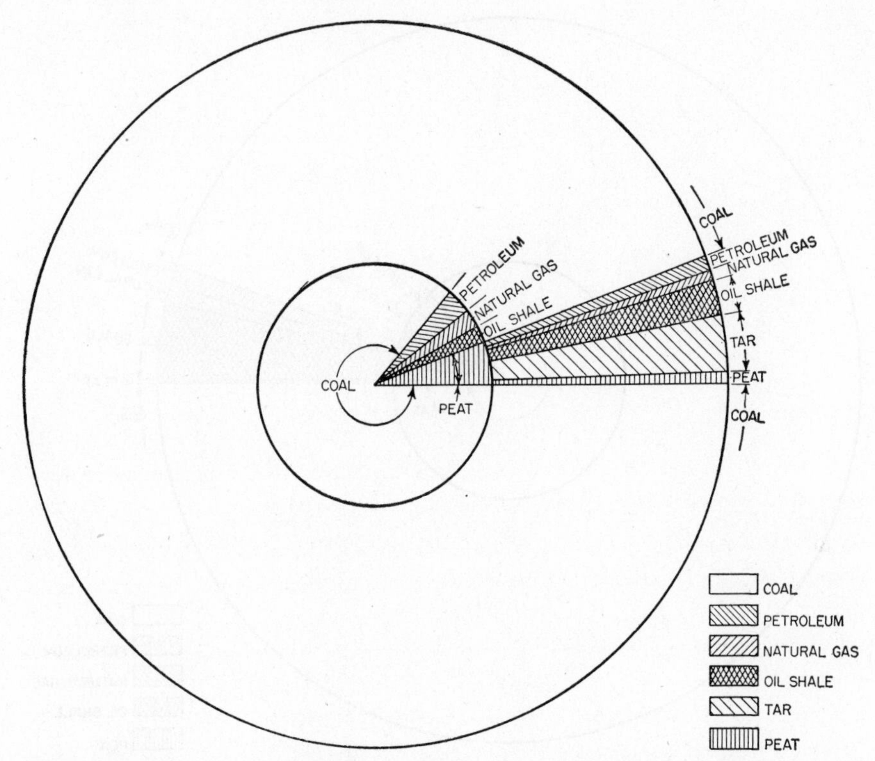

FIG. 1. The maximum (outer circle) estimates and minimum (inner circle) estimates of world fuel reserves.

TABLE 1. Ultimate Reserves of Energy from All Fossil-fuel Deposits of the World

In Horsepower-hours $\times 10^{14}$

	Maximum	Minimum
Coal	750	75
Petroleum (liquid)	5	3
Natural gas	3	2
Oil shale	12	2
Tar	20	
Peat	5	5
Total	795	87

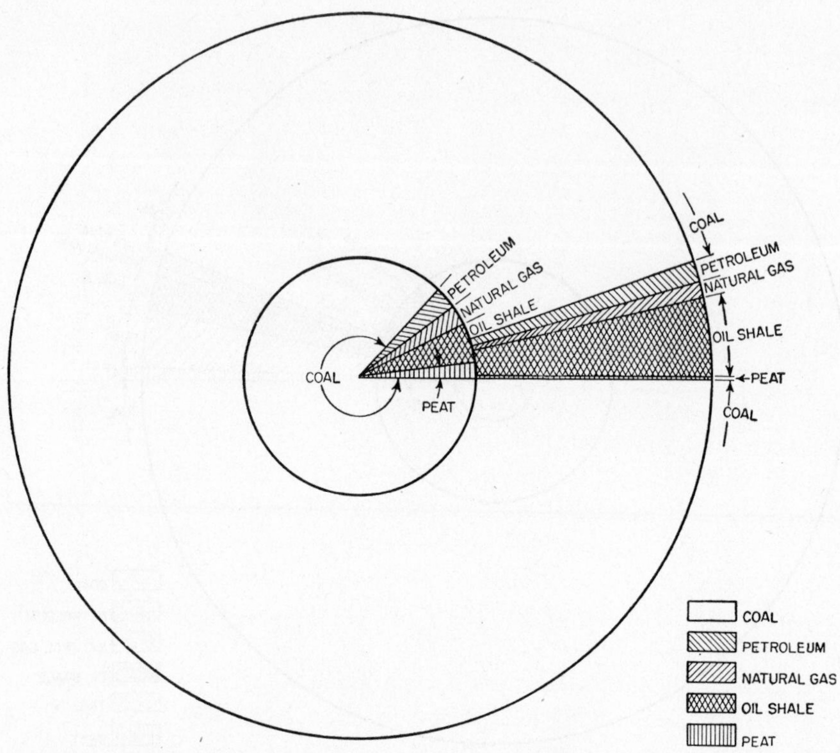

FIG. 2. The maximum (outer circle) estimates and minimum (inner circle) estimates of United States fuel reserves.

TABLE 2. Ultimate Reserves of Energy from All Fossil-fuel Deposits of the United States

In Horsepower-hours $\times 10^{14}$

	Maximum	Minimum
Coal	220	22
Petroleum (liquid)	2.3	0.7
Natural gas	1.6	0.7
Oil shale	8.5	1.4
Tar		
Peat	0.5	0.5
Total	232.9	25.3

whole is using wood more rapidly than the wood is growing, and as the use of wood falls off the use of fossil fuel must grow. The conversion loss of fuel is increasing because of the growth of demand for electric power. Conversion losses will increase to substantial proportions of total energy requirements when we begin large-scale manufacture of liquid or gaseous fuel from coal. In spite of technological progress in the devices for fuel use, the over-all efficiency of fuel utilization is tending downward. All of these factors will be discussed in turn.

The total energy reserves of the United States and of the world are almost the same when expressed in terms of the respective energy requirements. The reason for this is that the high proportion of the world's principal fuel (coal) located in the United States is offset by our relatively high energy demand.

Coal is so much more abundant than any other fossil fuel that inaccuracies in the other fuel reserve figures are of little over-all consequence. What is left of our fossil-fuel era depends upon coal. If we find twice as much oil and gas, or if we can recover ten times as much tar, or if we can produce all of our shale oil, the picture will not be greatly changed.

The maximum totals are almost ten times as great as the minimum totals. This does not mean that the fossil-fuel era will be nearly ten times as long if we can get the maximum amounts. The various factors that affect life conspire to subordinate actual reserve magnitudes. It will be seen that the energy picture of the future is fundamentally the same almost regardless of our choice of figures.

7

Patterns of Energy Use

The industrialized nations of the earth are moving constantly toward greater technological complexity in the *preparation* of energy supplies in order to secure optimum simplicity or convenience in the *use* of energy. The specific changes of energy pattern that have occurred in each country have depended, in part, upon the nature of the energy sources available. For example, countries like Norway, Sweden, and Switzerland have turned most rapidly to electricity because of high hydroelectric potentialities. In the United States the demand for liquid and gaseous fuel has increased disproportionately because of the abundance of petroleum. The trend away from wood fuel has been slow in Brazil because of the relative abundance of wood. Nevertheless it is possible to make certain generalizations.

Electricity is the most convenient of all sources of energy. Its use is growing more rapidly in all countries than any other energy form in relation to the total energy consumption. Almost everywhere electric lighting has displaced gas lighting just as gas displaced kerosene and kerosene displaced candles. In general, for domestic heat, the change is made from wood to coal to oil to gas, and finally to electricity. The shift to electricity is now in its earliest stages and is not likely to reach maturity in the United States until natural gas becomes much less abundant. However, in 1950 the ratio of gas ranges to electric ranges sold was but 3:2; while in 1935 the ratio was 16:1. The ratio of gas to electric ranges in service has declined from 20:1 in 1935 to 4:1 in 1950. The trend appears to be inexorable and probably cannot be reversed by advertising campaigns.

The increase in demand for electricity in the United States has been phenomenal. It has doubled every ten to twelve years since the industry began and is expected to double again in the next ten years.

Electric arc furnaces of huge size are contributing to the rapidly increasing demand for electric current. (*Westinghouse Electric Corp.*)

Modern steam locomotives came along just about in time to be replaced by the more efficient diesel-electric. (*Pennsylvania Railroad Co.*)

During the four years 1947 to 1950 inclusive, about 18.6 million kilowatts of generating capacity were added. This is about one-half of the industry's total generating capacity in 1940. The total United States power generation in 1950 (329 billion kwhr) was 12.7 percent higher than in 1949. This represents more than double the normal annual growth. And yet the margin of capacity over demand in 1950 was only 12 percent compared with 14 percent in 1949. In other words demand is more than keeping pace with capacity. Equipment on order will add another 22.8 million kilowatts of capacity by the end of 1953. In the five years, 1941 to 1945 inclusive, we generated over a trillion kwhr. From 1951 to 1955 inclusive we shall be able to turn out 2 trillion kwhr. New generating capacity installation is listed in Table 1.

TABLE 1. Additions to United States Generating Capacity, Industrial, Private, and Public

Year	100 000 kw
1946	3.6
1947	22
1948	40
1949	66
1950	57
1951	72
1952	81
1953	74*

* This includes only equipment ordered before 1951.

In 1949 the United States produced about 43 percent of all the electric-power generation in the world. Russia was a poor second with only about a fifth as much.

The Westinghouse Electric Corporation expects that by 1980 our generating capacity may be five times what it was in 1950. This seems like a reasonable estimate when it is realized that the average urban domestic consumer in 1950 used 1825 kwhr—nearly double the average use of 1940. The potential use of the modern home is nearer 10 000 kwhr (Table 2). Growth figures indicate that between 1950 and 1960 the average annual farm consumption in the eastern United States will jump from 2350 to 6000 kwhr, and this does not take irrigation into account. In forty years installed industrial power for each worker has risen from 2.9 horsepower (31 percent electrical) to 7.2 horsepower (93 percent electrical), and the trend continues. The aluminum and magnesium industries may more than double their installed capacity of about 2 million kilowatts in the 1950–1960 decade. The commercial production of titanium, an electric-furnace product, is looming.

Almost every new or expanded industrial operation means a greater demand for electric power. Ore beneficiation (because of the depletion of high-grade iron ore) will require a million kilowatts. Increased beneficiation of inferior coal will add several more millions. Full mechanization of present mines could easily treble the mining industry's installed capacity, for the huge coal mines of the future are expected to require far more electric power per ton of coal. (Plans call for an output

TABLE 2. **United States Domestic Consumption of Electricity**

In Kilowatt-hours per Annum per Householder

Year	Amount
1917	268
1927	446
1937	800
1950	1 825
Potential	10 000

of 100 tons per man per day, compared with 10 tons obtained now from our best equipped mines.) A 20 000-barrel-per-day shale-oil plant would require as much power as 50 000 homes.

The catalogue could be extended to include synthetic-rubber manufacture, welding, infrared heating, continuous annealing, electric-arc furnaces, resistance furnaces, radio-frequency heating, air conditioning (which is particularly important), oil burners, and automatic stokers—all of which are contributing to a rapidly growing load. Increasing the speed of nearly all processing lines will increase the electrical energy content per unit of output. General use of heat pumps in only our higher priced homes would multiply the total domestic electric-power consumption of the United States by 5. Unless military exigencies interfere, plans call for mass production of heat-pump units in 1952. The heat pump is discussed in Chaps. 10 and 15.

The reason for shifting from coal to oil, for example, may be economic or it may be that the supply is more dependable, but once a nation or an industry or a householder has taken the step—has experienced the simplicities of handling and control and the supplementary economies that are naturally associated with these simplicities—only compelling factors of price or supply induce a return to less convenient forms of energy.

Switzerland has almost no fossil-fuel reserves. In recent years the importation of coal has been displaced to an increasing extent by the importation of residual fuel oil. The reason has been economic rather than preference for liquid fuel. The refining capacity for Middle East

A substantial electrical power load is provided by installations for infrared heating. (*Westinghouse Electric Corp.*)

petroleum has been so much in excess of current petroleum demands in convenient marketing areas that it has been possible to supply residual fuel oil at a lower price per therm (100 000 Btu) than coal. Switzerland is unlikely to return to coal unless coal becomes cheap enough to counterbalance the intangible matter of preference as well as the tangible cost differentials of storage, transfer, control, use, and ash disposal, or unless political difficulties arise in the Middle East.

In Norway, homes are heated with wood gathered from local forests, coke imported from Britain, and electricity generated in hydroelectric plants. For many homes, electricity is the cheapest of the three, but wood provides by far the largest part of space-heating demand.

The United States, even with its abundance of both coal and petroleum, is marching down the same path as Switzerland. Many years

Industrial processes are finding new ways of applying more energy effectively. One is the increasing use of radio-frequency generators for localized heating purposes. (*Westinghouse Electric Corp.*)

ago ships turned from coal to oil. Ship owners will not willingly go back. More recently coal shortages arising from industrial disputes have led to the widespread substitution of oil for coal in the steam-generating plants of industries and public utilities. Between 1948 and 1950 this led to an increased consumption of oil amounting to some 35 million barrels per annum, or 85 percent. In the same two-year period the amount of natural gas used to generate electricity increased by 144 billion cubic feet (30 percent) while coal decreased by 12 million tons, or 12 percent. Some of these plants will return to coal only when coal becomes significantly cheaper than oil. This state of affairs is difficult for the coal industry and may be opposed, in the long run, to national welfare. For this reason the executives of some utilities have turned back to coal even when little or no favorable differential with oil existed.

Man's campaign for greater comfort is at a high cost of energy. Air-conditioning installations, such as this, are growing in popularity. (*Westinghouse Electric Corp.*)

Both coal and heavy fuel oil have been used in abundance to fire steam locomotives. The drastic substitution of diesel-electric locomotives during the past few years has led to further reductions in the demand for coal, and also reductions in the demand for heavy oil for this purpose. The shift from coal to oil in this case represents net conservation of energy reserves because, compared with fuel for generating steam, diesel oil can do ten times as much useful work in switching service, five times as much in freight service, and more than three times as much in passenger service. No wonder the railroads find it from five to ten times as profitable to spend money for the substitution of diesel-electric for steam locomotives as to retire a like amount of bonded indebtedness. The complete dieselization of our railway system will require the use of only slightly more diesel oil than the heavy oil used (in competition with coal) for the steam locomotives. Almost all railway traffic is expected to be handled by diesel by 1960. Locomotive purchases in 1950 were the largest in twenty-seven years. These

About 42 percent of the total electric power consumed in the United States for manufacture is for the production of primary metals, and the largest part of this is for aluminum. Ignitron rectifiers convert alternating current to direct current. (*Westinghouse Electric Corp.*)

included 3653 diesel-electrics, 15 steam, 6 electric, and 10 gas-turbine locomotives. The irrevocable nature of the change of energy pattern is indicated by the facts that displaced coal locomotives are being scrapped, roundhouses are being dismantled, and a considerable number of coal cars are pointed toward the scrap heap. Such alternative facilities will be no longer available.

The factor of greatest importance in the determination of our energy pattern is the way in which we are becoming increasingly insistent upon devices that require liquid fuels. We must have motor cars, trucks, airplanes, and agricultural machinery. Such mobile equipment can be powered conveniently only with liquid fuel. In 1950 about three-quarters of the world's cars and half of all trucks were operated within the United States. In 1950 more than six million cars, trucks, and buses rolled off American assembly lines—more than three times the output of all other countries combined. Automotive businesses accounted for

Modern petroleum refineries are beautiful examples of design and construction. Furthermore, they represent the highest of all fuel-conversion efficiencies. (*Gulf Oil Corp.*)

about one-fifth of all United States retail trade. In 1950 we consumed about 900 million barrels of motor fuel. This amounted to about 15 percent of our total energy requirement for that year. The wide use of the internal-combustion engine is the most distinguishing characteristic of the United States energy pattern.

The last few years have witnessed a skyrocketing use of natural gas. While oil has been displacing coal, gas has been displacing both coal and oil. For example, when natural gas reached New York City in January, 1951, it displaced about 5 million barrels of gas-enrichment oil that was used there annually for the preparation of manufactured gas. The impact of the wide distribution of natural gas on various other fuel markets will be marked but the pattern has not yet crystallized.

During the past decade billions of dollars have been spent to almost double the extent of our pipe-line system. In 1950 we had about 152 000 miles of pipe line that gathered the gas and 108 000 miles that transmitted it to centers of population. Additional pipe-line construction planned in 1950 should increase our annual capacity for long-distance transmission by nearly 5 trillion cubic feet. For a long time natural gas

Substantial portions of petroleum production are normally gases which can be conveniently stored in liquid form in spherical pressure tanks. (*Gulf Oil Corp.*)

has been priced lower per therm than oil or coal because it has been abundant at the source, although unavailable at many potential points of use. The pipe-line network will have the effect of bringing the price of gas more nearly to the same price level as oil or coal. While it is technically possible to convert natural gas to liquid fuel, the operation is not likely to become generally economical.

Between 1930 and 1950 the price of natural gas at the well head has varied between 5 and 7 cents per thousand cubic feet. The average of 6 cents corresponds to residual fuel oil at 35.6 cents per barrel and to coal at $1.52 per ton. Residual fuel oil at a normal delivered price of $1.65 per barrel would correspond to natural gas delivered at 27.8 cents per thousand, and coal at a delivered price of $8.65 per ton would correspond to natural gas at 34.2 cents. Natural gas appeals to the householder because of low installation and maintenance costs, extreme cleanliness, and freedom from dependence upon electric power for operation of fuel-handling devices. Gas appeals to the industrial consumer because of the additional reasons of price stability and relative dependability of supply. Those who have turned to gas are not likely to change to another fuel until gas becomes much more expensive.

Investors of great sums of money in gas transmission are under no illusion with regard to natural-gas reserves. Investments are based upon the assurance of not more than ten years' operation of pipe lines at rated capacity. After that the use of gas may gradually decrease until finally it becomes a minor part of our energy picture.

The gas utilities producing coke-oven gas are responsible for about 20 percent of the nation's coke and coal chemicals. The extension of natural-gas lines to the areas served with coke-oven gas will affect the production of needed coke and chemicals. The Bureau of Mines estimates that by 1960 about 3 percent of the nation's coke-making capacity may have to close down. This illustrates the close relationship of the various elements of a national energy pattern.

An interesting illustration of the impact on fuel consumption of changes in primary-metals manufacture is the comparison between aluminum and steel. About 1.4 tons of coal are required for the manufacture of every ton of steel. But nearly 15 tons of coal are required for every ton of aluminum. This assumes the use of coal instead of hydropower for the generation of electric current—a necessary assumption for the future. The coal equivalent of energy required for aluminum manufacture is arrived at as follows:

To produce the 2 tons of alumina required for 1 ton of aluminum requires approximately 1.4 tons of coal (or 23 000 cubic feet of natural gas) to supply processing heat, 0.05 ton coal to prepare 300 pounds of quicklime, and 0.06 ton coal to prepare 340 pounds of soda ash. The total for alumina preparation is thus about 1.5 tons of coal. To convert the alumina to aluminum requires the consumption of 0.65 ton of carbon (usually derived from petroleum), and 20 000 kwhr of electric power, which corresponds to about 12.3 tons of coal. The conversion thus totals about 13 tons, which, added to the 1.5 tons for preparation, gives a grand total of 14.5 tons. Since aluminum is now made with hydroelectric power, the present consumption of fuel is only about 2 tons, but even this is more than the energy required for steel, and the proper way to look at fuel requirements is to regard hydroelectric power as a part of the total supply of energy—a part that can be used for a variety of demands.

The significance of the aluminum picture is this: A comparison of production of the three years 1937 to 1939 inclusive with the three years 1947 to 1949 inclusive shows that steel did not quite double, copper increased only a trifle (because so much is being imported), and aluminum increased nearly four times (Table 3).

TABLE 3. United States Production of Some Metals
In Millions of Tons

	1937–1939	1947–1949
Steel	141	228
Copper	22	25
Aluminum	0.5	1.8

During the past few decades the consumption of petroleum (both oil and gas) has increased much more rapidly than the demand for total energy materials. The trend for the world is shown strikingly in Fig. 1,

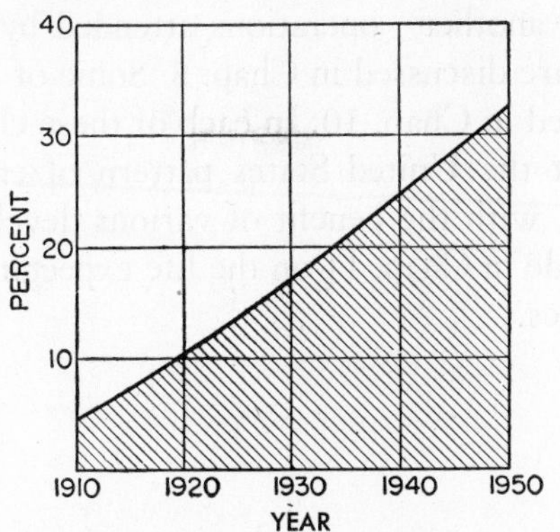

FIG. 1. Petroleum (liquid plus gas) is providing an increasing proportion of the world's total energy consumption.

which shows the increasingly prominent role of petroleum. The trend for the United States has been upward even more sharply. Table 4 shows data for 1940 and 1950 and estimates for 1960. Natural gas is

TABLE 4. Production of Energy in the United States (Excluding Wood and Nonfuel Uses)

In Trillions of Horsepower-hours

	1940	1950	1960
Hydroelectric	0.35	0.65	0.90
Natural gas	1.10	2.30	3.85
Coal	5.00	4.85	5.30
Oil	3.10	4.90	6.80
Total	9.55	12.70	16.85

expected to maintain its steep climb up to 1960, while coal demand increases only moderately. The next decade, to 1970, is likely to show an entirely different story, for gas may then begin actually to decline and a substantial part of our oil will be imported or synthesized. Coal should take the first halting steps toward its eventual destiny as the mightiest fuel source of all.

The above paragraphs suffice to sketch in some of the most conspicuous lines of the patterns of energy use. Each country has its own energy pattern determined by availability of domestic sources of energy, degree of industrialization, habits of life, distribution of wealth, and national economy as this affects trade with other countries. The energy pattern determines the extent to which it is necessary to convert one form of energy to another—operations attended by considerable loss. These operations are discussed in Chap. 8. Some of the losses in use of energy are discussed in Chap. 10. In each of these chapters, an attempt is made to project the United States pattern of energy use into the future, and finally, with the benefit of various developed assumptions, predictions are made in Chap. 11 on the life expectancy of total United States fuel resources.

8

From One to Another

It is technically possible to prepare almost any kind of fuel from any other kind of fuel. For example, motor fuel of equally high quality can be made from petroleum, coal, natural gas, shale oil, tar, peat, or wood. For that matter it can be made from carbon dioxide and water. But there are differences in cost and in energy losses. With occasional exceptions, the lowest cost comes with the lowest energy loss, and the energy loss is proportional to the amount of work required to accomplish the conversion. Optimum conservation would seem to call for the efficient use of each form of fuel without converting it to another form—to burn crude oil instead of converting it to the various petroleum products, to burn coal instead of using coal as a raw product for hydrogenation or gas synthesis, to manufacture no electricity by fuel combustion. The only reason these things cannot be done is that we would not be content with such an energy pattern.

In 1947 (the latest year for which all data are available at the time of this writing) 53 percent of our fossil fuel went into one sort of conversion or another. And the trend is upward.

Except for hydroelectric installations, almost all electric power represents an energy conversion from coal, oil, or natural gas. Motor fuel is now obtained by the conversion of crude petroleum. Later liquid fuels in general will be obtained by the conversion of solid fuels. These and other types of conversion will be discussed in turn.

From Crude Oil to Petroleum Products

Refining of petroleum, even with modern processes such as catalytic cracking, continues to be an example of conversion with relatively high thermal efficiency. This means that the heating value of the combined products, subtracting products that must be used as fuel to operate the refinery processes, is not much below the heating value of the crude oil taken in as charging stock. The actual efficiency depends, of course, upon how much work is done on the crude. A simple, well-designed "topping" plant, in which nothing is done to the crude except distillation, has a thermal efficiency of about 98 percent. Complete refineries prior to 1930, including thermal cracking (distillation under pressure), had thermal efficiencies of about 92 percent. The addition of catalytic cracking (distillation in the presence of clays) and of various other supplementary processes has brought the average thermal efficiency down to about 87 percent. This is still excellent compared with other conversions to be discussed. Catalytic cracking itself has a thermal efficiency of about 82 percent.

The processes used in petroleum refineries depend upon the kinds of petroleum products demanded. The reason for catalytic cracking is the desire to impart antiknock qualities to motor fuels. This applies also to several other processes. The demand for distillate fuel, which includes motor fuel, diesel oil, kerosene, and domestic furnace oil, has been going up more rapidly than the demand for residual fuel oil. At the same time average crude-oil production has tended to give higher yields of the relatively unwanted residual fuel oil. These two factors are leading to the adoption of means for converting residual oils to distillate. Both of the two available processes for such conversion involve energy loss.

One process is the destructive distillation of the oil until the only residue left is coke. The principle is identical with the coking of coal. The thermal efficiency is about the same as catalytic cracking—say, 82 percent. Coking is a process of removing carbon from a heavy oil to make a light oil.

The other is hydrogenation, which accomplishes the conversion not by subtracting carbon but by adding hydrogen. In each case the hydrogen-carbon ratio is increased, which means that the oils become lower in specific gravity.

Hydrogenation would necessarily be accomplished at the expense of fuel used for process heat, for the generation of steam and electric power, and for the manufacture of hydrogen. The thermal efficiency of petroleum conversion is a function of the difference in specific gravity between the charging stock and the total liquid products—or, in other words, a function of the work done (Fig. 1). To the extent that hydrogenation accomplishes more upgrading, it shows an impaired thermal efficiency compared with thermal cracking. This does not mean that hydrogenation of oil has no future, but it does mean that hydrogenation is not a means for extending our fuel resources. It is, instead, a means for improving the yield of one petroleum product at the expense of another. If, for example, one-half of the 1950 production of petroleum had been subjected to mild destructive hydrogenation, the conversion loss would have amounted to about 0.4 trillion hphr for that year.

Destructive hydrogenation differs from the classical organic hydrogenations, in which hydrogen is added to an unsaturated molecule to

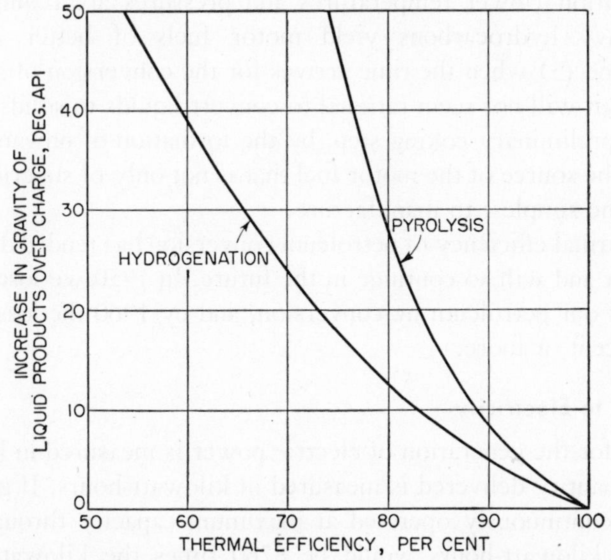

FIG. 1. Thermal efficiencies of conversion to petroleum by hydrogenation and by pyrolysis.

make a more saturated one. This latter is the process used, for example, in making vegetable shortening from vegetable oil. But destructive hydrogenation is accompanied by a reduction in molecular weight (instead of a slight increase) and a reduction instead of increase in the degree of hydrogen saturation. An illustrative reaction is the addition of one mole of hydrogen to one mole of diphenyl (a heavy oil) to make two moles of benzene (a light oil). Here we do not get the volume decrease characteristic of classical hydrogenations, because the consumption of hydrogen has been accompanied by decomposition.

Excellent catalysts have been found for destructive hydrogenation of heavy petroleum. Use of the process is quite likely to grow over the next decade. There are two variations of heavy-oil hydrogenation. In the one case the oil is distilled to convert it to coke, distilled liquid, and gas. The coke-still distillate is then subjected to high-pressure catalytic hydrogenation. In the other case the coking step is eliminated. By the end of 1950 the processes had not become sufficiently well-founded to compare economics, but it seems that the latter may become of special long-term importance for three reasons: (1) the high-molecular-weight hydrocarbons of heavy oils (the hydrocarbons from which coke is chiefly derived) are the easiest to convert to motor fuel by destructive hydrogenation (lower temperatures and pressures are required); (2) these heavy hydrocarbons yield motor fuels of better antiknock quality; and (3) when the time arrives for the conversion of solid fuels to liquids, it will not seem rational to convert liquids to solids. In other words, a preliminary coking step, by the formation of unwanted coke, destroys the source of the motor fuel that is not only of superior quality but also the simplest to manufacture.

The thermal efficiency of petroleum conversion has tended downward in the past and will so continue in the future. In 1950 we lost about 13 percent of our petroleum by conversion, and by 1960 the loss may run to 20 percent or more.

From Fuel to Electricity

Capacity for the generation of electric power is measured in kilowatts, and the quantity delivered is measured in kilowatt-hours. If generators could be continuously operated at maximum capacity throughout the year, the kilowatt-hours would be 8760 times the kilowatts. For a number of reasons this cannot be done—principally because the need for electricity is not constant throughout the day, week, or year. The peak load ordinarily occurs during some half hour in the early evening of a single day in December. With increasing air-conditioning loads, the peak may change to a day in the summer. This has already happened on some Southern power lines. The 1950 installed capacity of the United States was 67.5 million kilowatts, which at 100 percent load factor would produce 591 billion kwhr per annum. The actual production was 329 billion kwhr—about 56 percent of maximum.

One kilowatt-hour of electric energy, if there were no losses, would require the combustion of 0.26 pound of coal. The average coal consumption of the United States installed generator capacity in 1950 stood at 1.22 pounds per kwhr. This represents an efficiency of 21 percent. However, a number of modern power stations show a consumption under 0.87 pound of coal, which represents an efficiency above 30 percent. This marked improvement has been made possible by combining many things, such as improved combustion, higher steam pressures and temperatures, recovery of some of the waste heat by multistage regenerative water heating, steam reheating after partial expansion, larger plant size, and high load factor. It does not seem probable that much can be done to improve efficiencies of the best plants still further without very greatly increasing costs, but much can and will be done to improve the less efficient plants.

The improvement in steam generation efficiencies has had a broader application than the generation of electric power. A survey of commercial United States plants in 1947 indicates a number of clear relationships. As would be expected, the larger the station the better the thermal achievement, the largest stations showing thermal economy on the average about a third better than the smallest stations. Thermal economy was improved, of course, wherever higher pressures and temperatures were used. The 1200- to 1600-pound-per-square-inch plants required less than 0.87 pound of coal per net kilowatt-hour. The 600- to 700-pound-per-square-inch plants required about a pound. And the 200- to 400-pound-per-square-inch plants required anywhere from 1.06 to 2 pounds. The higher the percentage of time operated the better the fuel economy. On the average, plants with an operating factor of 80 percent showed the use of about a third less coal than those with an operating factor of 40 percent. The interconnection of power plants in the United States made it possible to make optimum use of the most efficient plants. For this reason the national average of 21-percent efficiency for electric power generation could be reached in spite of the existence of some plants as low as 14 percent. A few plants in the survey were slightly above 30 percent.

About 70 percent of 1950 electric-power generation was from fuel combustion (64 percent of this from coal-steam plants), and 30 percent was hydroelectric. Hydroelectric capacity is not increasing as rapidly as steam-generating capacity at this time, and is not expected to in the future because, normally, new hydroelectric plants, most of which may be somewhat less profitable than those already built, will be added only gradually as the rising cost of fuel makes them economically attractive. Of the new generating capacity under construction in 1950, 81 percent was in steam units, 18 percent in hydroelectric units, and not quite 1 percent in internal-combustion units (used chiefly for standby and peak-load purposes). As pointed out in Chap. 17, the amount of electric power that can be ultimately produced from waterfalls is definitely limited to about 50 million kilowatts, which is about three times our present hydroelectric power, and less than the entire 1950 generating capacity (67 million kilowatts). It is possible that, if we should have in 1980 the predicted generating capacity of 250 million kilowatts, not more than 50 million would be hydroelectric. This would leave 200 million for steam units—five times the 45 million in 1947 on which the tables in Chap. 21 were constructed. The 1.2 trillion hphr per annum representing energy loss for electric-power production (8.7 percent of the 1947 total energy requirement of the United States) will have been raised in 1980 to about 3.5 trillion hphr per annum. Thus, if the United States energy requirement remained constant, this loss would be about 28 percent of the total. Needless to say, the energy requirement of the United States will not remain constant, and it is certain that the production of electric power from coal will be improved; but, inasmuch as electric-power demand is increasing so rapidly, we cannot escape the conclusion that the percentage loss from this source will become materially higher in the future.

The apparently predominant position of electrical energy in the future—now from fossil fuels and later from constant sources—brings up the question of supply of metals suitable for electrical conduction. This is a grave problem that should be studied in detail. The life expectancy of our copper ores appears to be measurable in units of only decades. Fortunately, aluminum, which is potentially more abundant than copper, is already in the process of capturing some of the major electrical fields.

From Coal to Oil

Coal can be converted to liquid fuel in either of two ways. Both are wasteful.

Hydrogenation of coal is the same sort of destructive hydrogenation discussed under the heading From Crude Oil to Petroleum Products, but the process as applied to coal suffers in two respects: it is less facilitated by catalysts, and the technology of continuous operation has not yet been worked out. The original experiments in 1913 on coal hydrogenation were batchwise (noncontinuous) and slow. It is still batchwise and slow. There is enormous room for improvement in the catalysis of coal hydrogenation. The intense world-wide search since 1913 for catalysts for this purpose has been characterized by a frantic desire for patent protection rather than by a scientific quest for truth. All the metallic elements of the periodic table (except two rare ones), and endless combinations of them, have been patented as catalysts. These patents have now expired. The catalysts described are nearly all worthless; the best of them merely double the rate of reaction. In sharp contrast, a typical catalytic reaction in petroleum chemistry—the use of

In this coal-hydrogenation experimental plant at Louisiana, Missouri, a pattern of "know-how" is being cut for a future American industry based on the conversion of coal to oil. (*U.S. Bureau of Mines.*)

sulfuric acid to speed up the reaction between butene and isobutane to make an aviation fuel—produces an acceleration of the process of many million times—equivalent to a change in velocity from 1 foot per 5000 years to 186 000 miles per second, the velocity of light.

In the Bergius process for coal hydrogenation, powdered coal is mixed with tar from a previous run to make a thick mush. A little tin chloride or iron oxide is stirred in, and the heterogeneous mess is forced into a pressure vessel with hydrogen at several thousand pounds per square inch. Here it is heated for an hour or so, and the resultant stuff is separated into (1) crude products, (2) material for recycle, and (3) wastes, such as ash (Fig. 2). United States engineers have added little of importance to the fundamental conceptions of the German technologists. We have not yet succeeded in speeding up the reaction to the point where the hydrogenation of coal can be made truly continuous.

The products of coal hydrogenation are of about the same kind as those from the coking of coal, except that we get little or no coke. The proportions are different. Some carbon of the coal reappears in the liquid and gas; some is used to supply hydrogen and heat for the process. The latter factor creates an important problem. There are only two sources of industrial hydrogen—hydrocarbons and water. Each can be decomposed to make hydrogen. But hydrocarbons are the things we want to make rather than destroy. This leaves water as the only prac-

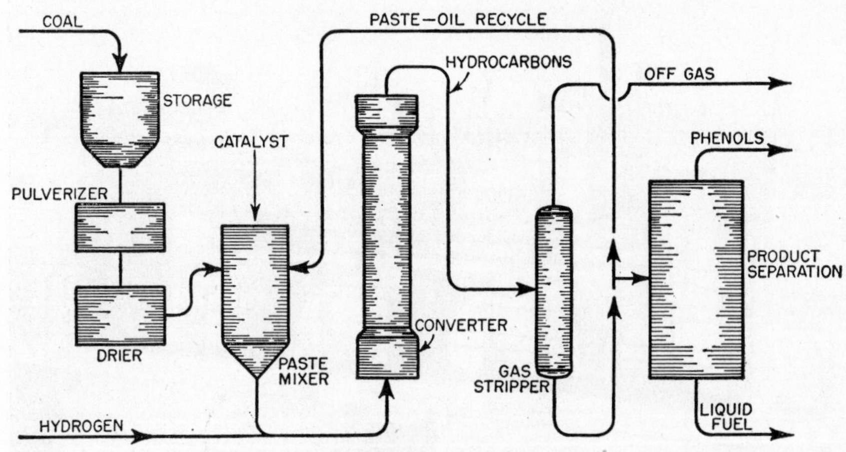

FIG. 2. The essential steps in the production of liquid fuel from coal by hydrogenation.

tical source, and to obtain hydrogen from water requires the addition of energy obtained by "burning up" carbon. A direct reaction between water and carbon forms hydrogen and carbon dioxide. The latter is readily removed. However, since carbon dioxide is an unwanted, though inevitable, product, generation of hydrogen through the aid of coal involves what amounts to destruction of a portion of the coal.

For this reason the Bergius process has so far not been seriously taken up as a method for producing liquid fuels, although the government and some chemical companies have considered the limited use of coal hydrogenation for the production of needed chemicals, with fuel as a secondary product. One such plant has already been announced and another is being promoted.

Benzene in the 1930's was in such oversupply that much of it was used as a constituent of motor fuel. Chemical demand has grown steadily until, in 1950, it was almost critically short. Benzene was formerly obtained exclusively from coke-oven operations. By the end of 1950 about 4 percent of it was being produced from petroleum. Additional petroleum-based benzene will be developed in the early 1950's, but such manufacture is wasteful of liquid-petroleum resources. Economics will become unfavorable to any large-scale operation of this sort. Coke-oven capacity has less than doubled between 1935 and 1950, whereas the demand for benzene has been multiplied in the same period by almost five. Future growth of coal distillation is not expected to be rapid if it is dependent upon demand for metallurgical coke, but applications of the process could expand enormously if the distillation of coal were to become incidental to the manufacture of liquid fuels. For the long term, coal will continue to be the primary source of benzene.

The same story is true of phenols. One commercial coal-hydrogenation plant could completely satisfy the United States market for phenols, and additional plants would probably have to "plow under" the phenols by recycling to convert to fuel. But petroleum will tide over periods of critical shortage.

A promising modification of coal hydrogenation is to convert only the easier portions of the coal to liquid and gas, the remainder going to coke. The idea may have possibilities, because the reactions are more rapid, require less hydrogen, and proceed at lower pressures. The process involves less over-all waste of fuel. The yield of liquid is lower than from complete hydrogenation, but additional supplies of liquid can be obtained from the coke by another avenue.

This is the so-called "Fischer-Tropsch process," an idea fundamentally different from that of Bergius. The raw product of the Fischer-Tropsch process is carbon monoxide and hydrogen. This mixture is known as "synthesis gas." It is possible to prepare this mixture from any carbonaceous material that burns. This includes wood, charcoal, oil shale, coal, coke, natural gas, and other hydrocarbon gases. When these materials are burned with plenty of oxygen or air, we get carbon dioxide, which can be reduced with hydrogen to carbon monoxide, which in turn can be reduced with more hydrogen to hydrocarbons.

$$C + O_2 \rightarrow CO_2$$
$$CO_2 + H_2 \rightarrow CO + H_2O$$

Such a procedure is extravagant in its hydrogen requirement. As we have seen, it is desirable to use a sequence of reactions that requires a minimum of hydrogen. This end can be attained in various ways. For example, incomplete combustion of carbon gives carbon monoxide instead of carbon dioxide, thus minimizing the need for hydrogen to reduce carbon dioxide.

$$2C + O_2 \rightarrow 2CO$$

Incomplete combustion of carbon in the presence of steam gives both carbon monoxide and hydrogen.

$$3C + O_2 + H_2O \rightarrow 3CO + H_2$$

The two gases can be obtained also from the incomplete combustion of hydrocarbons or by the reaction between hydrocarbons and steam.

$$CH_4 + O_2 \rightarrow CO + H_2 + H_2O$$
$$CH_4 + H_2O \rightarrow CO + 3H_2$$

The selection of the plan depends upon economics.

Some of these reactions give more than enough hydrogen for the synthesis while others give too little or none. The ratio of hydrogen to carbon monoxide in the product can be increased by a simple catalytic reaction between carbon monoxide and water to give carbon dioxide and hydrogen.

$$CO + H_2O \rightarrow CO_2 + H_2$$

This reaction is technically useful but essentially wasteful because it diverts some of the carbon to carbon dioxide.

Many of these reactions involve oxygen. Most continuous processes require reasonably pure oxygen, because when air is used the synthesis-gas product is diluted with nitrogen, which impedes satisfactory hydrocarbon formation. However, new techniques promise to yield nitrogen-free synthesis gas even when air is used instead of oxygen. Some of the more optimistic cost estimates for manufacture of motor fuel from coal by the Fischer-Tropsch process assume that air combustion can be made practicable.

The various reactions mentioned for preparation of synthesis gas are not new. Synthesis gas is merely the water gas of the nineteenth century, adjusted for ratio of components, and prepared according to identical chemical principles. Water gas is now being manufactured for use as a domestic fuel, as a source of hydrogen for synthetic ammonia, and in the synthesis of methanol. For these three purposes water gas has been cheap enough, but all the water gas now manufactured in this country would not make more than 16 000 barrels a day of motor fuel—a tiny fraction of our fuel consumption. If we are to use water gas as a basis for liquid motor fuels, we shall have to learn how to make it much more cheaply. The trouble with the old water-gas process is that it is not continuous and it works well only when coke is used as the solid fuel. The synthetic-liquid-fuel industry cannot afford to start with expensive coke.

Fischer-Tropsch synthesis itself is fundamentally simple (Fig. 3). You have a catalyst chamber. You put gas in at one end and take gas

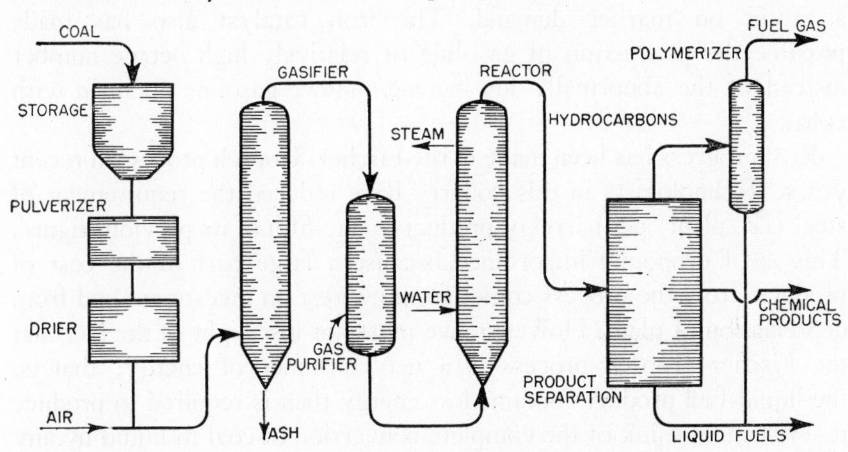

FIG. 3. The essential steps in the production of liquid fuel from coal by the gas-synthesis (Fischer-Tropsch) process.

from the other end. The input gas is a mixture of one part carbon monoxide with about two parts or less of hydrogen. The gas coming out contains hydrocarbons, some of which can be condensed out as liquids. The process can be regulated to give only gas or to give an optimum yield of liquid fuel. It can be made to give wax with up to 2000 carbon atoms per molecule, or to give a variety of oxygen-containing chemicals. Even under conditions believed to be optimum for gasoline, some ethyl alcohol is formed. So, in spite of the simplicity of the process idea, it is necessary to control many process variables in order to make the things that are relatively profitable and to avoid making unwanted things.

Successful development of this process would provide cheaper domestic gas, synthetic ammonia and methanol, and a convenient method for making many useful chemicals, such as alcohols, acids, esters, and various other organic compounds. This is important.

The proportions of the various hydrocarbon products yielded by the Fischer-Tropsch process depend on the catalyst used and upon a dozen conditions of operation. The catalyst preferred by the Germans was cobalt. The catalyst preferred in the United States is iron, because iron is cheaper and permits use of higher temperature ranges without bad effects. At higher temperatures the reaction is faster, which means that equipment for a given capacity is much smaller. Higher temperature also means that fewer chemicals are formed. Even with the iron catalyst, however, the volume of chemicals may ultimately prove to be a strain on market demand. The iron catalyst also has made possible the production of gasoline of relatively high octane number instead of the abnormally low-octane-number gasoline obtained with cobalt.

Real progress has been made in the Fischer-Tropsch process in recent years. Technologists in this country have reduced the requirement of steel (*i.e.*, plant) per barrel of product to one-fifth of its previous figure. This is of economic importance because a large part of the cost of products from the process comes from interest on investment and from depreciation of plant. However, we must not lose sight of the fact that the Fischer-Tropsch process is a net consumer of energy; that is, the liquid-fuel product contains less energy than is required to produce it. We cannot think of the complete conversion of coal to liquid by any process as conservation of fuel resources. It is, instead, a wasteful expedient justified only by a compelling necessity to produce more liquid fuel than can be obtained from other sources.

This is in sharp contrast with conversion of oil shale, which is not usable as fuel until it is treated to recover its oil. Every barrel of oil recovered from shale avoids the eventual destruction of a quarter of a ton of coal. Thus shale-oil recovery constitutes a most important measure of conservation.

The Fischer-Tropsch process requires power for its operation and also generates power. The essence of the problem of future development is the finding of means to balance the power required with the power produced, through the utilization of a minimum of plant and equipment per barrel of product. By the time it is necessary to use the process on a large scale many economies will have been developed, and the process will be applied in judicious combination with other processes. An example of such a combination would be low-temperature coking of coal in the presence of hydrogen, use of the coke as industrial fuel to the extent that markets could absorb it, and Fischer-Tropsch conversion of the remainder.

As for the choice between hydrogenation and Fischer-Tropsch, there is no doubt that coal hydrogenation can be greatly improved by research, but so can the Fischer-Tropsch process. It now seems most probable that hydrogenation will be applied in the future not to coal but to heavy oils for the manufacture of light fuels.

Beehive coke ovens are still required for the conversion of coal to coke despite their wastefulness. They are low in capital cost and hence suitable for occasional use to take care of peak demands for coke. (*United States Steel Corp.*)

Neither process of coal conversion has yet been tried on a commercial scale. Pilot-plant work has been done on certain parts of each process but not on all. Thoroughly reliable economic studies will probably not be available until 1955 because of the many unsolved phases of the problem of synthesis, but a careful appraisal was completed in 1951 by a petroleum-industry committee at the request of the U.S. Secretary of the Interior.

The Fischer-Tropsch process undoubtedly will grow in importance to our fuel economy. Ultimately it may play a huge role in the cleanup of our fuel resources. Much of the coal in the ground will never be mineable. Much of the oil shale contains too little hydrocarbon to justify handling. When oil fields are "exhausted," great quantities of oil, unrecoverable by ordinary methods, will still remain in the earth. There will also be large quantities of oil in inaccessible deposits of tar sands. The time may come when the gasification processes associated with Fischer-Tropsch will be used as scavengers to recover these precious residues in the form of synthesis gas. A little work has already been done on underground gasification of coal. The projects have been clumsy and unrewarding, but technologists are not overlooking the eventual necessity of "the last roundup."

By-product coke ovens recover gas and chemicals as well as coke. The use of such ovens has been increasing and efficiencies have been improved. However, the production of coal-tar chemicals has fallen behind demand. (*Koppers Co.*)

Incomplete conversion of coal to liquid fuel can be accomplished by simple coking. Coal is heated until only coke remains and the distillate is composed of gas and tar. The higher the coking temperature the less tar. Bituminous coal now used for metallurgical coke yields about 10 gallons of liquid per ton. The yield can be raised to 30 gallons per ton by careful retorting at lower temperatures, but the coke made in this way, while an eminently satisfactory fuel, is not suitable for blast furnaces.

Thermal efficiencies of various methods of converting coal are shown in Table 1. Yields of liquid fuel are comparable on a heating basis but

TABLE 1. Conversion of Bituminous Coal to Liquid Fuel

Process	Yield of Liquid, gal per ton	Thermal Efficiency, percent
Low-temperature distillation to tar	30	82
Low-temperature distillation plus hydrogenation of tar	30	77
Fischer-Tropsch	90	45
Hydrogenation	85	40

not on a use basis, for coking gives tar while other processes give mainly motor fuel. If tar had to be converted to motor fuel, an additional loss in liquid and in thermal yield would be incurred. The yield of liquid fuel from conversion of some lignites by the Fischer-Tropsch process would be about 45 gallons per ton—little more than one-half the yield from bituminous coal.

The analysis of our energy requirements shown in Chap. 21 contains no losses for conversion of coal to liquid fuel because this operation is not now being carried out. However, the time will come when liquid-fuel requirements cannot be supplied from domestic petroleum production. Then, for a time, it will be more profitable to import petroleum from foreign fields than to convert domestic coal. But there is a natural reluctance to be dependent for the lifeblood of our industries and our military establishment upon the friendliness of other nations. Furthermore, as other nations rise to a higher state of industrialization, international competition for oil will grow keener and the price will rise. Eventually coal conversion will be forced upon us.

When it becomes necessary to produce from coal a billion barrels of liquid fuel per annum (about one-half the present consumption of petroleum), the conversion *loss* would figure about 4.5 trillion hphr per annum—almost 38 percent of our present total energy requirement. Of course, this sort of operation will be postponed as long as there is oil safely available for importation. Eventually importation will cease either because of exhaustion of world petroleum reserves or because other countries will be in a position to outbid us. When this time comes —as it must—we may need to prepare from coal not 1 billion, but more than 2 billion barrels of oil per annum.

Unless great technological advances are made in coal conversion, the energy loss in this operation will eventually exceed 9 trillion hphr per annum—75 percent of the 1947 total energy requirements of the United States.

Any major dependence upon coal will be quite unsatisfactory unless the rate of supply of coal can be made reasonably uniform. When we talk about the possibility of satisfying our future needs for liquid fuel by the conversion of coal, we are assuming that measures will have been taken to guarantee the extraction of coal from the earth in a terrific and *constant* stream. Obviously, this will entail drastic social reforms. The real difficulties will be political and economic rather than technological.

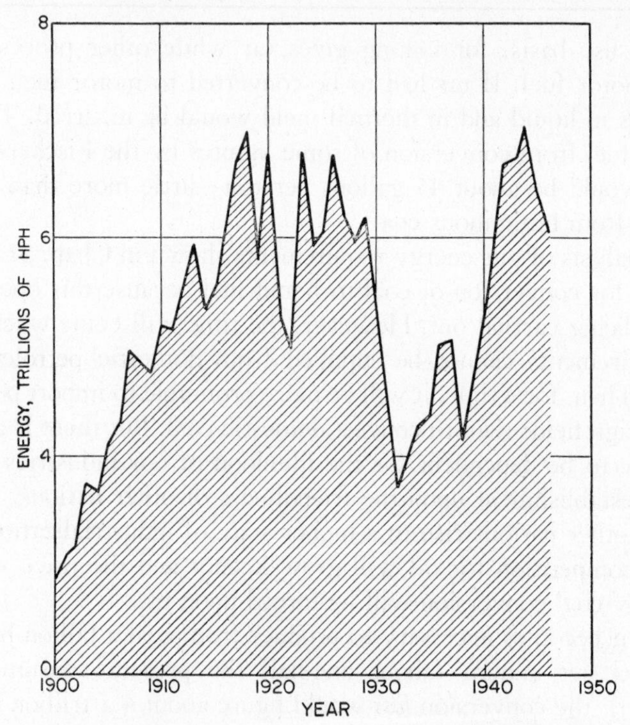

FIG. 4. Energy production from coal in the United States.

Our mines now are operated only part time, and even in the best years the stream of production is erratic and wholly unpredictable. The fault is primarily our archaic system of settling industrial disputes by force rather than by arbitration under law. The time will come when warfare between management and labor will be unthinkable. A part of the trouble, however, has been the shortage of railway cars during periods of high production. During the 1940's this factor accounted for the loss of about a quarter of the working time.

The saw-toothed production career of coal (Fig. 4) has become worse and worse as time goes on. This state of affairs would make a large coal-conversion enterprise unworkable because, if the stream of coal from the mine should dry up even for a few days, the whole complicated conversion plant would have to shut down. The mines could be brought into operation again within a few days, but the conversion plant would require, instead, weeks or even months. Also the rank of coal upon which we would have to depend is expensive to store for long periods because the composition of this coal makes it subject to spontaneous combustion. Thus it is not practicable to provide much of a cushion against the impact of production irregularities.

From Gas to Liquid

One consequence of the abnormally low market price of natural gas that prevailed a few years ago was the emergence of a project to convert it to gasoline. The Fischer-Tropsch process can be applied to suitable mixtures of carbon monoxide and hydrogen from any source. Natural gas is an excellent one.

But it is now clear that natural gas will not be used to supply a significant proportion of our liquid-fuel demand. Furthermore, it is becoming increasingly certain that natural gas should not be so used on a major scale. There are many reasons for this. Chief among them is the fact that natural gas is a valuable fuel in its own right. For most stationary heating purposes, gas is a more convenient form than liquid, and it might even seem more logical to convert liquid to gas than gas to liquid. The only excuse for the latter step would be a situation in which the urgency of our demand for gasoline would overbalance considerations of energy conservation.

Conversion of gas to liquid is wasteful of our over-all fuel resources. For every therm taken into the process in the form of natural gas, it is possible with present technology to obtain only about 0.4 therm in the form of liquid fuel. If we should make one-half of our motor fuel in this way, the loss would be equal to the energy equivalent of our present total motor-fuel production. If we transport 435 million cubic feet of natural gas per day to places where it can be used, this would have about the same heating value as 72 thousand barrels per day of fuel oil. But the Fischer-Tropsch process as applied to this gas would produce only about 33 000 barrels of liquid fuel. Of the other 39 000 barrels of oil equivalent, 10 000 barrels would be fuel gas, and 29 000 barrels would have been used largely to evaporate into the atmosphere about 30 million gallons of water per day.

Our present pattern of energy use is determined not by conservation but by economics. Fortunately in this case the two factors point in the same direction. The conversion of natural gas to motor fuel will become increasingly uneconomic because:

1. To pay out an investment in such a plant there should be available about a trillion cubic feet of gas—enough to supply from 100 to 200 million feet a day for twenty years. The reserve must be large enough to permit withdrawal of gas at an undiminishing rate for the entire period.

2. Every gallon of gasoline produced requires about 30 gallons of water. This water is not the amount circulated but that actually lost in the process by evaporation. Not many locations could supply this great amount of water.

3. The conversion can be profitable only when the cost of gas is a small fraction of the value of motor fuel (say, one-seventh). The cost of gas is rising more rapidly than the value of motor fuel.

Few if any plant locations will satisfy all of these conditions today. There will be even fewer tomorrow.

From Coal to Gas

The preference for gas for certain purposes (such as domestic cooking) far antedates the widespread availability of natural gas. The first manufactured gas was obtained from simple coking of coal. It was this kind of gas that was used, for example, in Great Britain in the early years of the nineteenth century. The thermal efficiency of coking (90 percent) was high but the yield of gas was low, for most of the product was coke. Toward the end of the nineteenth century a process was devised in which coke could be converted completely to gas. Steam was put in contact with red hot coke, and the result was a mixture of carbon monoxide and hydrogen with a Btu value of about 300. This was called the "water-gas" process. Then the "producer-gas" process was devised, which consists essentially of the burning of the coke with insufficient air to provide complete combustion. The two ideas have evolved gradually through the years with various combinations. But here, as in other conversions, the more work we do to convert, the more energy we lose. The water-gas process is now operated at a thermal efficiency of about 75 percent (including the tar as well as the gas), and producer gas (130 Btu from coke and 175 Btu from coal) is generated with an efficiency of 75 to 80 percent. In the latter case there is no tar.

These efficiencies apply to well-designed plants operating under reasonably steady conditions. Just as the national average efficiency of conversion of fuel to electric power is well under the efficiencies of many individual plants, so the national average for the preparation of manufactured and mixed gas appears to be only 54 percent. This is not surprising in view of the complex factors entering into this business. For example, by-product gases from coke ovens account for nearly a fifth of the fuel used for manufactured and mixed gas, and account for about a third of the heat content of the gas product. Some of the over-all energy loss may be caused by the sort of self-enrichment mentioned in later paragraphs.

Of the gas consumed in this country about 80 percent is natural gas and 20 percent is manufactured. The percentage of natural is rising. Of the manufactured gas about 40 percent is marketed, and the remainder, mostly coke-oven and blast-furnace gas, is used *in situ* for such processes as steel making. The amount of manufactured (and mixed) gas sold in 1947 was about 647 billion cubic feet, of which about 124 billion was natural gas mixed in for either economic or quality reasons. Manufactured gas also contained gas produced from 30 million barrels of oil (for enrichment), 4 million barrels of liquefied petroleum gas, and more than 6 billion cubic feet of refinery gas. Only 40 percent of the heating value of the gas came from coal, the balance coming from the various forms of petroleum. Details are shown in the tables of Chap. 21.

In spite of the seemingly negligible proportion of manufactured gas marketed in the United States, these tables show that about 1 percent of our total energy requirement represents losses in the conversion of coal and petroleum to gas. If manufactured gas should, for any reason, become much larger, the loss could become substantial. It seems doubtful that much larger quantities of manufactured gas will be made until our natural-gas reserves are seriously depleted—say about 1970; but when that time comes the story will be quite different.

Conventional water gas is made intermittently from coke by alternate passage of air and steam. Producer gas is made by a continuous partial combustion with air. Both processes can be theoretically improved by the use of oxygen rather than air, because the water-gas process could be made continuous, and the producer-gas process could be made to yield gas higher in Btu value. Various oxygen-gasification processes worked out, both in Germany and in the United States, show considerable promise. In these cases, thermal efficiency cannot be computed by comparing the heating value of what goes in to what comes out. Manufacture of oxygen requires energy that must be taken into account, but efficiencies are not necessarily less. Sometimes they are slightly higher.

Natural gas can be economically transported for considerable distances because its Btu value is high, around 1000. Water gas until enriched is 300 Btu or less, and must be used near its source. The problem of enriching water gas is of interest. In general, there are two ways, *viz.*, self-enrichment (by converting some or all of the carbon monoxide and hydrogen to methane) and the addition of outside materials of higher heating value. Self-enrichment is particularly wasteful. Methane produced in self-enrichment is formed at an efficiency, based on original coke, of only 50 percent. Heavy fuel oil used for enrichment shows efficiencies of around 85 percent. When petroleum and natural gas are gone, we shall have to be dependent upon self-enrichment, which has almost as low thermal efficiency as coal gasification followed by the Fischer-Tropsch conversion of synthesis gas to liquid fuel.

Gasoline from Air and Water

In Chap. 14 the possibilities are discussed of generating electric power from the solar energy of the deserts. If such electric power were adequate, railroads could be electrified, and stationary power and space heating needs could be met, but how about motor cars and airplanes? It is interesting to speculate a little on this problem. If there were no fossil fuels and too little convertible vegetation, but an ample supply of electricity, could liquid fuels be manufactured? The answer is yes—at a cost. One rather obvious cycle would be as follows:

By electrolysis, water would be converted to hydrogen and oxygen. Carbon dioxide would be separated from the atmosphere by one of the five processes outlined below. The hydrogen and carbon dioxide would be combined by the Fischer-Tropsch synthesis to form gasoline and other petroleum products. The only difficult part of the plan is the recovery of the 0.03 percent carbon dioxide from the air, because it would be necessary to handle a million cubic feet of air for every gallon of gasoline, and to handle this much air by any process would require considerable equipment.

At least five schemes are possible for carbon dioxide recovery: (1) liquefaction of air; (2) absorption in monoethanolamine followed by desorption with heat; (3) absorption in caustic soda solution to form sodium bicarbonate followed by hydrogen chloride acidulation; the caustic soda and hydrogen chloride would be produced by electrolysis of brine, and the brine would be regenerated by acidulation of bicarbonate; (4) absorption in caustic soda solution to form sodium bicarbonate followed by the electrolysis of the bicarbonate solution to regenerate caustic soda and carbon dioxide; and (5) absorption by limewater followed by electric calcination of calcium carbonate with regeneration of lime. Of the five schemes, the last two are probably the most economical, and would yield gasoline at a cost of around $3 per gallon. More than half of the cost would be from interest and depreciation, because sunlight and air are free and labor costs would be nominal. Steel requirements would be about 25 tons per barrel of product per day, *i.e.*, 3.5 times as much as the steel estimated for conversion of coal to liquid fuel. Such a process, even operated on a very large scale, would not deplete the atmosphere of carbon dioxide because all of the carbon dioxide would be returned to the atmosphere by combustion. Thus, with a sufficient investment in facilities, it would be possible to make almost unlimited quantities of liquid fuels year after year without exhausting any resource.

In these rather foolish proposals (foolish, unless fossil fuels were exhausted and liquid fuels were still required, and excess vegetation were inadequate) oxygen is a by-product to which no value has been assigned. If the time should ever come when, through necessity or through the development of better ways to collect carbon dioxide from the air, gasoline should be made by this process, the operation would probably be combined with the Fischer-Tropsch conversion of wood and the by-product oxygen would be used up in this way.

We may learn how to use the carbon dioxide of the air without a preliminary physical separation. Vegetation is doing this right along, and the carbon dioxide of the air may, perhaps, be used for the direct production of electricity. Research is actively under way on such photochemical problems. There are endless possibilities.

9

The Price of Possession

Energy has a way of evaporating. We start out with a comfortable amount of fuel in the earth, but we must use a part of the recovered material or some other fuel to accomplish the recovery, and then we must use some more of it to carry what remains to the point of use. Obviously, either of these losses can set an absolute limit to fuel

Fuels cannot be recovered from the earth without the expenditure of energy. About a quarter of the energy required for the mining of bituminous coal is in the form of electric power to operate mine hoist drives. (*Westinghouse Electric Corp.*)

resources. As soon as a ton of coal is required to recover each ton of coal from the earth, the net recovery becomes zero. From that time on, it does not matter whether a trillion tons of coal still remain in the earth or none. A million gallons of gasoline at the refinery is a million gallons. But if it must be carried by gasoline tank truck for 2000 miles, it becomes a half million gallons. At the end of twice that distance, the whole million gallons would have disappeared.

These are extreme examples—far from present reality. Coal and petroleum now being produced require acceptably small amounts of fuel to produce. For long distances, the present methods of transportation require relatively little energy. Nevertheless the energy required to produce fuels is a substantial proportion of the total amount recovered, and the energy used to transport them is far from negligible. Enough

Energy is required for the transportation of energy. Almost half of the cost of bituminous coal on the Middle Atlantic coast is for transportation. (*Norfolk & Western Railway* Co.)

coal and petroleum are now available to permit selection of the portions that give highest net recovery, and gross production rate is sufficiently high to allow us to ignore transportation losses. At present such losses simply add somewhat to the cost of fuel. For example, almost half the present cost of bituminous coal on the Middle Atlantic coast (near the coal mines) is for transportation. The economics of production and transportation will become gradually less favorable, and finally costs will rise abruptly. Then we shall know we are approaching the point where net yields become zero—a point where investment of energy yields no energy dividends.

The tables in Chap. 21 show that about 12 trillion hphr per annum of coal, petroleum, and gas were produced in 1947, and that 0.5 trillion hphr per annum were required to accomplish the act of production. This indicates the over-all efficiency of production is 96 percent. The fuel picture is far too complex to compare specific efficiencies of production for different fuels or for fuels in different locations. Much of the energy required for production of oil comes from natural gas. Some of the electric power required for coal mining comes from plants burning oil. And some natural-gas production is accomplished by electric power obtained from coal. The various technologies of production are hopelessly intertwined, and so we must be content to use the over-all figure for each fuel.

The energy efficiency of natural-gas production is likely to decline with gradually lower reservoir pressures. With both petroleum and coal the energy required for production is already on the way up.

The energy efficiency of transportation depends on the type of transportation and upon the distance. Table 1 shows the great range of

TABLE 1. Fuel Required for Transportation of Fuel

Method	Ton-miles per gal
Ocean-going tanker	2 360
Pipe line	1 090
Diesel-powered railroad freight	220
Diesel motor truck	80
Coal-steam railroad freight	30
Local gasoline truck	20

values for coal and oil. For long distances, coal is transported by railroad freight. Steam locomotives are still used to some extent for this service, but the much more efficient diesel-electric locomotives are rapidly taking over. Transportation of coal in 1948 was about 200 billion ton-miles. The coal required for this transportation would have been about 36 million tons in steam locomotives, while the coal equivalent of oil required in diesel-electric locomotives would have been about 13.5 million tons. The actual figure was somewhere in between. Even the smaller amount (which we are approaching now) is substantial when we consider that about a half million tons of coal (as gasoline equivalent) was required to deliver about 100 million tons of coal by motor truck to points of ultimate use. The best over-all transportation efficiency for coal can be taken as about 97 percent.

Long-distance transportation of petroleum is accomplished in five different ways (Table 2). Marine tankers, where they are applicable,

TABLE 2. Petroleum Moved in 1946 by the United States

Method	Barrels Daily
Pipe lines	4 404 000
Tank trucks	3 500 000
Marine barges	1 250 000
Marine tankers	2 000 000
Railroad tank cars	1 268 000

offer the form of petroleum transportation requiring the least fuel, as shown by Table 1. Because the total cost of this method is also usually less than pipe line, marine tankers are used when the water routes are relatively direct and when the terminals are near the markets to be

About 2 million barrels of petroleum are transported every day by marine tankers. These transport their loads at the rate of 2360 ton-miles per gallon of fuel, compared with 20 ton-miles for local gasoline tank trucks. (*Gulf Oil Corp.*)

served. Barges fall in this category and are favored for transport of petroleum to places adequately served by inland waterways.

To reach inland points not served by waterways, pipe lines and railway tank cars are used. Pipe lines are being used increasingly to reach relatively concentrated markets. In 1946, the transportation of petroleum in pipe lines was about 430 billion barrel-miles. To achieve this would have required about 52 million barrels for pumping if all pumping had been done by liquid fuels. If the pipe lines had been replaced by diesel-powered railway freight, 122 million barrels of fuel oil would have been used. Steam locomotives would have required 606 million barrels of fuel oil.

The transportation of petroleum in pipe lines amounts to about 430 billion barrel-miles per year. (*Gulf Oil Corp.*)

Motor trucks are used almost exclusively for the distribution of liquid fuel to retail customers, and to some extent also to haul crude oil from isolated wells to refineries and to transfer fuels from refineries and tank farms to jobbers. Motor trucks transport about 25 million barrel-miles per annum, consuming about 5 million barrels of gasoline in the process. Since the conversion of crude oil to gasoline has an energy efficiency of about 87 percent, this amount of gasoline corresponds to nearly 7 million barrels of crude oil. This is what it takes to make deliveries to service stations and retail customers. The major transportation losses for petroleum amount to about 60 million barrels per annum, or an overall efficiency of 97 percent (about the same as coal).

Gas is carried by pipe line. About 150 Btu of energy are required to transport one cubic foot of gas 1000 miles, which gives, for this distance, an energy efficiency of 87 percent because each cubic foot of natural gas has about 1000 Btu. For 1947, the energy equivalent of

To move petroleum from Texas and Oklahoma over the thousand or so miles to the industrial centers of the North and East requires many large pumping stations that annually consume many thousands of horsepower-hours of energy. (*Westinghouse Electric Corp.*)

about 130 million cubic feet of gas were required to accomplish the transportation of about a trillion cubic-foot-miles. For gas of lower Btu content the efficiency is naturally lower. Manufactured gas with Btu of 530 has a transportation efficiency of 78 percent (for a thousand miles) and producer gas with 130 Btu would have a negative efficiency. In other words, transportation of producer gas for one thousand miles would require more energy than the value of the gas delivered. It is easy to see why low Btu gas such as producer gas and the gas from underground gasification of coal cannot be transported to distant points.

A considerable portion of gas production is used near the wells. Another considerable portion is used in centers of population 1000 miles or more from the gas wells. If 500 miles is taken as the average distance traveled by gas, we arrive at an average energy transportation efficiency of 93 percent.

Transmission of electric power requires considerable energy. The production efficiency of electric power is measured at the bus bar of the

Transmission of electric power requires considerable energy. Losses are considerable before the current reaches our light bulbs and motors, but the smallest part of the loss comes from the high-voltage, long-distance transmission from the power station to the neighborhood of use. (*Aluminum Co. of America.*)

power station, but the losses are great before the current reaches our light bulbs and motors. The total transmission loss depends upon the distance, the extent to which the line is loaded, and the transmission voltage. The smallest part of the loss comes from the high-voltage, long-distance transmission from the power station to the neighborhood of use, and the largest part of the loss comes from local distribution at stepped-down voltages. Under average conditions the loss is about 20 percent, which makes the transmission efficiency about 80 percent.

Electric-transmission efficiency is controlled by economic factors. Losses could be reduced to an extremely low figure by increasing the cross-section of the conductors and raising the transmission and distribution voltages. But these expedients involve capital expenditures whose cost must be balanced by the savings in power. The point where this balance is effected varies in accordance with fuel costs, costs of copper and aluminum, and costs of transformation and associated apparatus.

Table 3 summarizes average transportation efficiencies for the United States for various forms of energy.

TABLE 3. Average Energy-transportation Efficiencies to Points of Use for the United States

	Percent
Coal	97
Oil	97
Natural gas	93
Electric power	80

10

Waste

We derive unwarranted satisfaction from the contemplation of our prodigious consumption of fuels. We are inclined to be proud of our lavishness instead of uneasy. But, after all, the measure of material progress is not how much fuel we are using but rather how much useful work or heat we are obtaining.

Energy is lost in all sorts of ways, such as transmission from one point to another (see Chap. 9), the generation of undesired heat, the evaporation of cooling water, mechanical friction, improper combustion, imperfect heat transfer, and low load factor. A large volume of research has been done on all of these factors, and such research will automatically expand as energy becomes more expensive. The question of probable years of supply of exhaustible sources of energy depends to a considerable extent upon the ways in which energy is used, and how well it is used.

Perhaps the ultimate contribution of an individual to the saving of sources of energy would be to insist upon living and working in unheated and unlighted buildings, walking instead of driving his car, eating only food that had not come from mechanized farms or factories, and avoiding the thousands of other conveniences that can come about only through the consumption of great stores of energy. This absurd example points up the complexity of the problem of conservation. The saving of one essential thing may lead to the waste or distortion of something else even more essential, such as health, comfort, opportunity for productiveness, environment favorable to creativeness, or political ideology. In short, energy is the basis of our way of life. Without abundant energy our standard of living would sink quickly to that of primitive man, and we would find the world immediately overpopulated.

In a sense, nothing is wasted if it is used. In a narrower sense, nothing is wasted if it is used with maximum efficiency. In a still narrower sense, nothing is wasted if it is used with maximum efficiency to accomplish the most desirable ends. It is this limited meaning of waste that concerns us here, but with such a definition the subject is controversial. The idea of "maximum efficiency" is hedged with considerations of economics and practicality, and there can be no easy agreement on "desirable ends." It is even possible to make out an excellent case for extravagance. For example, if we in the United States had not been extravagant in our demands for motor fuel before World War II, we would not have built up the great peacetime capacity for production that proved to be so important for military victory.

In spite of everything, however, we are disturbed by an intuitive suspicion that when "capital" instead of "interest" is being expended there must be some virtue in frugality, or at least in moderation. The only intelligent excuse for any other attitude is a confident expectation that when our capital is exhausted something else will turn up to keep us going. Nuclear physics has provided a welcome salve to the social conscience of the layman—if not to the technologist. If we are to have abundant atomic power in the future, why save our coal and petroleum? Of course the answer is that we may not have abundant atomic power and it is almost sure to be costly. When fossil fuels have been burned we shall still have the sun, but time is needed for the development of an engineered plant for solar-energy utilization.

What are the incentives to avoid waste? It has been thought that the peoples of the world have done a poor job of conservation. The reasons for poor conservation appear obvious. The subject of conservation seems unrealistic until a situation is acute, and then it is too late to do much about it. Historically, man has never done much planning for the future. We cannot expect anyone to sacrifice even a little of the known benefits to himself in the present for the unproven benefits to someone else in the future. The idea of such sacrifice may have some philosophic appeal but could never form the basis for effective concerted action.

These reasons account for the trend toward promotion of governmental projects. The legitimate function of government in this field has been to make it possible for industry to do things that, through conservation of fuel resources, lead toward the economic well-being of both suppliers and users of fuels. In some respects we in the United

States have done, and are doing, a magnificent job of conservation of fuels. The incentive has been profit. Nearly all conservation measures contribute to the economic well-being of the majority. If this is true it would seem that the battle for conservation of fuels is won even before it starts. Unfortunately the outcome is perpetually in doubt because of considerations of national security and because all of us are inclined to be swayed more by amenities than by economics. The primary task of the conservationist is to explore ways of making conservation more than philosophically or politically or even economically attractive.

The most successful national experiments in conservation have been associated with production and conversion. Chief among our failures are those associated with the end uses of energy.

The Motor Car

In a sense, the power plant of the motor car is one of the most remarkable fruits of the mechanical genius of this century. For its great power, it is low in cost and in size, it is versatile in action, and it is almost foolproof. It is so important to our way of life and so vital to two great industries that any criticism may seem like sacrilege. And yet its very indispensability makes it a proper subject of concern to the industries which it supports and, particularly, to the nation which it serves.

Unfortunately the motor car is a superlative example of short life and of low efficiency in use. Automotive engines are made to last (under favorable circumstances) from 200 to 400 hours under full load at 4000 rpm. In normal service, few engines outlive 100 000 miles. This represents less than six months of running time at a small fraction of its rated load. Steam turbines, electric motors, locomotives—almost any machines that come to mind—do far better than that. The internal-combustion engine used for automobiles is a fragile device compared with other prime movers—even compared with the internal-combustion engines used for diesel-electric locomotives that have been known to go over a million miles without mechanical overhauling. A number of very good reasons can be given for the relatively short life of the automobile engine, which must weigh and cost little per horsepower and must respond almost instantaneously to the throttle. Present economics are opposed to the manufacture of engines which would cost more and weigh more.

Something about the possession and operation of a motor car provides effective anesthesia for any awareness of economy. We may hesitate to spend a few dollars for a book or for a tool (things of more or less lasting value), but we think nothing of paying a like amount for a tankful of gasoline. In a few hours or days the gasoline is gone and we have left only the memory of a few miles on the road and perhaps many exasperating minutes in a line of stalled traffic. A few people for technical reasons keep an account of miles per gallon of fuel, depreciation per mile, and other costs of motoring, but the result is usually so appalling that the accounts are hurriedly discontinued and forgotten.

About 10 percent of the total energy consumption of the United States is for our acres of motor cars. In traveling we use about as much energy as is consumed in all manufacturing processes. (*General Motors Corp.*)

The highly competitive sellers of motor cars and motor fuels search earnestly for features in their products to advertise. The advertising specialists, conscious of the public pulse, do not waste much space and money talking about economy. They talk, instead, of performance, comfort, style, and reliability. Nearly everything said about a new car means lower fuel efficiency—for example, larger body, longer wheel base, greater weight, softer tires, more horsepower, more rapid acceleration, higher speed, automatic drive, improved flexibility of control. And now powered steering is almost upon us! No wonder car-miles per gallon of gasoline has shown no improvement over the past thirty years. Passenger-miles per gallon have probably shown a definite decline because an even larger proportion of motorists like to ride alone in about two tons of assembled steel driven by a silent power plant capable of more than a hundred horsepower. This decline is in spite of engineering changes that have made considerable improvements in *ton*-miles per gallon.

The motor-car operator is largely to blame. He insists on excessive weight, power, and luxury. He accelerates too rapidly. His speed is excessive. He knows, in a vague way, that he is paying for all this, but he feels that he is getting his money's worth of what may be called the "amenities" of motoring. He would be dissatisfied with the relatively feeble and unglamorous cars of 1920. But another factor has been the increased amount of traffic. Mileage in congested areas is about half what it is on the open road, and today a large proportion of motor-car use is in our towns and cities.

Statistics on miles per gallon are unreliable and confusing. It has not been practicable to develop accurate figures for total miles per annum. In particular, estimates for one year are not comparable with estimates for other years. Interpretation of statistics requires that we distinguish between ton-miles, car-miles, and passenger-miles, with the disturbing realization that the figures in each case are questionable. This is illustrated by the fact that official estimates of national car-miles divided by gallons of motor fuel usually show higher average mileage figures than those obtained by careful records of the performance of fleets of relatively high-mileage cars.

Great mechanical and chemical improvements have been made during the past thirty years. If these improvements could have been applied to economy instead of to performance the consumption of motor fuel should have been more nearly that obtained in other countries of the earth where gasoline is less abundant. We have paid a huge price for amenities, but this is not all. Another substantial fuel loss has come from the pattern of development of motor cars and motor fuels. This is an interesting story.

In 1920 gasoline was pretty much as you found it—largely the "straight-run" product of simple distillation of crude petroleum. The process of "cracking" to break down additional portions of crude oil to gasoline was just coming in. The thermal efficiency of gasoline manufacture was around 95 percent—about halfway between topping and an average proportion of thermal cracking (see Chap. 8). In 1920 automotive engineers conceived it to be their problem to adapt engine design to the available fuel.

Automotive engineers agree today, as they did in 1920, that the best single way to improve the efficiency of the internal-combustion engine is to increase the compression ratio. This means, in effect, to increase the pressure at which the fuel is burned, which raises the temperature of combustion and hence increases the amount of heat-energy available to do work. The average engine in common use in 1920 had a compression ratio of about 4:1. Higher ratios led to "knocking," which was unpleasant and harmful. But as long ago as 1914 experimental engines were devised to operate without knock with much higher compression ratios using the current straight-run fuels. The pattern of engine development at that time called for a gradual mechanical evolution away from the factors that limited the compression ratio.

Then something happened to put an almost complete stop to this sort of mechanical development—the discovery that "knock" could be suppressed by the qualities of the motor fuel. The lure of fuel chemistry became so fascinating that many men in automotive research were successfully metamorphosed from competent mechanical engineers to competent chemists. This has resulted in a gain for chemistry (even a distinguished president of the American Chemical Society), but a grievous loss for mechanical engineering. A generation of automotive engineers has occupied itself with a complex technology built up around an accident of design. A formidable mass of technical literature has been devoted to relationships between variable fuel qualities and engines that date back to the basic mechanical ideas of the 1920's. It was not until about 1945 that the automotive industry was able to extricate itself from its technological groove.

From 1920 to 1945 the petroleum industry conceived it to be its problem to make up in fuel quality what the engines lacked in mechanical quality. The task was not repugnant to the petroleum industry. Instead of selling a product that might have become as standardized as distilled water, it was possible to point to the superiority of one fuel over another. The appeal to sales and advertising departments was potent. But the improvement of antiknock qualities of motor fuels cost the petroleum industry around 6 billion dollars over the period in capital outlay and around 40 billion dollars over the period for additional operating expenses.

The thermal efficiency of modern refineries (using average proportions of catalytic cracking) is about 87 percent—a drop of 8 percent from the 1920 figure. A weighted average efficiency for the thirty-year period from 1920 to 1950 is about 90 percent. In other words, the 600 billion gallons consumed since 1920 represents about 5 percent more fuel than would have been required if it had not been necessary to improve the antiknock quality of the gasoline.

By 1945 it was becoming apparent that fuel quality was approaching a plateau above which it would be even more costly to go. This economic and technologic blockade came at a time when automotive engineers were becoming more conscious of the imperative need for more fuel economy. Mechanical progress has therefore resumed and is now making rapid headway. By 1950 we had learned how to make engines with 9:1 compression ratio to operate without knock with relatively low-octane fuels. By 1960 many cars are expected to have 12:1 compression ratio, and premium fuels may not be required.

The need for such development, not only of the automotive engine but of the other mechanical parts of the motor car, is underlined by the fact that the motor car is one of the least efficient of all machines. R. J. S. Pigott, past president of the Society of Automotive Engineers, made some calculations based on the performance of the Ford, Plymouth, and Chevrolet engines of 1947, which had a nominal average brake horsepower of 95 at about 70 miles per hour. The indicated thermal efficiency of the engines at full-throttle value was taken as 29 percent, and it was assumed that this efficiency was maintained at lower throttle openings. Motor cars are only occasionally operated at full load. In fact, they are operated most of the time well under half load. Pigott, therefore, figured mechanical and auxiliary losses for an average speed of 35 miles per hour, and found the engine mechanical efficiency (including fan, water pump, and generator) was about 71 percent. The "rolling efficiency," which represents the loss between the clutch and the road (including losses in the transmission, rear axle, and tire deformation), was about 30 percent. This assumed that the only useful work performed in the operation of the motor car was the work done in overcoming wind resistance.

With these figures we can calculate what happens to 100 hphr of crude petroleum by successively multiplying the energy figure by all of the efficiencies involved to arrive at an ultimate efficiency that may be termed the *energy-system efficiency*. In being produced the 100 hphr of petroleum becomes 96. In being refined it becomes 83. In being transported to the filling station it becomes 81. When it is burned in the motor, the energy produced is about 29 percent of 81, or 23.5 hphr. Engine (and auxiliary) losses bring it down to 16.7 hphr. Then, by the time the energy reaches the road, it is 5 hphr. With this definition of "useful work," the energy-system efficiency of the motor car with petroleum motor fuel is, thus, 5 percent. Some measurements made by the Ethyl Corporation indicate an energy-system efficiency of around 11 percent by ignoring all losses beyond the engine flywheel. This predicates that useful work includes not only windage but also losses in the transmission, rear axle, and tire deformation. Thus, any valid assumption shows the motor car to have an abnormally low over-all efficiency (Table 1).

TABLE 1. Energy-system Efficiency of the Motor Car
In Percent

	Efficiency of Each Step	Efficiency Including All Preceding Steps
Production of crude petroleum	96	96
Refining of petroleum	87	83.5
Transportation of gasoline	97	81
Thermal efficiency of engine	29	23.5
Mechanical efficiency of engine	71	16.7
Rolling efficiency	30	5

No one is proud of this accomplishment—least of all the automotive-design engineers, who are constantly exploring ways of increasing the energy-system efficiency to make it better than the now obsolete steam locomotive. The trouble is, every time the design engineer manages to save a few Btu it is more than spent answering the clamor for softer tires, for radio, for better heaters, more lights, cigarette lighters, and possibly even air conditioning. If synthetic motor fuel from coal or gas is used to operate a motor car, the energy-system efficiency drops to around 2.5 percent, putting the system at the very bottom of the list of energy applications. No one is proud of this either—least of all the chemical engineers, who feel that they are just starting down the long road of conversion technology to achieve something better than nineteenth-century efficiencies. The joint efforts of the automotive and chemical engineers have now reached the point where 95 percent or more of the energy in a ton of coal would be used not to move the car along the road, but (1) to evaporate huge quantities of water in the conversion plant; (2) to carry the gasoline to the filling station; (3) to heat the water in the radiator and the gas in the exhaust; (4) to operate motor-car auxiliaries; and (5) to overcome friction in gears and tires. With synthetic production, to obtain for motor-car transportation the energy equivalent of 1 gallon of motor fuel we would have to use the thermal equivalent of 20 gallons. At present, with petroleum motor fuel, we have to use 10 gallons, which is bad enough, but at least we are 10 gallons ahead of the widely heralded synthetic era.

The fault here is widely distributed between different efficiencies. The loss between the clutch and the road is particularly disastrous; and this loss, originating particularly in the tires, may make synthetic rubber more costly than natural (assuming the same price per tire and the same life) because of the greater road friction, with consequent greater energy loss. This is worth some study.

The aggregate horsepower of registered motor vehicles in the United States is about 4 billion. If all these vehicles operated constantly at full load (and if the presumed horsepower were actually generated), this would represent about 35 trillion hphr per annum—almost three times the total energy requirement of the country. As a matter of fact, the energy actually generated by these vehicles in 1950 amounted to about 6 percent of the motor-fuel equivalent, or 0.08 trillion hphr—less than 0.2 percent of the registered horsepower. This low utilization is caused by a combination of low energy-system efficiency and a use load factor under 4 percent.

The reason such huge amounts of energy are being wasted in the form of liquid fuel (and the reason the idea of wasting still more is being seriously entertained for the future) is that we insist upon operating heavy cars with dangerous and useless potentialities of speed and acceleration. This inclination, which is growing all the time, will do more to advance the end of the fossil-fuel era than any other factor. Higher automotive-engine efficiencies are announced from time to time as resulting from improved engines or superior fuels. But motorists have not realized any increase in mileage, since the potential efficiency increase has been offset by running more powerful engines under lighter partial loads and in hauling more tons of automobile at higher average speed. To take a simple example, a car designed for a maximum speed of 100 miles per hour must have 3.5 times as much installed horsepower per ton as a car designed for a maximum speed of 50 miles per hour. Other things being equal, the fuel consumption is about proportional to installed horsepower.

Histories written a few centuries hence may describe the United States as a nation of such extraordinary technologic virility that we succeeded in finding ways of dissipating our natural wealth far more rapidly than any other nation. At any rate, we are having a wonderful time doing it.

Generation of Electric Power

For a little relief let us turn to one of the most interesting examples of reduction of waste. In considering the generation of electric power in a steam plant, let us start with 100 hphr of fuel in the ground. By the time

One of the most encouraging trends in the fuel picture has been the steady improvement in the efficiency of steam-turbine generation of electric power. Some 1950 plants have an efficiency more than six times that of the best plants of 1900. (*West Penn Power Co.*)

this is collected and transported to a power plant, we have 93 hphr. When the fuel is burned to make steam to drive a generator, we come out with 20.5 hphr. By the time this power reaches our motor or stove, we have 16.3 hphr, and this is the energy delivered. In 1950 the average energy-system efficiency of electric power or heat was this 16.3 percent (Table 2).

Now this does not mean that we should not convert coal to electric power, but it does mean that we should be conscious at all times of the problem and take advantage of every technologic and economic opportunity to improve matters. We may well be optimistic when we consider that at the beginning of the twentieth century the energy-system efficiency for electric power averaged only 3.4 percent. By the end of World War I the energy-system efficiency for electric power averaged about 6 percent instead of 16.3 percent, and some of our production in 1950 ran above 20 percent. All of it will eventually reach this figure, and could even go a little higher if energy costs become high enough.

TABLE 2. Energy-system Efficiency of Electric Power
In Percent

	Efficiency of Each Step	Efficiency Including All Preceding Steps
Production of coal	96	96
Transportation of coal	97	93
Generation of power	22	20.5
Transmission of power	80	16.3

The manufacture of electric power in the United States for public sale in 1950 required about 138 million tons of coal (and coal equivalent). At the end of World War I the same amount of power would have required the consumption of 355 million tons of coal because of the lower average efficiencies of the power plants at that time. By 1960 efficiencies are expected to be high enough to require about 94 million tons for the 1950 load. Thus the work of the engineers and the progressive management of the power industry brought about an annual saving of 217 million tons during the period between the first two World Wars, and will probably bring an additional annual saving of 44 million tons before 1960. The incentive, of course, has been profit. This is of special importance because of the expected rapid increase in the use of steam-driven electric generators.

At the end of World War I the installed water-power-generator capacity of the United States was 3.7 million kilowatts. In 1950 such installed capacity had risen to 17.6 million. This, also, has meant the saving of coal, for without this additional 13.9 million kilowatts of water-power-generator capacity it would have been necessary to consume an additional 58 million tons of coal in 1950. Of this saving nearly 44 million tons has come from public projects. So we have a total saving during this period of 231 million tons of coal per annum stimulated by the hope of profit and an additional 44 million tons through governmental development of water power.

The total hydroelectric power eventually developed in this country will probably amount to several times what we have now. The coal savings from hydroelectric projects will grow. However, the major portion of the increased load of the future will have to be taken care of by steam plants. This makes steam-plant efficiency of the utmost importance. With the predicted steam-plant generating capacity in 1980 at

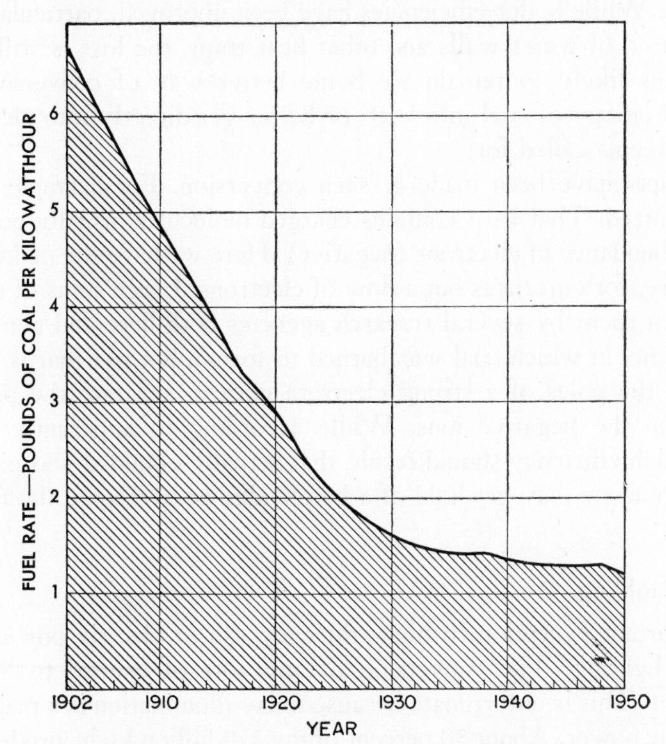

FIG. 1. The electric industry has set an excellent record in the improvement of energy-conversion efficiency.

around 200 million kilowatts (five times the maximum probable hydroelectric capacity), the coal saving represented by the difference between 1950 average plant efficiencies and those expected in 1980 will be about 100 million tons per annum. Progress in the past is shown in Fig. 1. We have not only made important progress in this field during the past few decades, but also we have every reason to expect continued progress in the future. No other nation has done as well.

Electric power starts out with the handicap of high conversion loss (*i.e.*, in the boiler), but many of its applications have very high working efficiency—approaching 100 percent. It is for this reason that electric power can often compete with gas—for example, for domestic cooking, refrigeration, and even space heating—without depending upon its unparalleled convenience.

Obviously the most fertile segment of the electric energy system for efficiency improvement is the conversion of latent Btu in fuel to the heat of steam. While boiler efficiencies have been improved, particularly by the addition of water walls and other heat traps, the loss is still great and seems likely to remain so. Some better way of converting the chemical energy of coal into heat, or better yet directly into electrical energy, seems called for.

Attempts have been made at such conversion. For example, a hot gas is ionized. That is, it contains charged molecules, usually positive, and an abundance of electrons (negative). Here we have the makings of electricity, for current is but a flow of electrons. Large sums of money have been spent by several research agencies both here and abroad on experiments in which coal was burned to form a hot gas that is blown between the poles of a strong electromagnet to separate the positive ions from the negative ions. While according to apparently sound theory high efficiency should result, that actually obtained was pitifully small. Someone may get hold of a better idea or overcome the flaw in this one.

Electric Lighting

An important exception to high-efficiency use of electric power is in electric lighting. The conversion of any sort of energy to light is inefficient. This is unfortunate because today illumination is a major use of electric power. About 30 percent of the 279 billion kwhr produced in the United States in 1950 was consumed by lamps. The electric industry was founded to provide light. Motors came later—in fact, not until the introduction of the polyphase system in the early 1890's. Meanwhile the electric-light industry had got a rapid start. Man has been largely successful in becoming independent of direct sunlight for all indoor activities and for those outdoors at night. But it is at an enormous expense of fuel energy. The amount of energy lost in the process always has been and still is high.

Efficiencies of some light sources are shown in Table 3. The superiority of electric lighting is apparent. The amount of fuel required in the most efficient device for the direct lighting of an area is roughly twice

TABLE 3. Energy Required to Produce 10 000 Lumen-hours of Light

Lamp	Horsepower-hours as Fuel
Average incandescent	3.7
Mercury-vapor, low-pressure	4.4
Mercury-vapor, high-pressure	1.6
Gas, Welsbach mantle	6.8

TABLE 4. Energy-system Efficiency of Electric Lighting
In Percent

	Efficiency of Each Step	Efficiency Including All Preceding Steps
Production of coal	96	96
Transportation of coal	97	93
Generation of power	22	20.5
Transmission of power	80	16.3
Light from incandescent lamps	10	1.6
Light from fluorescent lamps	20	3.2

TABLE 5. Outputs of Light Sources

	Light Output, Lumens per Watt of Input	Percentage of Input Radiated in Visible Part of Spectrum
Sperm candle	0.1	0.1
Open gas flame	0.2	0.1
Incandescent gas mantle	2.0	1.0
Carbon-arc lamp	50–55	10–25
Carbon-filament lamp (1910)	4	3
Tungsten-filament, gas-filled 100-watt lamp (1950)	16	10
White fluorescent 40-watt (1950)	62	20
Mercury-vapor lamp	37–57	12–16
Firefly	125	20
Theoretical equivalent of yellow-green light	680	100
Theoretical equivalent of "white" light	200–225	100

that of the indirect method of burning fuel to generate electric power to accomplish equivalent lighting with electric lamps. Nevertheless, the energy-system efficiency of electric lighting in the most efficient commercial lamp (fluorescent) is only about 3.2 percent (Table 4).

The outputs of various light sources are shown in Table 5. The reason for absence of proportionality between the figures in the two columns is that the amounts of energy represented by different parts of the spectrum vary widely. Light efficiency is a complicated matter. The most effective radiation optically is yellow-green light. Red is visually less effective. So-called "white light" is much less effective than yellow-green and, furthermore, varies rather widely. The figures for the firefly are estimates based on an assumption that 20 percent of the firefly's calorific food intake is expended in radiation. Almost the entire amount

The light output in lumens per watt of input is four times as high for the tungsten-filament gas-filled lamp as for the carbon-filament lamp. The fluorescent lamp shows a fourfold improvement over the tungsten lamp. (*Westinghouse Electric Corp.*)

of firefly radiation is not only in the visible part of the spectrum but is also in the most efficient part of the spectrum.

With efficiencies (ratio of visible output to total input) of best modern lamps running from 10 to 20 percent, clearly some entirely new and more efficient light-source principle would be highly desirable. In the pre-electricity age light was created by using combustion of fuel to heat gases to a temperature so high that a portion of their radiation extended beyond the heat and infrared regions into the visible. These lamps were loudly acclaimed. The fact that their efficiencies were less than 1 percent was unknown and unimportant.

Improvement came with electricity, in which the energy is applied to heat a solid (at first carbon, now tungsten) to a temperature such that some radiation lies in the visible. This has brought lamp efficiencies up to 10 percent for ordinary filament lamps.

Any process of producing light with heat as an intermediate step is wasteful. This step was eliminated by the fluorescent lamp, in which electric energy is converted first into ultraviolet radiation. The fluorescent lamp thus oversteps the mark. This invisible radiant energy is then transformed—*i.e.*, stepped down in frequency—by phosphors, which make this transformation with high efficiency.

But the fluorescent-lamp principle still involves an extra step. It is known that light can be produced without it. The principle is known as "electroluminescence." If certain phosphors, such as zinc sulfide, are subjected to high and rapid electrical stress, the energy in the field is directly converted to light. If an alternating current of several hundred volts and several hundred cycles is applied to a layer of phosphors, the layer glows with a pale blue-green light. The mechanism is not yet understood but apparently the rapid reversal of atoms within the phosphors causes them to absorb energy and reradiate a portion of it in the visible. This is light from electricity directly! But, all electroluminescent lamps to date have been woefully inefficient—about 0.1 lumen per watt input, compared to a white fluorescent lamp output of 2. However, it is a new light-source principle that, under research training, may someday be raised to some practical high efficiency.

Fundamentally the difference between radio-type radiation and light is solely one of frequency or wavelength. Radio-broadcast frequencies in the United States are 550 to 1500 kilocycles. Light frequencies are about 10 000 million megacycles. The gulf between them is enormous but since World War I electronics men have been narrowing it. Early in World War II klystrons and magnetrons were developed for radar that generated frequencies up to about 10 000 megacycles. Later high-frequency cavity-type resonators have produced frequencies of 50 000 megacycles. This is still a long way from visible-radiation frequencies and as generators of short-wave radiation they are inefficient.

To produce these ultrahigh frequencies these resonant-cavity generators have become smaller and smaller. Their dimensions have had to be more precise. It seems that the physical sizes of these cavity-type devices fashioned of metal have about reached their bottom limit. Some new way to carry this trend down into the visible is needed. In short, some way must be found to establish the oscillating chamber within the atom itself.

We have come a long way but obviously we still have a long way to go. While the thermal efficiency of electric-power stations will be improved somewhat, it will take a long time for the national average to exceed 35 percent. Transmission losses will not come down much, if any, as they are largely controlled by economics. Lamp engineers see improvements in incandescent lamps to perhaps 25 lumens per watt. (Thirty-two lumens per watt is an upper limit fcr tungsten filament, unobtainable because to produce even that the tungsten must be molten.) Considerable improvement is expected in phosphors as energy converters. Engineers believe they see 100 lumens per watt as commercially obtainable. But with all seemingly practical improvements we can hope for, the best coal-to-light efficiency with any illuminant now known will not be better than 5 percent. Clearly an entirely new way of producing visible radiant energy more directly is needed.

In spite of the great areas of improvement ahead we must not overlook the progress that has been already made. The development of electric lighting since World War I to its present stage has meant a saving (based on the present lighting load) of about 17 million tons of coal per annum. This is in addition to the saving brought about by improvements in generator efficiency. In terms of dollars, the consumers of electric power for light in the United States spent 9 billion dollars less in 1946 than they would have had to spend for the same amount of light in 1920. This saving was divided about equally between improvements in lamp efficiency and improvements in the thermal efficiency of power generation.

Locomotives

The energy-system efficiency in the use of coal in modern steam locomotives is about 7 percent, whereas for the experimental coal-burning gas-turbine locomotive power plant it is said to be 16 percent (Table 6). These efficiencies are low in spite of no conversion loss because the working efficiencies are low. The energy-system efficiency of diesel-electric locomotives is 23 percent (taking into account efficiencies for transportation, refining, and working); but, if the diesel oil were made from coal, the energy-system efficiency would be about 12 percent—not nearly as good as the coal turbine. On the other hand, heavy fuel oil in a steam locomotive has an energy-system efficiency of

The greater efficiency of the diesel-electric locomotive is greatly extending the life of our petroleum reserves. (*Baldwin-Lima-Hamilton.*)

The gas-turbine locomotive has a much higher efficiency than even the most modern steam locomotive but not as high as the diesel-electric. However, when diesel oil is made from coal, the gas-turbine locomotive may be at the top of the list. (*Westinghouse Electric* Corp.)

about 8 percent; and, if made from coal, would have about 4 percent (Tables 7 and 8). According to these figures some sort of coal-burning turbine, or some other relatively efficient use of coal directly as fuel, should have a great long-term future. In the meantime, diesel oil shows the best energy economy. However, it would be wasteful to make diesel oil from coal for use in locomotives (almost twice as much coal would be consumed).

TABLE 6. Energy-system Efficiencies of Coal-burning Locomotives
In Percent

	Efficiency of Each Step	Efficiency Including All Preceding Steps
Production of coal	96	96
Transportation of coal	97	93
Steam-engine efficiency	7.5	7
Coal-gas-turbine efficiency	17	16

TABLE 7. Energy-system Efficiencies of Oil-burning Locomotives
In Percent

	Efficiency of Each Step	Efficiency Including All Preceding Steps
Production of crude petroleum	96	96
Refining of petroleum	87	83.5
Transportation of oil	97	81
Steam engine	10	8
Diesel-electric engine	28	23

TABLE 8. Energy-system Efficiencies of Oil-burning Locomotives with Synthetic Oils
In Percent

	Efficiency of Each Step	Efficiency Including All Preceding Steps
Production of coal	96	96
Conversion of coal to liquid	45	43
Transportation of oil	97	41.7
Steam engine	10	4
Diesel-electric engine	28	11.7

It is interesting to note that the amounts of fuels statistically reported for gasoline-truck shipments and for diesel-electric-railway shipments show just about the same ratio as the energy-system efficiencies for the two cases (5 and 23 per cent respectively), provided that the fuel used for railway shifting is disregarded.

The rapid substitution of diesel-electric for steam locomotives brought about a coal saving by 1950 of about 40 million tons per annum. The picture will look even better when dieselization proceeds to its logical conclusion, or if the coal turbines now in the experimental stage become widely used. Diesel-electric locomotives were being manufactured in 1950 at a rate sufficient to subtract each year an additional 10 million tons of coal per annum. The course of development that will show the greatest economic benefit cannot be predicted, but the eventual savings in locomotive transportation on its present scale will be at least 85 million tons of coal per annum. It has been highly profitable to railroads and customers to make the present reduction of

TABLE 9. Diesel-electric Locomotives in Use in Class I Railroads

Year	Percent of Total
1937	0.5
1940	2.0
1945	9.0
1949	25.0

waste, and further reductions will also be profitable. The rate of railway dieselization is shown in Table 9.

Space Heating

When electricity is passed through a resistance wire, the wire becomes hot. All of the electricity consumed is converted into heat, and all of this heat is passed along to the environment of the wire. The efficiency of use of electric power for heating purposes is 100 percent. Likewise, when fuel is burned with adequate air all the heat of combustion is passed along to the environment of the fire. The efficiency of use of a fuel burner is also virtually 100 percent, if the fuel burner (like the electric wire) is in the room to be heated and if no chimney is provided to carry away the warm gases of combustion. But fuel burners cannot, or should not, be used in this way. The result would be both unpleasant and unhealthy. The reason electric heating is highly efficient in practice is that none of the heat has to be thrown away in order to get rid of objectionable by-products. There are no oxides of carbon, or water, or sulfur compounds—and no depletion of the oxygen of the air.

A fuel burner must be provided with a chimney through which some heat must escape. The fuel burner is usually located outside of the area to be heated. The part of the heat radiated to areas that need no heat is wasted. A third loss of heat comes from imperfect combustion. Taken together these losses give a use efficiency of about 65 percent for automatic coal furnaces and 75 percent for oil or gas in the average domestic installation. Theoretically gas should give a somewhat lower efficiency than oil because with the higher hydrogen content of the gas more water is formed by combustion and chimney losses should be higher. In practice the two give overlapping values. Because coal must be handled as a solid, its combustion is ordinarily not as complete as that of oil or gas.

The large majority of coal furnaces in use are hand-fired, and efficiency averages about 45 percent. Wood-burning heaters run about 25 percent, and open fireplaces around 10 percent.

TABLE 10. Energy-system Efficiencies for Space Heating with Coal
In Percent

	Efficiency of Each Step	Efficiency Including All Preceding Steps
Production of coal	96	96
Transportation of coal	97	93
Open fireplace	10	9
Hand-fired furnace	45	42
Stoker furnace	65	60
Industrial furnace	90	84

TABLE 11. Energy-system Efficiencies for Space Heating with Oil
In Percent

	Efficiency of Each Step	Efficiency Including All Preceding Steps
Production of crude petroleum	96	96
Refining of petroleum	87	83.5
Transportation of oil	97	81
Automatic domestic furnace	75	61
Industrial furnace	90	73

Industrial furnaces, where more attention is given to costs, show higher efficiencies than domestic furnaces. Insulation is better (less loss by undirected radiation), incoming air is heated by outgoing combustion gas (less chimney loss), and combustion is more nearly perfect. Efficiencies somewhat above 90 percent are reached with coal, oil, or gas.

In modern domestic-heating installations, the energy-system efficiency figures for coal (stoker), oil, and gas are, respectively, 60, 61, and 61 percent (Tables 10 and 11). If the domestic-furnace oil were made from coal or gas, the energy-system efficiency would be about 30 percent. We would certainly not elect such a use for synthetic oil as long as we have natural gas available.

The energy-system efficiency for manufactured gas is about 46 percent, which is reflected in its higher price. For completely self-enriched manufactured gas (which may some day be our only gas) the energy system efficiency is about 31 percent. Assuming a production efficiency of 35 percent for power-plant design, domestic heating by electric energy will have a future energy-system efficiency of about 26 percent. This suggests that electric energy may be used widely for space heating when oil and gas become less available. Where the heat pump (see Chap. 15) is used, the energy-system efficiency of the combination could be made even higher.

A good way to indicate the relative efficiencies of space-heating systems is to list the energy-system efficiencies as in Table 12. The figures, for the most part, are average and must not be taken too seriously. For example, fireplaces have been built to operate with efficiencies considerably higher than 9 percent. Some men are much more skillful than others at hand-firing a coal furnace. Many industrial

TABLE 12. Comparison of Some Space-heating Systems

System	Energy-system Efficiency, Percent
Coal, oil, or gas, industrial	84
Electric with heat pump (COP = 4)	65
Oil or gas, domestic	61
Coal, domestic stoker	60
Electric with heat pump (COP = 3)	49
Enriched water gas	46
Synthetic oil or gas, industrial	42
Hand-fired coal, domestic	42
Synthetic oil or gas, domestic	31
Electric	16.3
Open fireplace	9

furnaces are lower in efficiency than 84 percent. Electric heating supplied by the best power plants gives an energy-system efficiency around 26 percent.

As for heat-pump systems, the efficiencies shown are somewhat misleading because they are based only upon the coal required to generate electric current. A part of the energy supplied to the system is from another source, usually air or water. When this is taken into account the true energy-system efficiency of the heat pump is much lower. Expressed only in terms of the coal equivalent of electric current, the energy-system efficiency of the heat pump is computed simply by multiplying the energy-system efficiency of electric current by the "coefficient of performance" (COP) of the heat pump. If the average COP is taken as 3 the figure is 3 times 16.3. Some heat-pump installations have had COP values as high as 4. Some electrical supplies run as high as 26 percent. This means that with present technology energy-system efficiencies have been obtained somewhat above 100 percent. Heat is not generated from nothing. With the heat pump it is only cleverly manipulated. Further progress in heat-pump development could doubtless bring efficiencies even higher. Under conditions more nearly ideal than can be reached in practice, we could reach about 150 percent, which means merely that much more than half the energy would come from the water or air of the heat-pump evaporator.

A study of Table 12 makes it clear that the use of oil and gas for domestic heating will not outlast the supply of natural petroleum and gas. The wastefulness of oil and gas made from coal will be reflected in higher costs. Electric heating with the help of the heat pump seems destined to take over this market almost completely. This is a good thing from several viewpoints: (1) electric heating is more convenient than any other; (2) electric power is more easily derived from solar energy than is fuel; (3) the heat pump provides a way of utilizing the enormous waste of low-level heat; (4) the heat pump can be used in conjunction with the collection and storage of solar heat (see Chap. 15). When liquid petroleum and natural gas are no longer abundant, conservation will be developed from technologies now already well advanced.

Built-in electric radiant heat is being used even now for well-insulated houses, and the costs are said to compare favorably with other systems. This is in spite of the present energy-system efficiency of only about 16 percent for electric power.

Conservation should be regarded as almost synonymous with thrift. It is not thrifty in a sociological or nationalistic sense to heat a house with open fireplaces instead of using about one-sixth of the fuel in a central heating unit. Fortunately, it is also not thrifty for the householder. The only people who are hurt by this sort of conservation are the suppliers of fireplace equipment.

Space heating requires more than a third of the world's total energy consumption. It is estimated that the loss of energy in this important application is above 50 percent. With wider adoption of the more efficient heating appliances, which are presently available, this loss may be cut to 25 percent. The long-term trend upward of fuel prices will take care of this.

Carbon Black

The tables in Chap. 21 show the considerable amount of natural gas consumed in 1947 for nonfuel uses. Most of the gas so used went into the manufacture of carbon black.

There is no aesthetic appeal about a plant for the manufacture of carbon black from natural gas. Nor is there any appeal to the engineer concerned with conservation of energy. (*J. M. Huber Corp.*)

It may be argued that, although the yield of carbon black is notoriously low, the operation is not only economically attractive, but it satisfactorily takes care of an important technological need. Furthermore, it is obviously better to convert the gas to carbon black than to flare it. But let us look for a moment at the magnitude of the operation, and let us question the reality of its technologic importance.

We are accustomed to thinking of carbon black in automotive tires as representing only a trifling part of the energy consumed in transportation. Not many pounds of carbon black are in a set of tires. The tires are good for thousands of miles. We buy gasoline every few days, but we buy tires perhaps once a year. So it comes as something of a surprise when we compare the annual consumption of natural gas to make carbon black for the rubber industry with the annual consumption of motor fuel, and discover that on an energy basis the one has been 10 percent of the other, and that the amount of natural gas used for carbon black was almost one-half the total amount of natural gas used as a domestic and commercial fuel. This was the case in 1945 (Table 13).

TABLE 13. Fuel Used to Make Carbon Black for Tire Manufacture

Year	Heat Value of Fuel Used for Black as Percent of Heat Value of Motor Fuel Used
1941	7.60
1943	8.74
1945	10.66
1949	10.80

In view of this situation it has been gratifying to find a shift in technology toward the manufacture of carbon black from oil instead of gas. An equal amount of a satisfactory or even superior black can be made from oil with about one-sixteenth of the waste of fuel. The shift was well under way in 1950 and will be accelerated by the long-term trend upward of market price of natural gas. Here is another major conservation project that is being stimulated by progressive competitive business interests.

The importance of the project may be understood when it is realized that in 1949 our use of motor fuel was about 900 million barrels. The fuel value of about 97 million barrels of gasoline was required for the preparation of carbon black for tires. In 1949 nearly 20 percent of the fuel required for black was oil. In 1950 the proportion was nearer 30 percent. About a quarter of the carbon black made in the United States is exported. This is equivalent, energywise, to the exportation of about 25 million barrels of petroleum per annum.

Over-all Losses of Energy

In the above sections a few examples have been described of progress and retrogression in the use of energy. No useful purpose could be served in attempting a comprehensive survey here of every important energy application. In general there has been an economic incentive to reduce waste of fuel except where considerations of comfort and mode of life override. If it were more pleasant to consume electric power from an inefficient plant we would demand wasteful power. Fortunately thrifty electric power is just as nice.

In Table 8 of Chap. 21, an attempt has been made to allocate all production, transportation, and conversion losses between the principal end uses of energy. The data are summarized here in Table 14 with the

TABLE 14. Energy-system Efficiency for End Uses in United States, 1947*
In Trillions of Horsepower-hours

End Use	Energy Consumed	Losses: Production	Losses: Transportation	Losses: Conversion	Losses: Use†	Losses: Total	Energy‡ Obtained	Energy-system Efficiency, Percent
Primary metals	1.50	0.05	0.06	0.42	0.54	1.07	0.43	29
Other manufacturing	2.35	0.08	0.13	0.52	0.97	1.70	0.65	28
Railroads	1.31	0.05	0.11	0.09	0.89	1.14	0.17	13
Ships	0.19	0.01	0.02	0.02	0.10	0.16	0.02	11
Motor cars	1.82	0.06	0.15	0.28	1.24	1.73	0.09	5
Tractors	0.18	0.01	0.01	0.03	0.12	0.17	0.01	6
Residential	4.40	0.16	0.34	0.69	2.10	3.29	1.11	25
Miscellaneous	0.73	0.03	0.05	0.11	0.32	0.51	0.22	30
Total	12.48	0.45	0.87	2.16	6.28	9.77	2.70	

* This table is based on the figures derived in Table 8, Chap. 21.
† *Use* equals energy consumed in the conversion of *net energy* to *energy obtained.*
‡ *Energy obtained* equals energy represented by useful work accomplished.

addition of estimates on losses in use, based on average working efficiencies. In this way energy-system efficiencies can be computed for each end use, and the energy consumed for each use in the United States in 1947 can be compared with the energy actually obtained as useful heat or power. The over-all losses range from 70 percent to 95 percent. Internal-combustion engines are the worst offenders. The greatest losses come from low working efficiencies. As of today, more energy can be saved here than in production, transportation, and conversion, but tomorrow the story will be different.

Of the 12.5 trillion hphr of energy consumed, only about 2.7 trillion appears to have been represented by useful accomplishment. The loss of nearly 10 trillion is made up of about 6 trillion from low working efficiencies, about 2 trillion from low conversion efficiencies, and the rest from production and transportation. The relationship between losses from conversion and from application is likely to be reversed in the future because: (1) research is finding ways of improving working efficiencies; and (2) more electric power will be generated and synthetic fuels will ultimately be made from coal. So the one loss will go down percentagewise while the other will go up.

The increase in conversion loss is almost sure to exceed greatly the decrease in the other elements of the energy-system efficiency loss, because the area of possible improvement in energy-system efficiency is limited by a number of factors: (1) With the total energy requirement at the present level, perfect working efficiencies would save less than 6 trillion hphr per annum, whereas conversion of coal to liquid fuel would add 9 trillion hphr. (2) Not much can be done to improve transmission efficiencies. Only a few percent could be gained. (3) No system could conceivably be devised to bring working efficiencies up to 100 percent in the case of fuel combustion. It is dangerous to project estimates into the distant future; but, as it looks from here, even a century of development is unlikely to yield a reduction of more than 25 percent in our working efficiency loss of 6.3 trillion hphr per annum. This would give a credit of only 1.6 trillion.

The real conservationist roles will have to be played by the group of technologists who will labor to improve the production efficiencies of synthetic liquid fuels and by the other group of technologists who will labor to make liquid fuels less essential to our economy. Both will play their parts.

11

Life Expectancy

It is relatively easy to add up present losses of conversion of one form of energy to another. This is one of the many things included in the tables of Chap. 21. For convenience, these losses are included in Table 1

TABLE 1. Conversion Losses for United States Energy Materials
In Trillions of Horsepower-hours per Annum

	1947	1970	2050
Petroleum refining	0.6	0.4	0.2
Generation of electricity	1.2	5.0	10.0
Coal conversion	...	2.0	25.0
Gas, coke, and briquettes	0.4	0.6	5.0
Total	2.2	8.0	40.2

together with losses predicted for the near and more distant future. The predictions can be very wrong. They represent, at best, what *could* or *might* happen—not necessarily what *will* happen. The various bases for predictions are outlined below.

The trend of thermal efficiency in petroleum refining has been downward. It is expected to continue downward because the demand for distilled fuel will increase while the supply of crude will eventually decrease. The over-all thermal efficiency of refining operations for a given crude varies inversely with the proportion of distilled fuel (motor fuel, diesel oil, jet fuel, kerosene, domestic-furnace oil). An ever larger proportion of our crude, both domestic and imported, is of the sort that gives an abundant yield of residual fuel oil. This heavy residual is in demand largely in competition with coal and, therefore, cannot become much more expensive than coal. Hence, more and more residual oil will be converted to distillate (by coking or hydrogenation or equivalent processes). The rate at which such operations will be adopted depends upon general conditions of supply and demand. If, in twenty years, the peak of domestic production of crude is reached, and if world-wide demand has grown to keep pace with world-wide production, rather wide-spread residual-oil conversion could be expected. A substantial portion of residual oil is being converted today by coking, and commercial hydrogenation is "just around the corner." The loss for 1970 is computed on the assumption that half of our domestic residual oil is then converted.

Looking further into the future, natural petroleum will be a scarce commodity long before a century has passed. It is likely that all residual oil will then be converted and that marine bunkers will be filled with heavy oils prepared from coal. This follows from the fact that the conversion of petroleum residuals to distillate fuels is more efficient and economical than the preparation of distillate oils from coal or oil shale.

In spite of increased losses per barrel of crude, the national loss will amount to less in the future because less oil will be refined. In this forecast we shall assume that 1 billion barrels of petroleum a year is imported by 1970 and that domestic petroleum production in the year 2050 will take care of only 10 percent of our demand for liquid fuel.

The loss from the manufacture of electricity will tend to diminish somewhat on a percentage basis as generating plants are modernized and improved in efficiency but will tend to increase on an absolute basis with the demand for electricity. The net effect is sure to be a substantially increased loss, because even the most optimistic technologist would not expect the national average efficiency to rise from the 1950 figure of 22 percent to higher than 35 percent within the next two decades. But the amount of electrical energy is expected to be about four times what it is now.

At the end of a century the demand for electricity is conservatively assumed to be ten times the present demand and the national average efficiency is assumed to be 40 percent.

Unless political pressure is applied, the conversion of coal to oil will not be undertaken on a large scale until petroleum from domestic and adjacent foreign sources, such as Venezuela and Canada, can no longer supply the demand for liquid fuel. For the purposes of this forecast, it is assumed that conversion of coal to liquid fuel will be in its initial stages in 1970 (to supply 10 percent of liquid-fuel demand) and that by

2050 we shall be obtaining 80 percent of our liquid fuel from coal, the remainder being natural petroleum and shale oil.

To the multiplicity of assumptions outlined above it is necessary to add a few more.

In 1850 we were consuming fossil fuel and water power at a rate of less than 1 percent of present consumption. In forty years our consumption had been multiplied by 20. In the following thirty years our consumption had quadrupled. Between 1920 and 1950 our con-

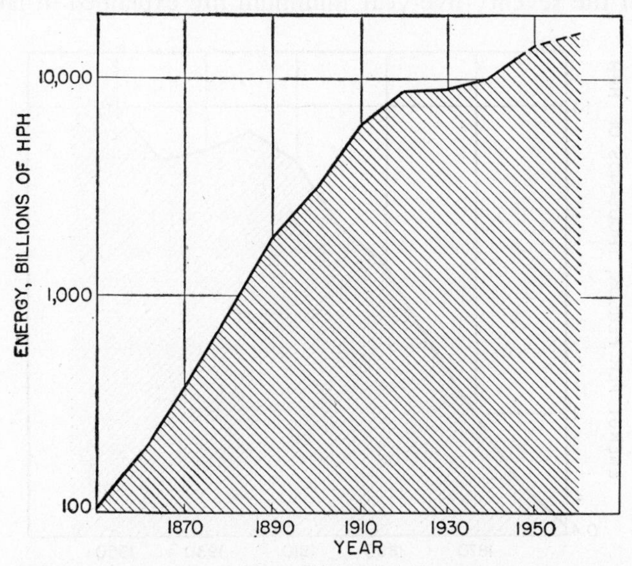

FIG. 1. The energy obtained in the United States from mineral fuels and water power. (*From J.F. Dewhurst, "America's Needs and Resources," Twentieth Century Fund, 1947.*)

sumption had almost doubled. A rate of increase of 50 percent in fifty years is assumed to be the rate of increase over the next century. The assumption should be conservative because it represents less than 1 percent compound interest, while some economists talk about an increase of 3 percent per annum. The actual rate of increase of energy consumption in the United States between 1900 and 1950 was 1.75 percent per year, and between 1940 and 1950 the rate of increase was 3.9 percent per year. Some economists predict an average rate of increase of 2.7 percent per year between 1950 and 1960, and this prediction is based upon the assumption that an increasing proportion of the total United States demand will be for electric power, the generation of which will require either coal or heavy oil. The oil would have to be largely imported.

Dr. Sumner H. Slichter, a leading American economist, believes that we shall double our output of goods between 1950 and 1980. Dr. Harold G. Moulton, President of Brookings Institution, suggests that by 2050 our scale of living may become eight times as high as in 1950. If such predictions should prove to be correct, the life expectancy of the United States fossil-fuel reserve would be cut down drastically. Instead of the seventy-five-year minimum life explained in later para-

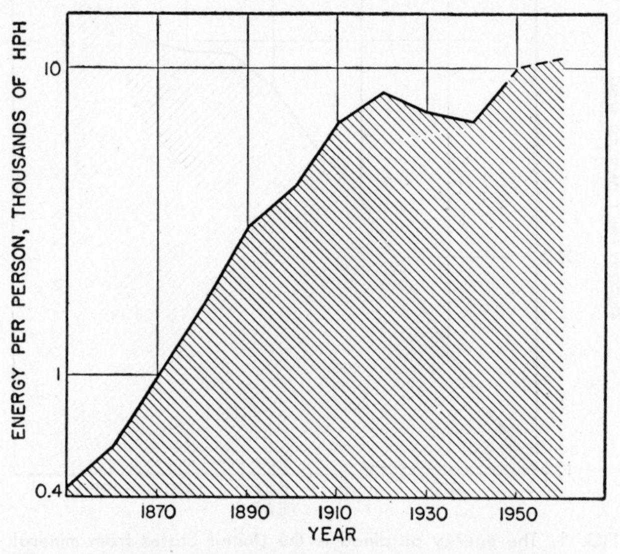

FIG. 2. The estimated supply of energy per person in the United States. (*From Dewhurst and the U.S. Bureau of the Census.*)

graphs, we would be confronted with something more like fifty years. No one can tell what the future holds for United States material progress. For present purposes it seems better to postulate a more moderate rate of growth in spite of the fact that the experts in the past have consistently fallen short in predictions of the rate of material progress. For example, a group of bankers in 1904, when we had about one million automobiles, warned that the motor industry was over-expanded. An investment firm in 1908, when we had one and a half million cars, said the industry was approaching the maximum limit. A business investment council in 1921, when we had twelve million cars, declared that the ceiling had been definitely reached. Later an economist said the limit would be twenty million. In 1934 an oil company forecast a 1950 car population that was actually reached in 1940. Keep in mind that if it is correct to be "bullish" as to rate of material progress, a rational corollary is that we must be "bearish" as to life expectancy of fuel resources.

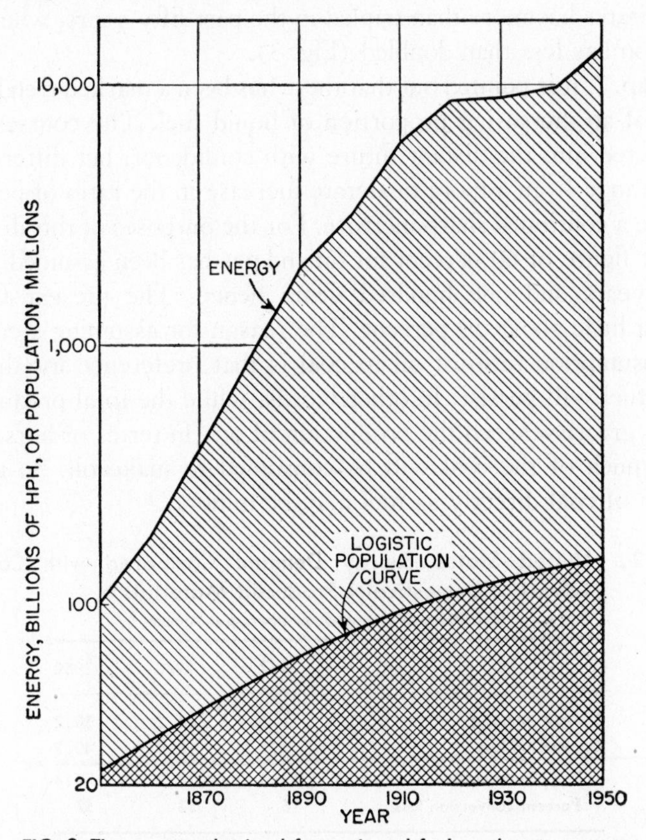

FIG. 3. The energy obtained from mineral fuels and water power compared with population growth. (*From Dewhurst and the U.S. Bureau of the Census.*)

The increase in energy consumption, expressed in ten-year averages, makes rather a smooth curve (Fig. 1), but the period from 1920 to 1935 shows a slower rise than earlier and later periods because of the depression in the early 1930's and because of the technological advances made during the 1920's that led to more efficient fuel utilization. These advances were too varied and numerous to mention here. But the improvement was so valid that the demand for energy per person in

1929, at the height of predepression prosperity, was 18 percent below the demand in 1920 (Fig. 2). The demand per person has now come back up to the 1920 figure, and is evidently on the way to further increases. It is significant to observe that, in spite of the discontinuity of the fifteen-year period just discussed, the energy demand of the United States has more than tripled in the past fifty years, whereas our population has less than doubled (Fig. 3).

In Chap. 7, it is pointed out that there has been a marked trend toward the use of an increasing proportion of liquid fuel. The courses cannot be projected into the distant future with confidence, but differences in opinion range from a more moderate increase in the ratio of petroleum to coal to a continued sharp increase. For the purposes of this discussion a modest figure of 60 percent for oil and gas has been assumed both for twenty years and one hundred years hence. The present figure is already a little above 50 percent. The reason for assuming a continued high consumption ratio of oil to coal is that preference for the liquid form of fuel will persist. In other words, while the total production of coal will greatly exceed the production of oil (in terms of horsepower-hours), much of the coal will be consumed to make oil. So the consumption of coal directly as fuel may be minor.

TABLE 2. United States Energy Demand Compared with Conversion Losses of Domestically Produced Materials

In Trillions of Horsepower-hours per Annum

	1947	1970	2050
Energy demand	11.6	16.2	30.2
Conversion loss	2.2	8.0	40.2
Total consumption	13.8	24.2	70.4
Percent conversion loss	16	33	57

Table 2 is computed from these various assumptions. By 2050 more than half of our domestic fuel production may be lost by various conversion processes. Where does this lost energy go? The processes evolve great quantities of heat, which is difficult to absorb except by the evaporation of water. The importance of developing generalized economic solutions to the problem of utilizing low-level heat cannot be too strongly emphasized. Our fossil-fuel era could be prolonged more by such developments than by any other, for such losses apply not only to conversion but also to the various ways in which energy is used. The problem is quite as much an economic one as technologic; for, no matter how useful recovered heat may be in a given case, there will be no recovery if it is unprofitable. Capital will not be invested to conserve unless the return is adequate. Also, no matter how easy (and cheap) it may be to recover heat in another case, nothing will be gained unless something useful can be accomplished by the recovery. Much heat lost by the Fischer-Tropsch process could be conserved if only we could figure out what we could do with the heat after we recaptured it. The great improvements in electrical-power production have been profitable. Conservation and profit can go hand-in-hand up to a point determined by the cost of fuel. This point rises with the rise in the cost of fuel. The best the technologist can do for conservation is to make sure that he is not lagging behind.

We now have an assortment of figures (including many guesses) that can be used to make estimates of the life expectancy of the total fuel resources of the United States. For convenience some of the necessary data will be repeated here.

The total fossil-fuel resources of the United States are 223×10^{14} hphr or 25.3×10^{14}, depending upon our degree of optimism. To compute the life of these reserves in years it is necessary to divide the total by annual energy demand. But the annual energy demand is not a constant. It is increasing every year, because of the trend toward a higher degree of mechanization and because of changing patterns of energy utilization which call for more wasteful energy-conversion processes.

In Table 2 the predicted conversion losses are totaled as 2.2×10^{12} hphr per annum for 1947, 8.0 for 1970, and 40.2 for 2050. Reasons have been given for believing that the natural increase of energy demand over the next century may be conservatively placed at 50 percent in fifty years.

Using this rate of advance, the 1947 energy demand (minus conversion loss) of 11.6×10^{12} hphr should become 13.7 in 1970 and 24 in 2050. Adding conversion losses we obtain total demands of 13.8, 21.7, and 64.2, respectively. Thus it is necessary to divide the total reserves by a lively variable. The mathematical solution to the problem involves the determination of the equation of a curve. This is scarcely worth while, for there can be too little sound basis for the numbers taken. But a graphical solution is simple, and gives a rough idea of what we may expect.

Two curves of energy demand are shown in Fig. 4. The lower curve is for demand of energy for end uses, while the upper curve represents the production of basic fuels required to give the necessary amounts of energy consumed in end uses. The lower curve assumes merely an increased demand of 50 percent in fifty years, whereas the upper curve adds the predicted conversion losses. The rate of depletion of natural reserves is determined, of course, by the upper curve.

The early part of the upper curve is fixed by the total demands quoted in this chapter. The later part of the curve assumes that conversion losses after the first century remain substantially constant.

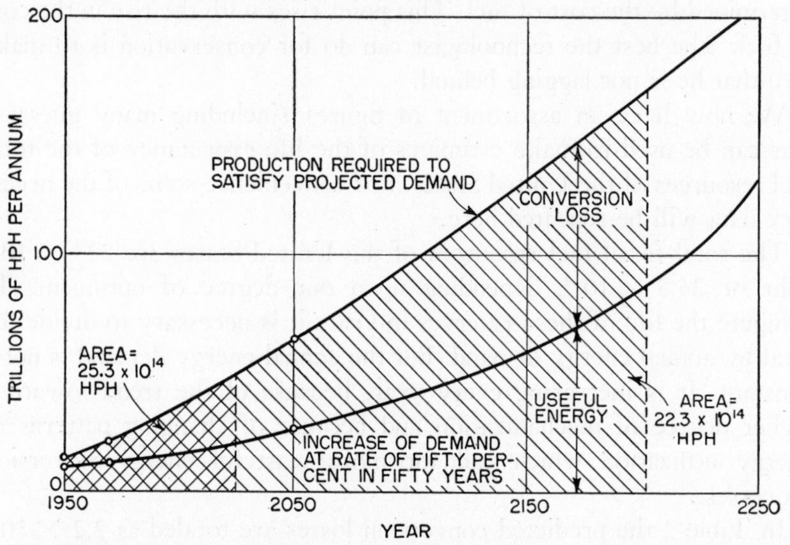

FIG. 4. An estimate of what future United States needs for energy will be and the cost in energy to supply them.

Two dotted vertical lines are drawn in such positions as to enclose areas of 25.3×10^{14} and 223×10^{14}, respectively. These lines indicate that the minimum life expectancy of United States fossil-fuel reserves is about 75 years (from 1950) while the maximum is about 250 years. The actual life may well be somewhere in between—say, 160 years.

These life spans must not be interpreted in too literal a sense because the rate of production of fuel will necessarily determine the rate of use. Thus while the demand for fuel keeps rising in the future the rate of production will be dropping (after the peak of production is once reached), and the excess of demand over production will have to be supplied by importation or by constant sources of energy. Fossil fuels will probably be produced for a thousand years or more—but finally in a mere trickle.

A rational prediction as to the date of peak of United States production of fossil fuels is quite impossible. If the rate of production can be kept high over the next fifty years, the peak will come early. But if the rate of production is kept low, the peak could conceivably come *after* the end of the predicted life expectancy (Fig. 5). In the latter case the constant sources of energy would have to be developed much earlier and used more abundantly. The future course of production will depend upon the timetable of research on constant energy sources. No one now can say whether progress will be rapid enough and successful enough to justify a long postponement of the time when we shall have to start burning up the last of our fossil fuels. Importation cannot be expected to be an important factor because other nations are likely to build up their demands for fossil fuels more rapidly than these demands can be supplied from areas outside the United States.

The life-expectancy curves are presented not with the idea that the figures can mean much in a quantitative sense, but rather to serve as a valid representation of our philosophy of energy as at present conceived. The shape of the curve is an affirmation of faith in the material future of our civilization, for it assumes a continuing increase in the demand for energy per person. It also assumes, perhaps wrongly, that the pattern of energy usage will not be greatly affected by radical changes in the economics of future fuel technology. During recent years liquid and solid fuels have had competitive prices. In the future liquid fuels will become relatively more expensive. It is difficult to say what effect such a condition would have upon comparative consumption.

Another plausible source of error is the assumption that demand for energy will not be greatly impaired by increased costs of energy. Perhaps this possibility is offset by the adoption of the low rate of increase of demand (50 percent in fifty years) instead of estimates that have been made of more than twice as rapid progress.

To extend the life of our reserves, we need to change the shape of the demand curve. The most radical improvement would be to eliminate all conversion of coal to liquid fuel. The next in importance would be to eliminate the production of electric power in coal-steam plants. Neither of these things are likely to come to pass.

The life-expectancy estimates assume the eventual total production of 80 billion barrels of shale oil. This has only a minor influence on the life

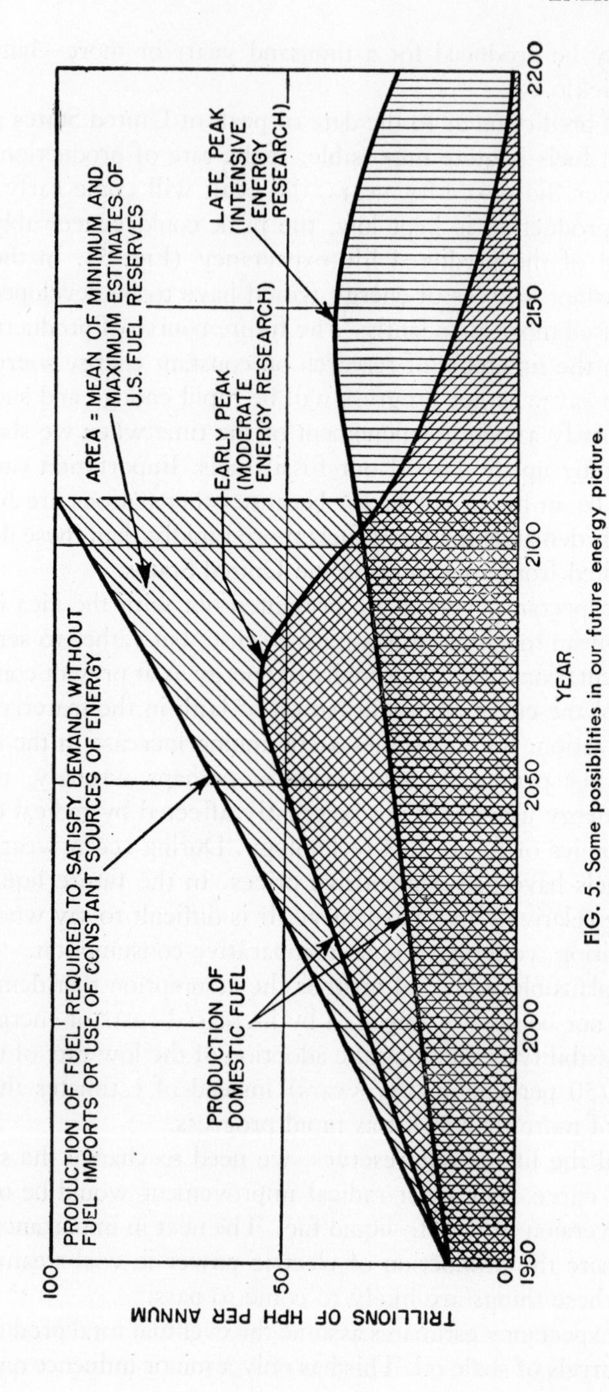

FIG. 5. Some possibilities in our future energy picture.

of our fuel resources. If the shale oil were not produced, the life expectancy of our total reserves would be shortened by only about five years. This seems strange at first glance; because if we divide 80 billions by two (the 1950 annual production), we get forty years. But the net effect of any fuel increment can be measured only by throwing it into the whole energy "pot," *i.e.*, using it as a part of the areas in Fig. 4. Obviously shale oil used now, when consumption is relatively low, would not extend the life any more than using it toward the end of the life period when consumption will be relatively high.

Some of the figures in this analysis may be very wrong. Perhaps we shall discover many times as much petroleum as we now expect, and perhaps we shall be able to recover hundreds of billions instead of 80 billion barrels of shale oil. But such good fortune will be short-lived. The eventual solution of the problem would thereby be postponed for one generation at the most.

If it should be necessary for us to live with a long-drawn-out semimilitary economy, or if we should be confronted by a series of global wars, what will be the effect upon the life expectancy of fossil-fuel reserves? This is an interesting question with many facets, but it is probably safe to assume that wars are likely to have little effect.

The idea that wars tend to accelerate the depletion of natural resources is not borne out by statistics. World Wars I and II make no consistent impression upon curves of annual consumption of coal or oil or on total energy demand. The reason is obvious. Maximum production of such basic things as fuels and metals is fixed by plant investment and supply of skilled labor. In our expanding economy production has been close to maximum except in periods of depression, and cannot be easily expanded during a war emergency because of the limits imposed on both manpower and materials of construction. Instead of increasing production, wars merely divert the use of produced materials from civilian to military channels. It is necessary to subtract from civilian economy what is needed for military purposes. The reason we feel that wars are opposed to conservation is that we sense the material futility of military dissipation of resources. What we sometimes fail to realize is that even peacetime objectives are ephemeral, and fuel is the most ephemeral thing of all. In either war or peace, a few weeks after fuels are taken from the ground they are burned. Things made of steel last a little longer, but after a few years they disappear. Even massive structures are temporary. Buildings and bridges do not ordinarily last fifty years. Automobiles, refrigerators, and washing machines usually return to the junk yard in a dozen years. Tire chains are good for about ten hours of service. During a war we recover iron from natural concentrated deposits (ore) and distribute it so widely that it can never be recovered. In peacetime we do the same thing a little more slowly. But the net effect is the same. In the United States our steelmaking capacity has expanded over the years at a sufficient rate to more than offset the rate of obsolescence of fabricated steel. Hence we have an expanding economy. In wartime civilian expansion stops, and if a war should last long enough our economy would contract—*i.e.*, steel would disappear more rapidly than it can be replaced.

During World War II about as much fuel was used for essential transportation as in prewar times. The fuel diverted from civilian use was largely fuel consumed for convenience or pleasure. Who can say that pleasure is more constructive than the attainment of a military objective? In either case the fuel is gone forever and we may have little or nothing to show for it. War gives a purposeful direction to the dissipation of fuel.

This is not intended to serve as an apology or defense for the philosophy of war, but rather to refute the fallacious idea that war is more wasteful than peace. If anything it is less wasteful. During World War II we averaged the consumption of 665 million barrels of motor fuel per annum. During the four years after the war our average annual consumption was 850 million barrels—an increase of 28 percent!

One way in which long wars might increase the rate of use of fuel resources would be by interfering with importation of petroleum to such an extent that we should be compelled to resort prematurely to the conversion of coal to liquid fuel. However, a war might have the opposite effect. Up to the end of 1950, the importation of oil had been hindered to some extent by import duties which would have been eliminated if the need had been great. Also, the retorting of oil shale (which is not accompanied by conversion loss) might well precede the conversion of coal.

Consideration of all the factors appears to lead to the conclusion that maximum and minimum estimates of life expectancy are likely to be almost independent of military events unless, indeed, war were to be so prolonged and disastrous that our whole way of life would retrogress.

An assumption of 160 years as the probable length of time that the total United States fuel resources will last is based, of course, upon two important "ifs": (1) if we depend almost entirely upon domestic production; and (2) if it is physically and economically possible to produce fuels at the rate of demand. We are already depending more and more upon imports, and we know we are approaching the time when production will become necessarily below demand.

12

The Nucleus

Much has been written about the possibility of competitive nuclear power for the future. All of such studies are necessarily speculative and range from high optimism to the deepest pessimism. No one has the prescience to appraise inventions and discoveries that have not yet been made. All that can be done at this time is to paint the picture with the colors of our present conception of nuclear technology. With this picture each one of us can use his imagination to reach his own conclusions.

It is necessary at the outset to have clearly in mind the great difference between energy for useful power and energy for destruction. If an automotive engine could be designed to operate with nitroglycerine, we would complain bitterly about miles per gallon with such a fuel. A pound of gasoline contains six times as much energy as a pound of nitroglycerine. The earth is struck by lightning about a hundred times per second. But the energy represented by the whole of the electrical potential gradient between the earth and the atmosphere is less than a third of the present world consumption of energy. The violence of the lightning disguises its weakness.

An evaluation of the place of nuclear energy in the total energy picture seems to resolve itself into four questions. First, can energy-producing nuclear reactions be performed on a workable, controllable basis? Second, do we have enough suitable fissionable material to make the energy product a major factor in the resources total? Then, if the answers to these two questions are positive, will the cost of that energy make it competitive with that from other sources at the time it becomes available in quantity? Finally, if the relative costs prove high, does this form of energy have special characteristics that warrant its use where other forms are less applicable?

Today there is no doubt about an affirmative answer to the first question, although as recently as 1942 it would have been no. In December, 1942, when Dr. Fermi and his group working in the West Stands of Briggs Stadium, Chicago, withdrew the control rods from the world's first nuclear pile and a steady flow of heat resulted—albeit only 250 watts—there was no further doubt that man can control nuclear reactions to provide a net energy output. Since then many energy-producing piles have been built, some of them large ones such as the one at Hanford that produces heat equivalent to several hundred thousand kilowatts. With all these piles, heat has been a by-product of some other objective, and simply dissipated to air or water. But, that is incidental to the question, can it be done? Piles producing commercially usable energy will be built.

The second matter—the amount of nuclear fuel—cannot be disposed of so quickly. We have two nuclear fuels. One is uranium, the material on which the atomic bombs and all presently operating piles are based. The other is thorium, which is still a nuclear fuel only in theory, at least in so far as the public has been advised.

Uranium occurs in the earth's crust rather plentifully, but unfortunately not much of it is in concentrated bodies like coal or iron ore. Principally it occurs as a minute constituent—perhaps one pound per ton or less—with other minerals. The greatest announced source is the pitchblende deposits in the Belgian Congo. The best United States reserves are in Colorado in carnotite ore, which contains less uranium than pitchblende. Uranium occurs in minute proportions in phosphate rock. The grade is probably much too small to warrant processing for uranium alone. But we need agricultural phosphorus (see Chap. 16). With two ends in view, working the vast Idaho deposits may become practical.

The total amount of uranium that will be available is uncertain. Even the known facts are restricted. However, the chances are that uranium metal will be extremely limited in quantity. The order of magnitude is more likely to be tens of tons than hundreds of tons. Uranium metal in thousands of tons seems quite improbable.

Thus, from an energy angle, discovery of the fissionable properties of uranium is similar to finding large new petroleum pools or coal fields. The amount has been estimated as being more than equivalent to the world's petroleum reserves but less than the coal reserves. Certainly the amount of energy obtainable from uranium is not infinite. It does not justify the assumption that our energy worries are over.

Having gotten, say, a hundred pounds of pure natural uranium metal, less than a dozen ounces is the right kind for fission—the process by which a neutron causes a nucleus to break up into smaller fragments and a lot of energy. Uranium consists of three types, or isotopes. The more common kind, uranium with mass 238 (U^{238}), is not itself a nuclear fuel. It is the second kind, U^{235}, that can support the necessary chain reaction. And this is present in natural uranium only in the ratio of 140 of U^{238} to 1 of U^{235}. The third kind, U^{233}, is even rarer. We'll return to it later.

If we were dependent on U^{235} as the fuel for nuclear power plants nuclear energy would, quite surely, remain in the category of minor energy sources. But there is more to the story. It happens that U^{235} nuclei are caused to explode by slow-moving neutrons. In the cataclysm, some neutrons (up to three on the average) are ejected at high speed. At least one of these must be slowed down and caused to strike another U^{235} nucleus to keep the process alive. But the spare high-speed neutrons can be put to other good use. It is a fortunate circumstance that when the 140 times more prevalent U^{238} nuclei are struck by neutrons they are converted first into another element, neptunium of mass 239, but which—and this is the important part—changes to a still different element, plutonium of mass 239 (Pu^{239}). Plutonium, like U^{235}, is fissionable by neutrons.

Thus in causing the disintegration of a relatively rare fissionable nucleus, U^{235}, we have created, theoretically, at least one more fissionable nucleus (Pu^{239}) out of the nonfissionable U^{238}. It's startling but we wind up with as much, if not more, nuclear fuel than we started with. At least in theory. Breeding, as the process is called, has not yet been put to large-scale demonstration, but seems assured of success. If it is we can place all natural uranium—not just the rare U^{235} kind—in the nuclear-fuel resource column.

Breeding does not lead to an unlimited amount of nuclear fuel, as some have concluded. This is an important point. We cannot, even by breeding, make more nuclear fuel (of uranium origin) than we have uranium. By breeding we stand to increase our nuclear fuel up to 140 times more than it would be if we were dependent on U^{235}.

Breeding has another fortunate aspect. As the product, plutonium, is another metal, chemically different from uranium, its separation from uranium is simple by comparison with the separation of U^{235} from U^{238}. Thus the elaborate, costly, and enormously complicated separation processes such as are established at Oak Ridge for separation of the two kinds of uranium are unnecessary.

Then there is thorium, a metal about four times more abundant than uranium. According to theory, it, like U^{238}, can be converted to a fissionable material. Supposedly, when a thorium nucleus absorbs a neutron it is converted to U^{233}—the rarest of the three naturally occurring kinds. Whether or not this has been actually accomplished has not been disclosed. For the time being we shall have to hold this as a distinct possibility by which the stock of nuclear fuels can be multiplied further.

One must conclude that while fissionable materials are available in sizable quantities, they are not abundant. They are, after all, earth minerals—and rare ones at that. To be sure, a little goes a long way. Energywise, a pound of any of the three fissionable materials is worth about a million pounds of good coal. Nuclear fuels will be a means of extending our inventory of earth-stored energy. The factor is still in doubt.

Nuclear fuel, having been demonstrated to be capable of producing large amounts of energy and to be available in important quantities, still has another obstacle to hurdle before it becomes competitive with other energy forms. These are the engineering problems—which boil down to cost. Production of energy from nuclear processes is hedged by problems that in both size, number, and complexity make every engineering project heretofore attempted seem like a Tinker Toy operation. The problems that surrounded the development of television are child's play by comparison.

Some concept of these hurdles can be gathered from looking at the several expensive and difficult steps to supply and maintain a nuclear-power plant. These are based on the necessary assumption that the pile will simply replace the fuel supply, fuel-storage and -handling facilities, and boiler of a conventional electric-power plant. No idea has yet been found how nuclear energy can be converted to electric energy more directly. The intermediate heat steps with their losses and complications seem inevitable. Enormous quantities of electric charges are present at the time of a nuclear explosion but no way to capture them has appeared. About 80 percent of the nuclear energy produced is in the kinetic energy of the flying product particles—*i.e.*, heat. About 5 percent lies in subsequent—and perhaps long-delayed—radiation from fragment particles. The remainder is in immediate gamma radiation and the motion of nuclear components (electrons, neutrons). If someone steps up with a more direct energy-capture process the entire picture will be changed. The chances don't appear good.

The first step in power generation will be, of course, the separation of the uranium from the ore.

The second step will be the purification of the uranium compound. This is important because the presence of the impurities would capture neutrons at an intolerable rate. The degree of purity must be high.

The third step is to reduce the uranium compound to metal. Uranium has a great affinity for oxygen and must be processed in a vacuum or in an inert atmosphere. All melting and casting is done in this way.

The fourth step is fabrication and machining into long cylindrical rods. This requires many man-hours of highly skilled work and is usually carried out at low temperatures to minimize oxidation.

The fifth step is to jacket the rods with aluminum to protect the uranium from corrosion by water and air in the plutonium-producing reactor.

The sixth step is the operation of the reactor. The design of the reactor will have to represent a compromise between what is believed to be best for power generation and what is believed to be best for the efficient conversion of U^{238} to plutonium. We must assume that a satisfactory compromise can be found. It is hoped that the first reactor designed to test the feasibility of breeding will also produce "a small amount of useful power." Conversely, it is hoped that the reactor designed primarily to produce power will also succeed in breeding fissionable material more rapidly than it is consumed.

The seventh step is the removal of heat from the reactor to a power-generation system. Possibly this will be with a molten metal. This heat-transfer metal must be fairly light, must remain in a liquid state over a wide range of temperatures between a low melting point and a high boiling point, must have good heat-transfer characteristics, and, above all, must have the proper nuclear characteristics. We must assume that a suitable medium can be found.

The eighth step is the removal after a considerable time of the uranium rods from the reactor for chemical processing. This must be done after only a very small percentage of the fuel has been consumed. If one dared to look at the rod at this stage, it would be found to have a blue-white glow from its intense radioactivity. The rod within its aluminum jacket is no longer pure uranium. In addition to uranium there will be small amounts of plutonium and neptunium (which soon decays to plutonium) and somewhat larger quantities of impurities that must be removed before the breeding reaction can be resumed.

The ninth step is the "cooling" of the radioactive rods—a time of storage to permit the high level of radioactivity to subside.

The tenth step is chemical reprocessing of the rods. This is the major step and will represent probably 80 percent of the power plant. The beautifully machined and jacketed rods must be completely dissolved in chemical reagents. In the first reagent only the jacket is removed. The second reagent dissolves everything else, and this solution is processed to obtain (1) pure uranium; (2) pure plutonium; (3) about 40 other elements as free as possible from uranium and plutonium. The great bulk of the product, uranium, is then put back into the third step in the process (reduction to metal), and then through all the succeeding steps (fabrication, jacketing, etc.). The plutonium is stored as active fissionable material. The 40 impurities are radioactive and must be disposed of in special ways.

The eleventh step is the disposal of these radioactive wastes. This is a problem that has not yet been satisfactorily solved. So far, the nonvolatile products of fission have been stored. Some of the elements lose their dangerous radioactivity in a few hours, while others are dangerous for many years. Even in the manufacture of atomic bombs—an operation that has been negligible in magnitude compared with industrial power requirements—the storage has become embarrassing. The volume of liquid waste has been reduced by evaporation of the water. Some of the materials with short radioactive lives can be diluted and run into streams, but in spite of precautions, the mud of such streams is becoming increasingly radioactive. Gaseous wastes are discharged to stacks from 200 to 300 feet high, where the waste can be safely diluted with a strong wind. In such a case, the power plant must be slowed down or shut down when the weather is unfavorable. The waste-disposal problem is helped somewhat by increasing by sixty days the "cooling" period between the time the rods are removed from the reactor and the time the chemical processing begins. The many facets of radioactive waste disposal must be solved before any nuclear power plants can be put into operation.

The continuous generation of nuclear power is thus a process in which 95 percent or more of the nuclear fuel must be continuously recycled through the most costly and complicated chemical process now known and through a high-grade machine shop. The cycle must be made many months long because of the time it takes to react, to "cool," and to repurify. Thus a correspondingly large amount of fissionable fuel must be "in process."

There are two reasons for the costly nature of the nuclear chemical plant. Both have to do with poisons. On the one hand is the problem of avoiding the "poisoning" of the nuclear reaction itself—the accumulation of the 40 or more elements that slow down and finally stop the formation of plutonium. In most industrial operations, removal of reaction poisons is relatively simple. Catalysts, for example, can be regenerated at intervals *in situ* or even continuously. The ashes from fuel combustion can be shaken out. In other processes, volatile products can be distilled off, and insoluble products can be precipitated. Many processes depend, for their economic status, primarily on the difficulty of eliminating the things that interfere with reaction. In the nuclear-power plant everything is against us. Nothing can be done in the reactor itself to remove impurities. The entire charge must be removed and processed—not promptly but after a long "cooling-off" period—not through simple operations such as heating or cooling or gas blowing, but by putting the charge into complete solution and carrying out a nightmarish succession of chemical-engineering steps.

In most industrial operations the ratio of recycled material to fresh charge is less than unity. This recycle ratio is the major factor in determining capital costs because it determines the capacity of equipment for a given input of raw product. In certain petroleum processes, the capital cost is regarded as excessive if it is necessary to recycle more than five times the volume of the charge. But for plutonium manufacture the recycle of uranium amounts to more than twenty times the rate of fresh uranium input. If yields could be disregarded and the operation were carried out as a once-through process, the chemical plant and reactor, per pound of converted uranium, would be only one-twentieth as large.

All stages of plutonium manufacture must be carried out by remote control. The control rods which regulate the intensity of the nuclear reaction must be able to move five feet in a tenth of a second, and must also be controllable within fractions of a millimeter. An inkling of the problems involved may be obtained from the simple statement that once the pile is in full operation *no one* can *ever* go inside the shield thereafter to repair or lubricate or adjust any of the reloading or control equipment inside. If any important part of it becomes inoperable, the reactor must be shut down and another one built. The remote control makes use of servomechanisms, hydraulic actuators, periscopes, and television. Chemists and operators must be separated from their work by six or seven feet of concrete. In some cases, they must keep more than 300 yards away from the zone of operations.

These are some of the factors that skyrocket the cost of getting rid of the reaction poisons.

The other "poison" problem is, of course, the matter of waste disposal. There is no practicable way of speeding up radioactive decay. Radioactivity persists through all chemical reactions and is ordinarily unaffected by changes in physical conditions. We simply have to "stand and wait" for days or decades until materials are safe.

The cost of power to the consumer is made up of various items, the largest of which is fixed by the investment. Water costs nothing, but hydroelectric power is usually as costly as coal-steam-electric power because the higher investment in the hydroelectric plant offsets the cost of coal. It has been estimated that if nuclear fuel could be made without cost, and used in a conventional power plant, the cost of the resultant power to the consumer would be about 75 percent of what it is now. But it cannot be used in a conventional power plant. The extra investment required for its use would ensure a *higher* cost to the consumer even if the nuclear fuel itself cost nothing. But nuclear fuel cannot be made without cost.

One can hardly escape the conclusion that, even when the engineering problems are solved—and, for all their magnitude, they most surely will be—power from uranium-fueled plants will not be cheap power. It is almost idle to speculate at this juncture. The problems are not likely to be solved quickly enough to permit a commercial nuclear-power plant to go into operation before 1960, perhaps 1970. What can be done in the meantime to reduce the costs of the nuclear-fuel portion of the endeavor we cannot say. In the meantime, costs of other fuels can be counted on to rise. Sometime they may meet.

It is quite possible that nuclear-power plants will not have a chance to prove their economic competitiveness. Because of the military interest in nuclear energy and the necessary government controls that result, it may well be that the operation of power plants will be related to the production and processing of the nuclear fuel for military purposes, with the result that the cost of the nuclear part of the plant does not represent its true cost.

While the cost of nucleus-produced energy seems uncompetitively high, it is certain that nuclear-power plants will be built. As with any new thing, nuclear energy has characteristics unlike any other form. It thereby has potential applications where other types of power producers are not so well suited. Mobile power plants are the most obvious ones, because the nuclear-power plant, while large itself, needs to carry with it no large quantities of fuel. For ships this is particularly important and is why the first power plants built are designed for naval service. Nuclear-propelled military aircraft—having unlimited range—is attractive and is the subject of intensive research. However, the chance of extending this form of energy to locomotives seems remote, and to automobiles, completely fantastic.

A nuclear-power plant, in addition to not requiring a continuous supply line or large hoard of fuel, uses little water. This combination opens other interesting possibilities. There are arid regions such as our West where a power plant indifferent to fuel and water problems would be attractive. To speculate, should minerals be found in the Sahara, or at either of the polar regions—which are without fossil fuels—a nuclear-power plant could provide the energy to make their exploitation practical. Once again, we should not view the new wholly in terms of the old.

13

The Patron

Ancient peoples looked up to the sun, worshiping it as a deity. At a time in the future much nearer than the era of sun worship we will again look up to the sun, not as a god, but for the daily ration of energy to keep the machines of civilization running. For, when stored fuels are gone, the one important source of energy will be the continuous radiation showered on the earth by the sun, unless nuclear energy vastly exceeds expectations. The mechanism by which the sun provides this bountiful store of heat and light is interesting. It may be instructive as well.

For all that the sun is a blinding ball of fire riding the sky some 93 million miles distant, a surprising amount is known about it. Much of this has been learned in the last dozen years. In fact the new evidence is contrary to many of the long-believed popular conceptions of the sun. For example, perhaps the sun is not cooling off but getting hotter! It does not consist principally of superhot molten iron and heavy elements but is predominantly hydrogen and helium. Also, to a degree, the sun is refueling itself. As it speeds at 650 000 miles per hour through the cold "void" within our galaxy it sweeps up atoms of hydrogen gas that comprise the "ether" of interstellar space. And hydrogen is the fuel of the solar furnace. While this hydrogen drawn from space is not adequate at present for the solar fires, it does add to the sun's stock of fuel. (The sun is 81.76 percent hydrogen, and 18.17 percent helium. This leaves but a small fraction of 1 percent for all the other elements, which are present in about the same proportion as they are in the earth.)

The sun is not a solid. Not at the temperature and pressures present. The main body is a "gaseous" ball 865 000 miles in diameter whose density at the center is about ten times that of lead—a cubic foot weighs about 3½ tons—and is under a pressure of a billion tons per square inch. The body of the sun is quite commonly spoken of as being a gas but undoubtedly this is not a gas as we know it because nothing in our earthly experience is subjected to anything like such pressures and temperatures. At solar interior pressures the atoms of any substance would literally collapse were it not for the high temperatures, believed to be 20 million degrees C. Moving from the sun's center toward its periphery the pressures, densities, and temperatures decline. At the surface—*i.e.*, at the bottom of the 200-mile thick layer of gas called the "photosphere" (which is what we see)—the temperature has dropped to a mere 6000 degrees C and the gas pressure is only one-fifth that of our sea-level atmosphere. The average density of the sun is but 1.42, about equal to that of a lump of coal. The total mass of the sun is 2.24×10^{27} (2.24 billion, billion, billion) tons, or about 330 000 times greater than the earth.

We cannot see the sun's surface, only the upper layers of gas that comprise the photosphere. This is a turbulent mass of gas whose outer temperature varies from about 6000 degrees C at its base to about 5000 degrees C at its outer layer (200 miles) where its pressure has become equivalent to the vacuum in an average radio tube—about one one-hundredth of an atmosphere.

Why the solar atmosphere, which is so tenuous, should be opaque when our much denser atmosphere is almost transparent was long a mystery. It has since been discovered that the photosphere contains copious quantities of negative hydrogen ions—hydrogen atoms to which are attached one more than the one normal electron. Negative hydrogen ions are almost nonexistent on earth. These extra electrons very readily absorb almost any visible or ultraviolet radiation, which they must eventually give up again, of course, but by then the damage is done. Thus light coming from the sun's body itself that would tell us something directly of its character is, in effect, diffused by the photosphere much as light is scattered by a sheet of ground glass.

On the surface of the photosphere appear the sunspots, blamed for so many things. Much mystery about their origin and nature still surrounds them. They are quite surely turbulent, perhaps cyclonic, disturbances in the sun's atmosphere. Although called "spots," they are dark only by comparison with the surrounding photosphere. Their temperature is only about 1000 to 1500 degrees C cooler and they

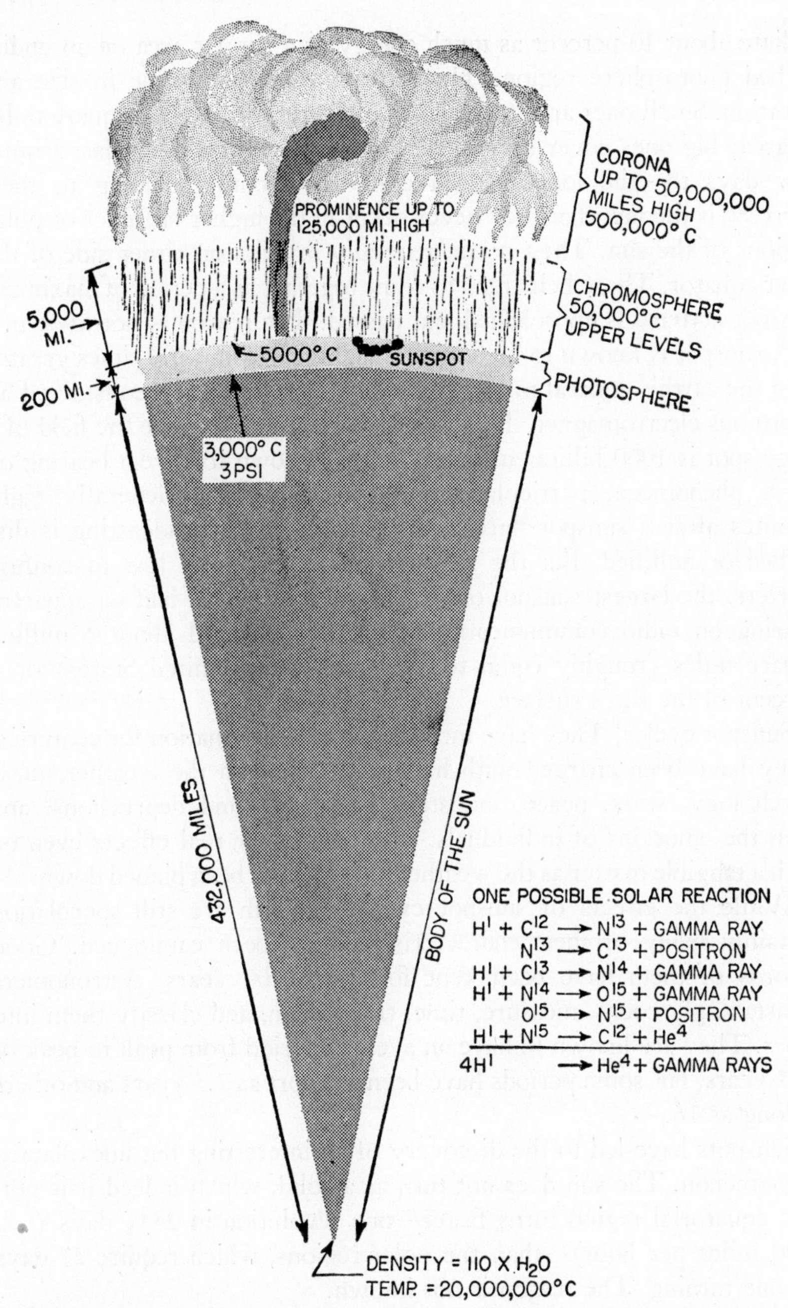

FIG. 1. A diagram, not to scale, of the solar structure, based on latest views of the astrophysicists. Shown is one set of probable reactions by which hydrogen is converted to helium, via carbon as a catalyst, with an attendant release of large quantities of radiant energy.

radiate about 10 percent as much energy as a similar area on an undisturbed photosphere region. They are extremely variable in size and duration. Small ones are 500 miles in diameter, or 250 000 square miles in area; big ones cover several million square miles. They last from a few days to—the longest on record—18 months. Adding to their mystery is the fact that they never occur in the higher latitudes or polar regions of the sun. They occur generally in belts on either side of the solar equator. These belts tend to come together as a period of maximum sunspot activity is approached and passed. The reason is not known.

A sunspot is known to be fiercely magnetic—some 500 times greater than the earth's general magnetic field. A sunspot can be considered an enormous electromagnet. The current required to produce the field of a large spot is 1000 billion amperes. This is known to have a bearing on earth phenomena, particularly radio transmission. Generally eight minutes after a sunspot flare activity short-wave broadcasting is disturbed or nullified. But the relationship is not clear. Just to confuse matters, the largest sunspot on record—April, 1947—had no apparent bearing on radio communication. This spot covered about 6 million square miles (roughly equal to the area of the United States) or 1 percent of the sun's surface.

Sunspot cycles! They have intrigued man's imagination for centuries. They have been charged with having influence on the weather, mass psychology, wars, peace, industrial prosperity and depressions, and even the emotions of individuals. However, their real effects even on such a tangible matter as the weather have not yet been pinned down.

While the effects of sunspot cycles on earth are still speculation certainly many of their characteristics have been catalogued. Good records of them have been kept for about 200 years. Astronomers painstakingly count, measure, time, track them, and classify them into types. They are known to have an average period from peak to peak of 11.2 years, but some periods have been as short as 7.5 years and others as long as 16.

Sunspots have led to the discovery of an interesting but unexplained phenomenon. The sun does not turn as a solid, which indeed it is not. The equatorial region turns faster—one revolution in 25½ days (*i.e.*, 4500 miles per hour)—than the polar regions, which require 27 days for one turning. The reason is not known.

Another interesting and somewhat mystifying sun feature is the solar prominences. These are flamelike emanations that come in a wide variety of sizes, types, and durations. Some rise to a height of only a few thousand miles; others climb a quarter of a million miles above the solar surface—and do so at the fantastic speed of 100 miles per second. Some prominences rise to a peak and then quickly fall back, as though their mass—as much as a billion tons—were sucked back by the gravity of the sun. All evidence may be gone in an hour or so. Others form and remain essentially unchanged in shape for days.

The photosphere is not the sun's only atmosphere. It has at least two more. Above the photosphere is a layer called the "chromosphere,"

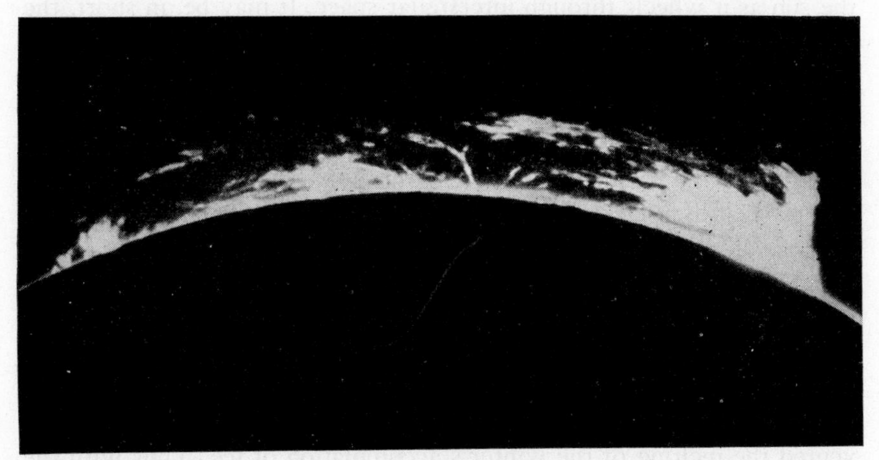

Enormous turbulent masses of hot gases rise several hundred thousand miles above the sun's surface and can be seen at times of natural or artificial eclipses. (*Harvard Observatory.*)

so named because at times of solar eclipse it exhibits a distinct color. The chromosphere is decidedly nonuniform. It appears to be made up of moving filaments and has been likened in cross section to the grass of an unkempt yard. The individual filaments, or spicules, are threadlike only by comparison with solar dimensions. Many of them reach 5000 miles and some 10 000 miles, which gives the chromosphere an indefinite depth.

The chromosphere has a surprising and unexplained characteristic. One would expect its temperature to be much lower than that at its boundary with the photosphere underneath (5000 degrees C). Quite the contrary. Astronomers have evidence that its temperature must be at least 20 000 degrees C.

Far beyond the chromosphere is the "corona," a pearly, fan-shaped halo that becomes visible (white in color) at the time of a total solar eclipse. Its form is always indefinite but, in general, at times of sunspot minimum, the corona displays enormous extensions along the equator. The converse is true at sunspot maximum, indicating that corona and sunspots are somehow interrelated.

The composition of the corona is still a matter of speculation. It has generally been assumed to be some form of ash from the sun's nuclear reactions. Recently, however, a very different and extremely interesting idea has been proposed. It is that the corona is not of solar origin at all but is really clouds of hydrogen gas being scooped up by the sun as it wheels through interstellar space. It may be, in short, the sun refueling itself.

The corona temperature? An astonishing one million degrees!

In the fact that the sun (as do the other stars) draws to itself hydrogen gas as it swings through the galaxy may lie the explanation of the ice ages on the earth. The sun is moving relatively rapidly now, too fast to suck in hydrogen in any such volume as it consumes. But some astrophysicists hold that at times in its life the sun has moved much more slowly. Thus it scooped up or "tunneled" a much larger volume of hydrogen. These periods were associated with a slight rise in solar radiation, which had the seemingly contrary result of causing the ice ages. The greater sun's heat caused more evaporation of the earth's water, creating dense clouds that hung over the polar regions and prevented the melting of the winter's accumulation of ice. Thus with the protective umbrella of clouds the ice sheets slowly crept downward.

Should the solar radiation have increased much more, the trend would have reversed, causing a melting of the ice sheets and extending the temperate zones to the polar regions, which could account for the presence of huge coal deposits as far north as Spitzbergen.

Why the change in sun speed is not known. But it is expected that as the sun ages—in another forty or fifty billion years—its temperature will again increase and bring the earth to a molten mass.

The Solar Nuclear-power Plant

But the point of greatest interest about the sun is where all that energy comes from. Only recently has that been established with any definiteness. Obviously it cannot be any earthlike fire. Had the sun consisted at the outset entirely of carbon and oxygen it would have burned out in 1500 years. The sun is known to have been in business at least two billion years. Further it is a young star, has about fifty billion more to go.

Until a few years ago astronomers held that the energy came from the slow contraction of the sun, and consequent heating of its constituent gases. As late as 1939 it was believed that sun heat might come from the decay of radioactive substances heavier than those that exist on earth, *i.e.*, beyond uranium. That idea is now wholly discarded.

The beneficence of the sun can be imagined taking many, many forms, as the artist has it here. (*American Petroleum Institute.*)

It is pretty generally agreed that solar energy emanates from a nuclear reaction. On earth we have achieved an energy release in the atomic bomb and uranium piles, by the fission of heavy atoms—specifically, uranium and plutonium—into middle-sized elements, such as barium and krypton, about midway in the scale of elements. The sun does it differently. It converts four atoms of hydrogen—the lightest element—by probably many different sets of reactions to one of helium, the next heavier element. The mass of four hydrogen atoms is slightly more than the helium product, the remainder—*à la* Einstein's $e = mc^2$ —appears as radiant energy. Such indeed is the proposed H-bomb.

In the sun, four atoms of hydrogen become one of helium by way of probably many different nuclear-reaction routes. However, astrophysicists give a fairly simple mechanism, which we can take as representative, if not predominant. The steps are these:

An atom of carbon (C^{12}) collides with a proton (H^1), which is the hydrogen nucleus. The result is a kind (isotope) of nitrogen. However, its mass is less than that of its parents. The difference, according to the inexorable mass-energy relationship, must come out as energy, which it does as a gamma ray. Hence the reaction has already netted some energy. But there is more to come.

The nitrogen isotope is unstable and in a few minutes ejects a positive electron (*i.e.*, a positron, e^+). This makes it a heavy isotope of carbon (C^{13}), which meets with a second hydrogen nucleus to form a different isotope of nitrogen (N^{14}) and again a gamma ray. A third hydrogen nucleus collides with this nitrogen isotope to create oxygen (O^{15}) and more gamma radiation. This oxygen atom likewise is unstable and it expels a positron to become a third kind of nitrogen (N^{15}). Hydrogen nucleus number four strikes this nitrogen atom, this time causing it to split into two, one of which is the helium nucleus (He^4). The other is the nucleus of carbon (C^{12}), which is ready to start the whole chain again.

In effect with the aid of carbon as a catalyst, four hydrogen nuclei have been converted to one of helium plus an enormous amount of energy. In total some 564 million tons of hydrogen are converted into 560 million tons of helium, leaving 4 million tons of mass converted into energy each second. Thus each second the sun pours into space energy equivalent to about a million times the earth's original heritage of stored fuels—coal, petroleum, and natural gas.

What are the chances of copying the sun's trick of creating energy? We have plenty of raw materials. Hydrogen can be made in large quantities at small cost. We could easily spare a cubic mile of sea water for the purpose if necessary, which contains almost exactly as much hydrogen as the sun consumes each second. And the energy realized even at only 10-percent efficiency in converting the hydrogen in 1 cubic mile of sea water into helium would be 1.14×10^{18} kwhr, or enough to satisfy our energy wants at the 1950 rate for about 300 centuries.

A few years ago any such prospect would have been suitable subject matter only for the wildest of pseudoscience fiction. But with the likely prospect of the H-bomb—which is nothing but a short-lived solar reactor—this idea must be hauled out of the realm of the fantastic. To be sure, the difficulties of performing the reaction—which takes place only at temperatures of several million degrees—on anything like a steady, controllable basis seem insurmountable at present. But so was the A-bomb in 1938.

14

Power from the Sun

We are engaged today in an intensive search for anything that can be burned. Just a century ago wood was our principal fuel, and the art of the woodcutter embodied all the necessary technology of fuel procurement. Today, with fossil fuels we are dependent on a host of technologists in almost every branch of pure and applied science—physics, chemistry, metallurgy, geology, geophysics, and all kinds of engineering. We have reached a furious tempo of effort to find and produce and destroy. The climax of this effort will certainly be reached within the lifetime of some of our children. The whole technology of geophysics as applied to the discovery of petroleum is contained within the past thirty years. By the end of this century such use of geophysics may be regarded as an interesting historical episode in applied science—a device that supplied us with the means of satisfying our appetites for energy, and that accelerated the age of mechanized industrialism.

The use of energy is habit forming. We cannot now conceive of a satisfactory way of life without abundant and economical power, heat, and light. So, while we continue to find and produce materials that can be burned, we are beginning a new search—a search for elements suitable for nuclear fission. This search too will promptly reach a climax if and when technology makes industrial nuclear power practical.

Three Days' Worth of Fuel

While these two enterprises are being prosecuted to their inevitable ends, we are having showered upon us an essentially perpetual supply of energy from the sun. How abundant is this energy? A conjecture makes this startlingly clear.

Suppose all the earth's coal, lignite, peat, tar sands, crude petroleum, natural gas, and oil shale that we are ever likely to produce in the future (according to the more optimistic forecasts) were collected and that all our timber were cut into cordwood. Suppose we segregate all the uranium and thorium that we are likely to produce in the future (based on estimates by Lawrence R. Hafstad) and that it is all purified for nuclear fission. Thus we have at hand for immediate use all the earth's stock of fuels. Then, suddenly, we extinguish the sun. We ignite our fuel in such fashion as to give us energy at the rate at which we are accustomed to receive it from the sun. In about three days our entire supply of combustible fuel would be gone. Then we would get the nuclear reactions under way. This would last us less than an hour if the "breeder principle" could be applied—otherwise only a few seconds At the end of a few days the earth with its load of ashes and radioactive wastes would begin its descent toward some temperature only slightly above absolute zero.

This gives a rough idea of what it would mean to try to compete with the sun.

What We Get from the Sun

There are two particularly interesting things about the sun. One is the high order of magnitude of the amount of energy it radiates. The other is the low order of magnitude of the rate of the nuclear reactions that are believed to be responsible for this energy. Both are quite beyond our terrestrial experience and hence are difficult to comprehend. The transmutation of hydrogen to helium in the sun is incredibly slow. It has been pointed out that only 1 percent of the hydrogen in the sun is transformed into helium in a billion years. The sun is usually regarded as being about two billion years old. If it has lost only 2 percent of its hydrogen during its lifetime, this is, nevertheless, a source of a stupendous amount of energy.

Much of the heat and light of the sun is due not to degraded or stepped-down gamma radiation, but rather to the collision of the material particles involved in the hydrogen-helium cycle. But why does the sun radiate almost none of the original gamma rays? The only difference between the gamma rays generated in the sun and the light that reaches the earth is frequency. Both are narrow portions of the great electromagnetic spectrum that spreads from radio frequencies to infrared to visible light to ultraviolet to X rays to gamma rays, in order of increasing frequency. The earth receives a little of all of these radia-

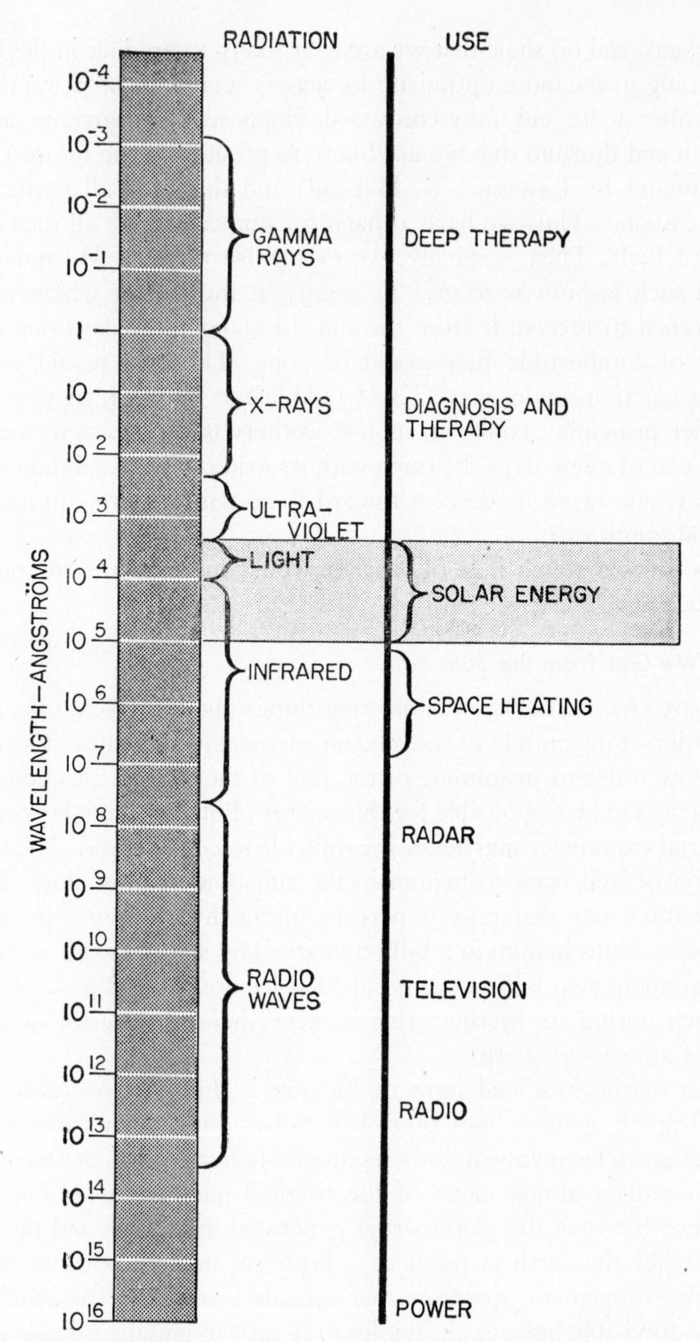

FIG. 1. The solar energy that can be utilized for power is concentrated in the relatively narrow band of the electromagnetic spectrum.

tions. But, nearly half of the sun's radiation that reaches us at the bottom of the atmospheric ocean is in the visible spectrum, and most of the remainder is short-wave infrared with less than 4 percent on the opposite side of the visible in the ultraviolet. The range of more than 99 percent of solar radiation is only a tiny segment of the known frequency range of the electromagnetic spectrum. The total amount of thermal radiation (infrared) is fairly constant over the year for most of the temperate areas of the earth, whereas the amount of light is much less in winter. Thus the percentage of the total radiation that is thermal is higher in winter than in summer.

Fortunately for us the sun's own photosphere functions as a step-down frequency converter because even a moderate amount of gamma radiation would destroy life instead of fostering it. The rays formed in the center of the sun take such a tortuous and interrupted journey that they may be on their way for ten thousand years before reaching the surface of the sun. By that time they have been almost entirely degraded to lower frequencies. And any frequencies higher than light tend to be intercepted by atoms in the sun's corona and by the molecules of our atmosphere. Otherwise life on the earth would not be possible.

Development of industrial power from nuclear fission of uranium is enormously more complicated than utilization of solar energy. The two projects are alike in the respect that in both cases radiations from nuclear reactions must be converted into some form of useful work. But, whereas the sun is both a nuclear-energy generator and a radiation shield, man-made radiation retains all of its virgin malignity. While the generation of solar energy presents no problems for us, generation of nuclear energy from uranium is beset with dozens of very serious problems. Whereas solar energy is essentially perpetual, supplies of fissionable materials are definitely limited. The sun's essential monopoly as our primary energy source remains unchallenged.

The Prospects of Utilizing Wave Motion

Solar radiation can be utilized in two conceivable ways: (1) by taking advantage of its wave motion; and (2) by the use of various quantum phenomena. The first is perhaps unlikely; the second is what has put the earth in the energy business.

What are the prospects of using the wave motion of solar radiation to fashion a more direct energy supply than the present more complex and efficient methods employing discrete quanta? We have become adept at using the energy of radio waves for communication. More recently we have learned how to generate and use frequencies as high as 30 billion cycles per second (1 centimeter wavelength) for radar. Such frequencies approach those of the longer heat waves, which start at about fifty times the frequencies employed for radar and end where light begins. Since we already have electrical circuits capable of dealing with electromagnetic radiation approaching the frequency of heat waves, it might seem but a step to the use of equivalent circuits and techniques for directly harnessing solar radiation.

The Stone Wall of Dimensions

However, the attempt to handle higher and higher frequencies with man-made equipment is met with some apparently insurmountable difficulties. Electrical circuits and thermionic tubes used in such equipment must have appreciable dimensions if useful amounts of power are to be produced. Moreover, the electrical-circuit constants must be below certain maximum size requirements or the circuits cannot be made to respond to the high frequencies. Thus, as we approach the higher frequencies, the physical size of the apparatus becomes vanishingly small to conform with the wavelength of the radiation, while the power-handling capabilities of the equipment decrease correspondingly.

Thus, while the handling of radiation of 1 centimeter wavelength is practical in circuits fabricated by man, the handling of heat radiation of 0.02 to 0.00007 centimeter wavelength involves physical dimensions approaching the molecular. In nature, heat and light radiations generated by molecular and atomic phenomena apparently require molecular or atomic mechanisms for their absorption and utilization.

The Helter-skelter of Natural Radiations

These facts bring out another and equally important difference between man-made radio waves and those of heat and light. Radio waves, even of the shortest wavelength, are produced by a single generator or, at most, relatively few generators or oscillators operating synchronously so that their outputs combine additively to excite a single radiating system (antenna) with a single oscillating current. In this way a single source radiates a relatively large amount of power. On the other hand, radiation of light wavelength is produced within single atoms by the spontaneous change in energy state of electrons from a higher to a lower level, the difference being emitted as electromagnetic radiation. The frequency is determined by the change in energy within the configuration of the particular atom involved. The dimensions of the "generator" are those within the atom. The total energy emitted from a given light source may be large, indeed, since countless billions of radiating atoms are involved, but this energy may be scattered over a wide band of frequencies. Moreover, even if each atom emitted the same frequency, the "generators" are not triggered simultaneously but at random. The resultant radiations are not synchronized. Each atomic source is independent of every other source, and hence the phase of each wave is random with respect to that of every other wave. Instead of marching in regimented order, the waves move like a disorganized mob.

As early as 1924, the gap between the then known radio frequencies and heat radiation was filled by the experiments of Dr. Ernest F. Nichols, of Cleveland. He used the earliest and simplest form of radio-wave generator. A high voltage was impressed across the ends of a tube loosely filled with metallic filings. At the points of contact between each pair of metallic particles, a spark occurred. This excited electrical-current oscillations in the pairs exactly as in the early experiments of Hertz. However, because the dimensions of the radiators were very small, the electromagnetic radiation from each of the numerous individual dipole antennas was of correspondingly short wavelength. Since each pair of filings radiated independently of every other pair there was no uniformity in either the frequency or the phase of the radiated pulses. Replace the numerous metallic particles by a far greater multitude of atomic mechanisms generating waves of light, and the analogy is excellent.

Dr. Nichols was able to demonstrate that the wavelength of the radiation spanned the gap in the electromagnetic spectrum between the thermal waves from a heat radiator and the wireless waves received by a radio. But there has been no indication that the one can be converted to the other. It does not appear likely that the step from radiant energy to power can be made without an intermediate step involving the molecular or atomic intervention of matter.

This pessimistic viewpoint is supported by the fact that nature produces no orderly electromagnetic radiations of appreciable energy comparable in wavelength to those of man-made radio waves. An insignificant amount arises from atmospheric disturbances, and at the very high-frequency end of the radio spectrum, radiation from cosmic or stellar sources has been detected. The absence of appreciable natural radiation in this region of the electromagnetic spectrum is indeed fortunate, or man's development of electrical radiation for communication purposes would have been plagued by intolerable interference. Here is perhaps a broad hint that if man is to convert solar radiation to power, it is likely to be done only through processes involving the intervention of matter after the fashion of nature.

At any rate all that can be done now is define some of the problems. If some genius can find a way to make use of the oscillatory properties of the natural electromagnetic radiations, the discovery might be of far greater importance than the development of nuclear science. Some work is being done now on the direct conversion to electric power of the gamma radiation from nuclear reactions—a variation of the general problem outlined in the foregoing paragraphs. The Atomic Energy Commission is also supporting valuable work on photosynthesis. These by-products of nuclear research may eventually overshadow the present primary objectives.

The Use of Energy Particles

Meanwhile, we must take light as we find it and direct our efforts to make use of the individual photons or quanta, as in photosynthesis, other photochemical reactions, photoelectrical phenomena, and development of heat. Because of the dual nature of solar radiation (and all other electromagnetic radiations) we can now forget the oscillatory characteristics and think of solar radiation as simply a shower of tiny particles of energy (photons, or quanta). The energy of each particle is proportional to the frequency of the radiation. According to this conception, a receiver or absorber of such radiation must be capable of responding to energy levels commensurate with that of a single photon, and the receipt of such energy is manifested as the summation of all the countless individual photons. This is the way light is utilized in nature and the basis of all successful attempts, so far, to develop artificial methods of utilization.

Distribution of Solar Energy

The sun, of course, radiates impartially in all directions. Only a tiny fraction of this radiation impinges upon the planets of the solar system. The vast remainder passes on into space. About one two-billionth of the sun's radiation lands on the earth, but about half of it is radiated into interstellar space by our atmosphere. We receive at the earth's surface about 10^{18} hphr per annum.

Now let us consider what happens to the sunlight and the sun heat that reach the earth.

Because the earth rotates we have alternate periods of night and day. Hence we have alternate periods in which the net flow of energy is toward and away from given points on the earth. If we regard the earth as a whole, however, we have a steady condition in which the outflow and inflow are almost equal. The outflow is very slightly higher because of the generation of heat in the earth itself.

In the simple case of the moon, 90 percent of the solar energy received during the day is absorbed (the other 10 percent is being reflected) and all of the absorbed energy is radiated away during the night. (This refers to *net* inflow and outflow.) The earth's situation is more complex not only because of the atmosphere, which turns back about half of our allotment of sunshine, but also because of the peculiar effects of our vegetation and our hydrosphere (the water surface of the earth). The moon has no atmosphere, vegetation, or hydrosphere. The effect of vegetation is peculiar because, while it utilizes a little of the light falling upon it to form food and combustible material, it rejects most of it at once. The world's annual growth of vegetation (excluding marine vegetation) utilizes about 6×10^{13} hphr per annum of solar energy—less than a ten-thousandth of the incident sunshine. About 30 percent (or 3×10^{17} hphr per annum) of the energy that reaches the earth from the sun is reflected into interstellar space without waiting for night to fall. Most of the reflection of sunshine during the day is from vegetation which rejects, for all time, a thousand quanta of light for every quantum that it usefully employs. Vegetation is essential to life because it provides not only the food we eat but also the oxygen we breathe. We must forgive its extravagance.

What happens to the 70 percent retained during the day? About 15 percent of it is absorbed by bare earth, and the remaining 85 percent is used to evaporate water from the hydrosphere and from vegetation, to raise the temperature of surface water, and to cause the growth of marine vegetation. The rate of growth of marine vegetation has been estimated at eight or nine times terrestrial vegetation—nearly 5×10^{14} hphr per annum. The energy used for evaporation cannot be recovered as power because it is balanced by nocturnal radiation away from the earth by the atmosphere with the resulting condensation of water vapor to rain or snow. But the energy required to lift water vapor above the earth is partly recoverable in the form of water power. As a practical matter about 0.001 percent of the sunshine absorbed by the earth can and probably will be recovered as hydroelectric power. This is about 10 times what we are recovering now.

Photosynthesis

While an almost inconceivably small fraction of the sun's total radiation (about one ten-trillionth) is utilized for growth of plants on the earth, nevertheless, to us, photosynthesis is big business. The energy absorbed by both terrestrial and marine vegetation is about 5×10^{14} hphr per annum. On the average each horsepower-hour leads to the production of 0.05 pound of vegetation and 0.05 pound of oxygen. Thus the total production for the earth is of the order of around 100 billion tons of vegetation and a like amount of oxygen. Without both of these things constantly forming, life on the earth would not be possible. If we did not suffocate first, we would starve to death.

The amount of energy absorbed by vegetation is equal to the amount of energy that can be generated by burning of vegetation. Thus if all the vegetation of the earth produced in one year were burned we would have 5×10^{14} hphr—almost 100 times the energy produced by the world's annual combustion of coal. In Chap. 16, it will be explained that unless considerable vegetation is permitted to return to the soil, vegetation must be considered an exhaustible instead of a continuous resource. But the equality of the two phenomena illustrates the over-all mechanism of photosynthesis, which may be represented by the simplified equation

$$CO_2 + H_2O + 112 \text{ kilocalories} \rightleftarrows \text{carbohydrate} + \text{oxygen}$$

Like many other chemical equations, the reaction is reversible. When we ignite a splinter of wood the reaction goes from right to left, and that is the way we derive energy from all the fuel we burn. Man does not yet know how to cause the reaction to go from left to right. But nature does. We are proficient in destruction of fuel to provide energy, but we must depend upon the radiation of the sun to create fuel.

The reaction as shown tells nothing about the actual steps, and little can yet be told. Various theories have been advanced but all seem faulty. A few interesting discoveries have been made. For example, while no catalyst is required for combustion (the temperature is high enough to eliminate the necessity), synthesis will not take place at an appreciable rate without a catalyst. The catalyst employed by nature is a complex substance called chlorophyll—the green pigment of vegetation. The 112 kilocalories of energy must be supplied not only at moderate temperatures (what we regard as comfort temperatures) but also at moderate intensities.

In the equation for photosynthesis, the 112 kilocalories has a special significance because this is the amount of energy that must be supplied to each mole of reactant. To provide this much energy per mole we would expect to have to use radiations well above visual frequencies—well into the ultraviolet. And yet photosynthesis is carried on by almost the entire range of the visible spectrum. Short ultraviolet radiation tends to destroy all life. Green light (55 kilocalories per mole) would require two photons and red light (40 kilocalories per mole) about three photons to provide the required 112 kilocalories for the reaction. In a sense chlorophyll appears to act as a step-up frequency converter, but the actual mechanism is probably much more complicated than this. For some curious reason, the infrared radiations of the sun (heat rays) are ineffective or, at least, much less effective in the ordinary case. There is some evidence that red light is more effective than blue, but too little is known of the effects of short-wave infrared. We are not yet sure whether, in the growth of vegetation, we can make use of less than one-half of solar radiation, or whether, under optimum conditions, we could contrive to use nearly all of it.

The present assumption is that through the agency of chlorophyll the photosynthesis is accomplished by step-wise utilization of light. The exact nature of the steps is still controversial but the study will be aided by a discovery that has been made through the use of radioactive tracers, that the oxygen of carbohydrate all comes from carbon dioxide while the free oxygen all comes from water.

Symptomatic of the confused state of our present knowledge is the difficulty of deciding whether the efficiency of the reaction under optimum conditions is about 25 percent or nearer 70 percent. Another obscure phenomenon has been the tendency of light of high intensity to inhibit growth of varieties of plants (*e.g.*, phytoplankton) accustomed to dim light. Studies are, of course, immensely complicated by the great variation between different plants and between different experiments with the same plant, by the importance of the kind and amount of mineral traces in the nutrient, and above all by the fact that living systems are not subject to the laws of closed-system thermodynamics, such as the laws of conservation of energy.

Carbon Dioxide Supply

The earth has plenty of water but not too much, in the right places, of fresh water required for vegetation. On the other hand, there is an abundance of carbon dioxide everywhere. Carbon dioxide is, of course, not a source of energy, per se, but it is a raw material from which carbon can be recovered by application of energy. Most of the carbon of the earth is insoluble and, therefore, not immediately available for photosynthesis. This carbon amounts to the stupendous figure 7×10^{16} tons. The available carbon in the form of carbon dioxide amounts to only 0.03 per cent of the atmosphere, and to only 0.0012 percent of the hydrosphere; but the atmosphere, which seems so unsubstantial to us, weighs 5×10^{15} tons, and the hydrosphere 12×10^{17} tons. These amounts are so great that the total carbon of the atmosphere is about a thousand times the carbon in the annual coal production of the United States, and the hydrosphere contains 7000 times our coal. The distribution of carbon dioxide is shown in Table 1.

TABLE 1. Distribution of Carbon Dioxide

	Weight, Tons	Carbon, Percent	Carbon, Tons
Atmosphere	5.7×10^{15}	0.008	5×10^{11}
Hydrosphere	1.2×10^{18}	0.0003	3.6×10^{12}
United States coal production	5.6×10^{8}	87	4.9×10^{8}

This great volume of carbon dioxide is maintained on a rather even keel. Carbon dioxide is absorbed by vegetation at about the same rate as carbon dioxide is "breathed out" by soil from the bacterial destruction of organic matter and from root respiration. Some carbon dioxide is lost by formation of insoluble carbonates, but some is emitted from volcanic vents. At this period of rapid depletion of fossil fuels it appears that we are forming carbon dioxide by combustion at a rate at least a hundred times as great as the losses to sediments. On the other hand carbon dioxide from combustion is small compared with the cycle volume of photosynthetic fixation and respiration. The carbon dioxide content of the atmosphere close to the earth has shown a measurable increase since 1900, but this could easily be accounted for by deforestation of the earth during the period.

Even with the low concentration of 0.03 percent, each acre of land has about 15 tons of carbon dioxide in the atmosphere above it. If the amount could be increased, the rate of growth of vegetation could be increased. This is possible only through industrialized farming under "factory" conditions (see Chap. 16).

Practical Efficiencies

The actual utilization of sunlight in photosynthesis ranges from 0.1 to 0.5 percent of the radiation falling upon the land. In most cases land is not completely covered by vegetation, and the growing season is often less than a third of the year. Plants have a mechanism by which they are able to exclude carbon dioxide. For some strange reason they sometimes close the door for considerable periods. During such periods no photosynthesis occurs.

The efficiency of photosynthesis is greatly reduced by the fact that only a portion of the sun's radiation (visible spectrum) is absorbed by the plants, and also that of the amount absorbed only a fraction can be used for reaction as determined by quantum yield. Efficiencies have been computed by assuming (1) that the plant mechanism can absorb all the light between 0.30 and 0.73 microns; (2) that the quantum yields are constant over the entire effective spectrum. Since the energy of the photon changes with wavelength, it is necessary to integrate efficiencies over the effective spectrum. When this is done, we come out with efficiencies of 11.3 or 28.25 percent, depending upon our preference with regard to quantum yield.

The structure of chlorophyll has been determined but it has not yet been synthesized. Fascinating research is now under way to uncover its mysteries and to provide new ways for conversion of light to power and food. Some of the questions are (1) Do some of the so-called "plant nutrients" function as catalyst accelerators for photosynthesis? (2) What are the optimum conditions for rapid absorption of light? (3) What are the effects on photosynthesis of molecular modifications of chlorophyll? There is no reason to doubt that the mind of man can improve on nature, just as it has been found in numberless cases that certain desirable properties of other natural substances can be improved ten-thousandfold by scientific understanding. Chlorophyll is the only catalyst we have for photosynthesis. Perhaps some day we shall know how to synthesize catalysts that can utilize not only visible light but also the infrared of solar radiation to produce from carbon dioxide and water substances less complicated than the components of vegetation.

Photochemical Reactions

The remarkably efficient job done by chlorophyll for plant growth has been just about equaled with some synthetic dyes and inorganic chemicals. Photosynthesis is, of course, a species of photochemical reaction. Many photochemical reactions are exothermic chain reactions. The results are out of all proportion to the energy applied (hydrogen and chlorine, for example). But for endothermic photochemical reactions in the inanimate world efficiencies have usually been quite low. There have been some recent exceptions.

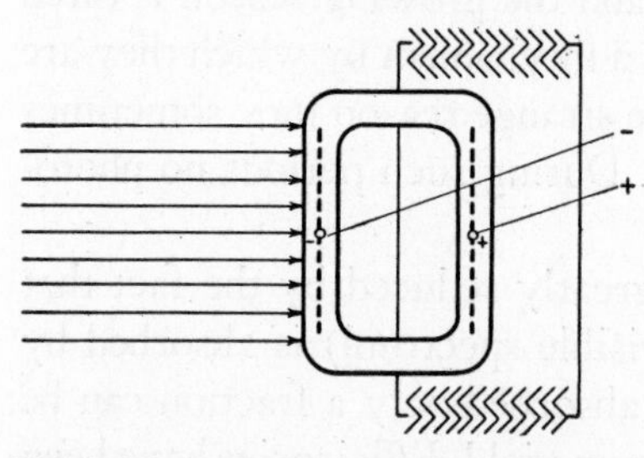

FIG. 2. The iron-thionine cell is based on the light-sensitive oxidation-reduction equilibrium between the two substances. When half a cell is exposed to light and the other half kept in the dark, electric current is produced.

Lawrence J. Heidt and Maynard E. Smith, of the Massachusetts Institute of Technology, have done some interesting work on the photochemical decomposition of water in the presence of ceric perchlorate and perchloric acid. Under optimum conditions the amounts of cerous and ceric compounds remain unchanged, *i.e.*, they act as true catalysts. Hydrogen and oxygen are evolved. The solutions were irradiated with monochromatic ultraviolet. The quantum yield was not quite as high as that of photosynthesis but of the same order of magnitude. Further research may point the way to the development of practical methods of generating hydrogen from water by solar irradiation. If the over-all efficiencies can be made high enough, this sort of process will be of fundamental importance.

The interesting work of E. Rabinowitch, now of the University of Illinois, on the thionine-iron system indicates a quantum yield about as high as chlorophyll. The oxidation-reduction equilibrium between iron and thionine is highly sensitive to light. A potential difference can be maintained between illuminated and dark cells, and it is conceivable, therefore, that a direct conversion of sunlight to electric current might be arranged by this means.

Another photogalvanic effect is illustrated by the photocell—the most familiar form of which is the photographic exposure meter. This has a low over-all efficiency, but research on liquid and solid photogalvanic cells is proceeding and may turn out important power developments in the course of time. Because of the engineering simplicity of direct conversion of sunlight to electric power, the photogalvanic cell would not need to be as efficient as photosynthesis, but to compete with nature we shall have to find ways of multiplying over-all efficiencies by at least ten.

The Familiar Quanta-to-Heat Phenomenon

The simplest utilization of quantum energy is, of course, in the development of heat.

A large amount of excellent work has been done to evaluate the possibilities of collecting solar energy for space heating or power.

About 1670 the concentration of solar energy by means of lenses was practiced by François Berniere, French physicist. (*Bettmann Archive.*)

Space heating will be discussed in Chap. 15. In appraising the work on solar power, Hoyt C. Hottel, of the Massachusetts Institute of Technology, has given a figure of about 50 horsepower per acre that might reasonably be salvaged in the form of power from solar energy that reaches an acre of the earth's surface in Arizona on an average annual basis. This would mean about 440 000 hphr per annum per acre. The best photosynthetic production of energy figures about 216 000 hphr per annum per acre if the vegetation were used directly as fuel, and only about 60 000 hphr per annum if the fuel were used to generate power. So the simple conversion of solar energy to heat and the use of the heat to operate an engine would seem to be about seven times as efficient as the most optimistic agricultural proposal, and so far photosynthesis is well out ahead of any substitute plan for the harvesting of quanta through chemical intervention.

In 1884 a paraboloid reflector was used to print a newspaper by means of solar energy alone. (*Bettmann Archive.*)

To produce by optical means all the heat and power now consumed in the United States would require an area of about 50 000 square miles—about two-fifths of the state of New Mexico. The installation would preferably be in arid country that has a maximum amount of sunshine.

Simple collection of solar heat may be carried out with or without optical concentration. Hottel believes that the most efficient and economical method may be the use of the flat-plate collector described in Chap. 15, if the glass is specially treated to increase transmission of solar radiation to a maximum.

Some useful things are now being accomplished with solar-energy collectors. Aside from space heating, solar heating of domestic water supplies in our Southern states has become a general practice. The equipment is rather crude but is effective for the purpose. One large water-heating system in Switzerland is said to have obtained a maximum of 36 percent of the theoretical maximum of heat inflow during July, with monthly averages of around 10 percent for March and August. This is excellent.

Under optimum conditions it is possible without optical concentration to secure temperatures well above the boiling point of water if the heat is not carried away. Some of the power-generating proposals, however, require reflectors of various sorts.

The Power Institute of the USSR Academy of Sciences is said to be sponsoring development of means for utilizing solar energy. The mirrors proposed by this group are roughly of paraboloidal shape made up of sections of flat glass. The first mirror was 33 feet in diameter. Later mirrors were planned to be many times larger. The solar installations were to be in Tashkent, Uzbek (latitude about 40), and at other places in Central Asia where the highest power requirements coincide with the sunny season of the year (vegetable-oil canneries), where shipment of fuel involves considerable expense, or where the local supply of waste combustibles is insufficient to take care of the annual fuel requirement. Such installations were expected to provide steam at all temperatures and pressures required in local industries.

In the above paragraph the subjunctive tense is used because the final working out of the plan has not been described.

It is reported that in Stalingrad in 1941 a solar installation was used to demonstrate the feasibility of melting iron. Felix Trombe of France believes that solar energy, which can be concentrated about 50 thousand times with modern optical systems, is even more adapted to high-temperature processes (possibly approaching 5000 degrees C) than to industrial-power levels. He notes that to melt a pound of iron one needs much fewer calories than to heat and vaporize one pound of water. Trombe has found it possible to melt a number of highly refractory materials by this means.

Dissimilar Metals + Heat = Electricity

One application of the high-temperature technique is in the use of thermocouples to develop electric power without the intervention of the steam cycle. Thermoelectric power of metal couples does not increase without limit as the temperature increases. This is one limiting factor. Another is that the relationship of thermal to electric conductivity should be as low as possible. Maria Telkes, of the Massachusetts Institute of Technology, has obtained a 7 percent useful conversion of heat to electrical power by the best materials available at the time. This represents real progress and research is continuing.

Phosphors as Converters

About a quarter of the electric power we use is for lighting. Westinghouse engineers have predicted future use of phosphor powders as components of paint and wallpaper. Thus some of the light absorbed during the day would be emitted at night. Because phosphors are essential to fluorescent lamps and picture tubes used in television, the interest in the development of phosphors is keen and much improvement in phosphor efficiency can be expected. In view of the interesting new information being accumulated, the Westinghouse prediction does not now seem farfetched. Here is a quantum phenomenon that need not be efficient to be useful because it involves the use of a little of the light that is now wasted. Clear daylight varies from about 2400 foot-candles in winter to above 8000 foot-candles in summer. A room lighted at night with more than 100 foot-candles is considered brilliantly lighted. The average is more like 10. In other words, we need at night only a few percent of the illumination intensity of the day, and we do not commonly need even this except for a few hours.

The future will probably see some of these things coming to pass. Even the clumsy application of the primitive scientific knowledge that we have at this time could ensure a plentiful supply of *energy at a price*. With the fuller understanding of the fundamentals of radiation sure to come later on, this price in capital and in labor will shrink. The sun will again be recognized as the most important of all natural physical phenomena—the same sun that was worshiped as a deity and valued for its comfort and healing by all ancient peoples. Now we have better understanding of the reason for that homage.

15

Windows

We take window glass for granted. But two hundred years ago, Dr. Samuel Johnson, who lived for a short time in Stourbridge amidst the glowing fires of Britain's infant glass industry, marveled at a substance that "could admit the light of the sun and exclude the violence of the wind." We have almost lost the salutary capacity to wonder. And yet we have no more idea than had Dr. Johnson why glass can be made transparent to light, why it is a solid instead of a liquid, or why it is, in general, opaque to thermal radiation. It is because of these qualities that glass is so important in our energy analysis and specifically to space heating of the future.

More energy is required for warmth in homes and in places of work than for motor cars, for industrial power, or for lighting. Space heating of building interiors is a prime requisite, for without adequate warmth for living we can live only briefly and with distress. Nearly a third of the total energy requirement of the highly industrialized United States is for the heating of homes and offices. Space heating is the one major energy demand in poorly industrialized communities, containing the great majority of the population of the earth. Every other energy use is secondary.

We seem destined to become more and more dependent upon the sun for all energy. It happens too that sunlight is somewhat more easily adaptable to space heating than to the development of power. These two circumstances taken together are full of fortunate significance.

Solar heating of houses is not new. It has been going on ever since houses were first built. Before fuel was sufficiently available for general use, it was necessary to depend on the sun. Its use was primitive and ineffective. As fuel becomes less available, we shall become even more dependent upon solar heating. Blueprints for future solar heating call for effectiveness comparable with modern standards of fuel or electric heating.

Before window glass could be made abundantly and cheaply, windows were either mere apertures for ventilation rather than for light, or closed with mica, alabaster, shells, thin sheets of horn, or varnished parchment. Later small pieces of glass without parallel plane surfaces were used in the same way. The materials were translucent or irregularly refractive or even opaque. They "excluded the violence of the wind" and sometimes admitted a little light, but they did not possess the optical properties necessary for the entrapment of solar energy. Many homes had little or no fuel to burn, and habitability was dependent upon the warmth stored up by materials of construction during capricious periods of sunshine.

Machine-made window glass did not come until 1905. From then until 1930 the production of window glass in the United States remained at a practically stationary rate of three square feet per capita per annum. This was enough to take care of the prevailing style of house building. During the past two decades there has been a virtual revolution in window-glass manufacture because of a number of changes in attitude toward windows. By 1940 production per capita had doubled. By 1950 about ten square feet of window glass was being produced per capita. The increased demand for window glass coincided with an increased demand for plate and sheet glass for motor cars (which take about 75 percent of plate-glass production) and, more recently, for fluorescent lamps and the tubes of television sets. Windows are no longer luxuries. Now, for the first time in history, window glass is cheap enough to be available to everyone. At present glass manufacture in the United States requires nearly two million tons of soda ash annually. In the days of Dr. Johnson it is doubtful that the world consumption of soda ash for glass of all kinds could have been more than a few thousand tons, for it all had to be derived from the burning of vegetation. The British consumption of soda ash in 1810, long after the development of the Leblanc process, was only about 2000 tons.

Today the poorest house in the United States, except in the Deep South, is equipped throughout with window glass. This is the first technological step toward solar heating because glazed windows are traps for sunlight. This is why an automobile parked in the noonday sun becomes unbearably hot, and why greenhouses are made of glass.

Ordinary window glass is transparent to nearly all solar radiation. A little is reflected and a little is absorbed, but about 90 percent of both the light and the heat of the sun pass through. On the other hand, window glass is almost opaque to the long-wave infrared reradiated by interior objects heated by sunshine. Thus the solar energy can come in but it cannot be radiated out. Glass, in short, is a radiant-energy filter. Some heat, however, escapes because the glass is cooled by the outside air and the cool glass absorbs heat from the warm interior air

One of the most effective ways of increasing our energy reserves is to reduce the waste of space heating. Double-pane windows, such as the one through which the dog is looking at the outside world, offer a means of greatly reducing heat losses. The double heat losses through single-pane windows are evidenced by the well-frosted window at the right. (*Pittsburgh Plate Glass* Co.)

in contact with it. So, while the glass is effective in preventing loss of heat by radiation, it cannot prevent loss of heat by convection.

When this phenomenon was understood, storm windows were devised to capitalize on it. The quiet air space between two sheets of glass serves as insulation. The outer glass may cool while the inner glass remains warm. The quiet air in the space between conducts heat poorly. The function of the storm window is not to seal the window more effectively but rather to provide somewhat the same degree of insulation for windows as in house walls, while still permitting the sunshine to deliver its warmth. Now, instead of storm windows, it is possible to use double panes of glass manufactured as units with dry air space sealed between. The insulation with double glass is not perfect, of course. It is about equivalent to an ordinary wall 8 inches thick.

Many houses are now designed with south walls almost completely of glass. In some houses glass comprises three-fourths of the wall area. This has been made possible by several things. Large sheets of glass are relatively less expensive to manufacture. Since 1930 the price of glass has risen only 31 percent while the average price of all building material has gone up 114 percent. Now window glass costs no more per square foot than lumber, tile, or brick. Large glass windows cannot be conveniently hinged for ventilation but need to be permanently placed. Architectural designs have been evolved for ventilation independent of the windows. This is accomplished by means of screened louvers between panes or above and below.

In summer large glass windows can be objectionable unless they are shaded. Selective shading is sometimes accomplished by an overhanging roof with dimensions determined by the latitude of the location. No inflexible arrangement can be a perfect control of solar radiation because of the lag of the seasons. Nature herself provides a better solution in deciduous trees, which do not accumulate leaves until shade is desirable and which do not lose the leaves until shade is not required. Properly placed trees or vines provide an automatic seasonal control of solar radiation because if the summer is late, foliage will also be late, and an early fall will see the premature dropping of the leaves no longer needed for shade.

Properly designed glass houses in favorable locations require less than normal amounts of fuel. It is difficult to generalize because of the many variables, but in Philadelphia and Chicago, for example, fuel bills are sometimes reduced to one-half when double-paned south walls are supplemented by low-temperature radiant heat from floors, ceiling, or walls. With ordinary convection heating systems the fuel bills can sometimes be reduced by about a third in the same solar climate.

More supplemental heat is required when single sheets of glass are used, and especially when there is no provision for drawing curtains over the interior glass surface at night. The imprisoned air space between the curtain and the glass acts as an insulator to decrease the loss of heat at night. With double glass, curtains are not so effective, although they still prevent some loss of heat. Such homes possess a certain charm—a feeling of living outdoors and an awareness of the perpetual drama of nature. The charm is dependent, of course, upon the attractiveness of the landscape and is unfortunately completely absent for many urban (or even suburban) locations. Architects are studying ways of placing houses on small lots with appropriate planting and arrangement of fences.

While the cost of supplying supplemental heat to such homes can often be made appreciably less than for conventional buildings with less glass, the homes are usually built to take advantage of the psychological and physiological attractiveness of sunshine rather than for heating economy. Nevertheless certain of the architectural principles can be generally applied to fuel conservation.

The floors of houses using these principles are usually of heavy concrete with imbedded heating elements, thermostatically controlled to maintain a moderate temperature. The heating elements may be electrical or hot-water tubes. Sometimes ethylene glycol is used to make an antifreeze solution like those in automobile radiators, thus avoiding risk of freezing when the heating system is shut down in cold weather. When the sun shines in upon the floor the solar energy is absorbed by the concrete and stored therein. Hours after the sun sets or is obscured by storm, the concrete continues to radiate heat to the room. Eventually it cools down to the point where the heating elements must begin to function. During periods of bright sunlight there is usually no controlled maximum. Uniform temperatures are not always sociologically desirable.

We turn now from windows designed primarily for the amenities of living to those possessing a more severely scientific function. These are termed "flat-plate heat collectors." Perhaps they should not be called windows at all for they can be used neither for ventilation nor for light. However, the collectors are essentially multipaned windows (usually two or three sheets of glass) permanently curtained with a black sheet of copper. Their difference from the multipaned window construction mentioned earlier is that instead of depending upon normal interior objects, such as floor or furniture, to absorb heat from the sun and alter its wavelength, all the heat is absorbed by the copper backing, from which the heat can be carried into more effective storage than is provided by the concrete floor. In this way none of the solar heat is used directly. It is withdrawn from storage only as required. The collectors serve one purpose only—the relatively efficient accumulation of solar energy.

A large amount of work has been done (particularly by the Massachusetts Institute of Technology in a research program financed by Dr. Godfrey L. Cabot) to determine the functional properties of heat collectors with glass of various quality and thickness, with different numbers of glass plates variously spaced, and with several basic structures. Efficiencies of collection have been determined for all angles of incidence of sunlight and practical experiments have been made to provide the necessary constants for mathematical equations relating the many factors. According to University of Denver and M.I.T. experiments, flat-plate collectors, properly disposed, are capable of trapping about one-third of the sunshine falling upon them. This is a "mean" value, taking into account periods of highest solar intensity and other periods when the rate of collection is lower than the rate of heat loss.

The amount of solar energy reaching the earth is dependent upon the variable nature of the atmosphere. The transmissivity of the atmosphere is expressed as a percentage, with 100 percent indicating no atmospheric interference at all—an impossible condition. In practice the transmissivity even on the darkest day is well above zero.

Solar research has indicated that with the kind of weather encountered in Boston, houses can be solar-heated completely without fuel when the mean atmospheric transmissivity is above 55 percent. This is based on house walls of conventionally good insulating properties, and an area of solar collectors one-fifth of the total house envelope. The mean atmospheric transmissivity in Boston is often definitely lower than 55 percent in winter. Therefore it is not yet certain that a solar-heated house could be operated in New England without some auxiliary heat. It would be necessary at least to use a larger ratio of heat collectors to total house envelope, and the walls would need exceptionally good insulation.

Boston is a good place for experimental development of this sort because climatic conditions there are less favorable than in some other areas of the United States. In Fig. 1 the United States is divided into three areas: (1) a southern region where houses comfortably warmed by solar energy alone could be designed without difficulty; (2) an intermediate region (including Boston) where houses could receive at least the major part of their heating from the sun; and (3) a northern section where only a minor part of space heating could be obtained from the sun. Region 3, of "minimum feasibility," includes Ohio, West Virginia, all of Pennsylvania except the eastern part, and, of

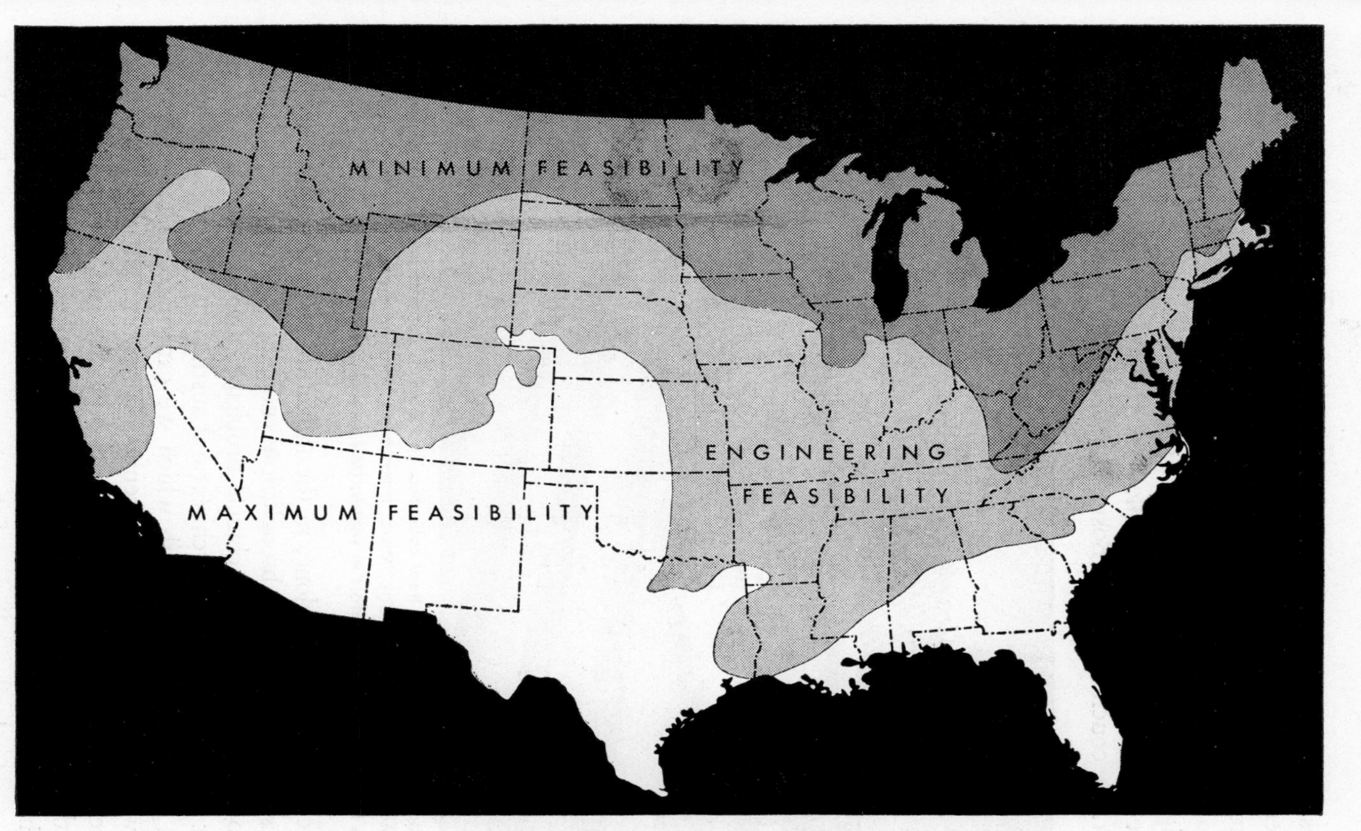

FIG. 1. The regions of the different degrees of feasibility of heating houses by solar energy. In the white areas houses may be entirely heated in this fashion; in the light-gray areas a large portion of the heat can be obtained; and in the darker areas only a small part of space-heating needs can be provided by trapped solar energy.

course, the Northern states. This interesting map is based upon the present state of technology.

Professor Hoyt C. Hottel of M.I.T. has pointed out that solar climates exist in which the yield of heat from collectors would be twice as high as the yield in the Boston area. In these more favorable areas, the economic value of the collectors would, therefore, be twice as great. He concludes that in Boston a householder would not be justified,

By placing the glass areas of heat collectors on the south slope of the roof of this house at 450 Memorial Drive, Cambridge, Mass., it has been possible to provide from the sun most of the heat required for comfort in winter. (*M.I.T. News Service.*)

on economic grounds alone, in the utilization of solar-heat collection. Costs have not yet been brought low enough.

To the economic and technical problems of solar house heating we must add the problem of architectural aesthetics. The idea of a house with many windows through which we cannot see is not appealing. We want to look out, and in the temperate zone we want the advantages of personal contact with all the sunshine we can get in the winter months. Proposals have been made to combine the felicity of maximum sunshine in the living areas of the house with effective collection and storage of solar heat. Some of the many ways of doing this have been described. All of the combinations will doubtless be tried. Two such houses are briefly discussed below.

The M.I.T. house is provided with large south windows and with flat-plate collectors forming the south slope of a tilted roof. An insulated body of water is used for heat storage, consisting of 25 pounds of water per square foot of collector area. This has been found sufficient to take care of the house-heating load for two average sunless winter days in Boston. A larger storage system would, of course, carry over

The sun-heated house in Dover, Mass., was engineered by Maria Telkes; the architect was Eleanor Raymond; and the owner is Amelia Peabody. This is the first example of the use of vertical flat-plate solar-heat collectors in combination with chemical storage of heat. (*Maria Telkes.*)

for a longer period. If the house were to be redesigned the water storage would be placed in the living area instead of in the "attic," where it is now. This would bring any heat leakage into the area where it is needed.

During two winter seasons solar energy contributed 91.3 percent and 81.3 percent, respectively, of the total heating load, the remainder being supplied by combustion. It is of particular interest that about one-third of the total heating load was contributed by the south windows and about one-half by the roof collector.

The famous Dover house was engineered by Dr. Maria Telkes, Research Associate, Department of Metallurgy, M.I.T. In this case, the flat-plate collectors are placed on the vertical south wall of the house above a tier of large south windows. The fundamental difference between this and the M.I.T. solar house is that a salt instead of water is used for heat storage. This represents such a long forward step that it merits description.

That certain solids (like ice) require considerable heat for melting is well known. But not so familiar is the idea that the same amount of heat must be given up when the liquid solidifies. Perhaps the reason for this intellectual blind spot is that we intuitively associate heat with relatively high temperatures. An effort is therefore required to realize that when water, at the freezing point, is congealed to ice, a tremendous amount of heat is evolved—the same amount, in fact, that is required to raise the temperature of the water from the freezing point to about 176 degrees F. But this is "cold heat," which can be used only to raise temperatures from subfreezing up to freezing.

TABLE 1. Chemicals for Heat Storage

Salt*	Melting Point, degrees F	Heat of Fusion, Btu per lb
$Na_2CO_3 \cdot 10\ H_2O$	90–97	115
$Na_2HPO_4 \cdot 12\ H_2O$	97–118	114
$Na_2SO_4 \cdot 10\ H_2O$	88–90	104
$Ca(NO_3)_2 \cdot 4\ H_2O$	104–108	90
$Na_2S_2O_3 \cdot 5\ H_2O$	120–126	90
$CaCl_2 \cdot 6H_2O$	84–102	75

* The heat storage capacity of the above materials is about 10 000 Btu per cubic foot.

The heat absorbed or evolved in changing from solid to liquid or vice versa is called the "heat of fusion." Many substances possess this property to a marked degree, but not all. Ordinary glass, for example, has very little heat of fusion. Water has a higher latent heat of fusion than almost any other common material. Ice would be a highly effective agent for storing heat if we were content to limit the temperature of our homes to, say, 25 degrees F. Since we do not regard such a low temperature with favor, we must hunt for materials that have not only a high heat of fusion but also a melting point in the range of solar-heat storage—say, between 85 and 110 degrees F. Dozens of substances have both qualities. Some are cheap and abundantly available. Hydrated sodium sulfate, for example, has a melting point around 88 degrees

F, and its heat of fusion is substantial enough to give, in practice, as much heat storage as from four to eight times as much (by weight) of common construction materials that depend entirely on temperature differentials without change of physical form. Disodium phosphate is another of the materials which have been successfully used. Table 1 lists the properties of a few salts.

The scheme works this way: Air or water is heated by the sun to a temperature above the melting point of the salt. A cloudy day would slow down the rate of collection of solar energy, but would not completely stop it. An insulated tank is filled with small sealed cans of the salt, and the sun-warmed air or water is circulated through the tank. The temperature of the flow of air or water away from the tank to the space heating of the house is near the melting point of the salt as long as much of the salt is liquid. Thus, with a sufficient mass of the salt, heat can be delivered to the house for several days after heat has been received from the sun (Fig. 2). It is not impractical to thus store enough heat to tide over two weeks of cold, sunless weather.

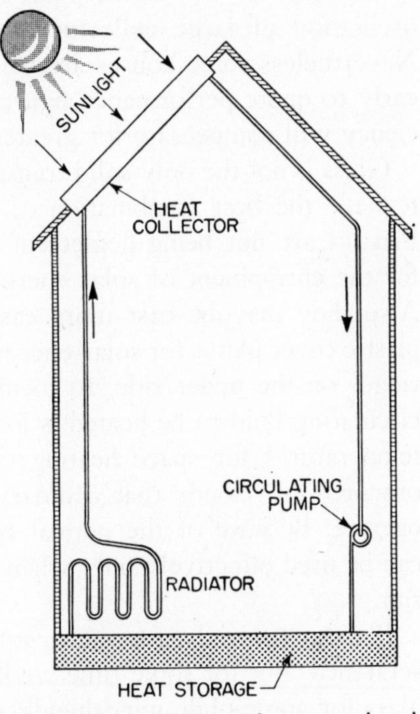

FIG. 2. Solar energy can be trapped and stored for space heating as needed.

The salt does not need to be contained in a tank. It can be located, instead, in the concrete floor of the house, or in the walls or ceiling. This plan has the advantage of simplifying the problem of insulation, because some leakage of heat from storage to the living areas can be tolerated. When such solar-heat storage is coordinated with electrical heating elements the "power factor" of the system is raised. This means a lower cost of operation because the demand for electricity is at a more nearly constant rate. Effective heat storage occupying as little as 1 percent of the space to be heated will become an essential element of space-heating designs of the future.

The two experimental houses just described have their solar-heat collectors in fixed position. The maximum rate of absorption of solar energy is at the time when the rays of the sun fall perpendicularly (instead of obliquely) upon the glass covers. Theoretically, of course, the collectors should move with the sun in the same fashion as a telescope is made to follow the course of a star. This is somewhat complicated because the apparent motion of the sun across the sky is different every day of the year. And the precise or even approximate oscillation of large collector areas presents engineering difficulties. Nevertheless some houses are being constructed in this way. It is too early to quote performance figures—to know whether the higher efficiency will compensate for greater cost of construction.

Glass is not the only solid transparent substance, but it seems, so far, to have the best combination of economic and technologic qualities. Plastics are not being neglected. Some have the necessary properties for the entrapment of solar energy and the advantage of low weight. Also they may be cast more easily in certain shapes. For example, plastic cover plates for solar-energy collectors are now being made with ridges on the under side, to focus sunlight along a line. The pipe of circulating fluid to be heated is located on this line. In this way useful temperatures for space heating can be obtained when the sun is so obscured by clouds that ordinary flat-plate collectors would fail to operate. Because of the optical concentration effect, focusing covers can be used effectively only when the collectors follow the path of the sun.

Plastic materials are much softer than glass and so more easily scratched. But for some time we have had combinations of plastic and glass for automobile windshields. Combinations can be worked out, if desirable, for solar-heat collectors.

In Boston, Philadelphia, or San Francisco it should be possible through radiant heating and south windows to cut down the consumption of fuel by at least one-third. Also with the use of solar-heat collectors and heat storage the fuel can be cut down by at least another one-half. This leaves about one-sixth of the normal amount of fuel still to be supplied. If the supplementary energy for heating is electrical and if electric rates are high, there is an economic incentive to reduce energy consumption still further. This can be done by means of a device called a "heat pump," which, under most favorable circumstances, can cut the one-sixth in half. Thus it is technically possible today to design a home (for a favorable solar climate) without chimneys or the odors or soot of combustion, to keep comfortably warm in winter with only one-twelfth of the customary consumption of energy. Furthermore, by a turn of a valve, the system can be reversed and the house can be cooled in the summer.

The heat pump operates on principles identical with those of the household refrigerator. By the circulation of a substance that is gaseous under ordinary pressures but liquid at higher pressures it is possible to pump heat from a low temperature level to a higher temperature level. The familiar refrigerator removes heat from food at relatively low temperatures and delivers this heat at higher temperatures to the room in which the refrigerator is placed. The heat pump does the same thing in the same way on a larger scale except that instead of cooling food it cools water or air or earth. The amount of heat that can be efficiently delivered to the house depends upon an ample supply of material to be cooled. Obviously, if the supply is too limited the temperature of the supply will be lowered and more energy will be required to raise the heat to the relatively high level of house heating.

The most convenient supply of low-level heat is a lake or a river or a deep well. In these cases the heat required for an average house-heating load could be obtained without a significant drop in the temperature of the water. When coils are buried in the earth below the frost line, an area of at least 3000 square feet is required. The heat delivered by the heat pump originates, of course, in the sun, which maintains the ambient temperature of the earth, water, or air in which the coils are immersed. More air-to-air heat pumps are likely to be used than any other.

In a sense, the energy involved in heat-pump operation is analogous to monetary capital, since a certain amount of energy must be "invested" to yield a return of an increased amount. One therm of coal or oil or gas will produce about three-quarters of a therm of space heating when burned in a furnace. This same fuel, when converted to electric power to drive motors, or when used to operate internal-combustion engines, can produce (as a maximum) about one and one-half therms of space heating in the heat-pump radiators.

The heat pump is sometimes called a "reversed-cycle heating system" or a "reversed-cycle refrigerator." Such terminology is confusing because it implies that the heat-pump is opposite in principle to the household refrigerator. Even when a heat pump is used for air conditioning the cycle is not "reversed." It is simply a matter of using the cooling effect of the evaporator instead of the heating effect of the condenser. The only respect in which a heat pump is "reversed" is that the cycle is the exact opposite of a heat engine, in which heat is converted to motion. In the case of the heat pump, motion is converted to heat.

An even more confusing thing about heat-pump technology is the "coefficient of performance"—commonly abbreviated to COP. This is the ratio of heat output to heat input and, as such, should represent the efficiency of the process. But this expression, like all other efficiencies, needs careful definition. COP values for actual installations run as high as four, which is commonly interpreted to mean that for each unit of heat supplied by the electrical system four heat units are made available for space heating. Careful analysis of the problem shows that the heat pump, in such a case, does not cut fuel requirements to one-quarter unless the comparison is limited to electrical heating alone.

In Chap. 10, various energy-system efficiencies are derived. For electrical heating the figure is 16.3 percent, while for domestic coal-stoker heating the value is 60 percent. Thus simple electrical heating requires about 3.5 times as much coal as domestic coal-stoker heating. If, therefore, the COP of a heat-pump installation is four, the net result is that the heat pump has brought down coal consumption for electrical heating only a few percent under coal consumption for the coal furnace. (Some authorities consider a COP of 3.33 as equivalent to coal.) If everything about a heat-pump system were ideal, the COP could be around 7.5, which would mean that fuel consumption had been cut in half. But the average COP of heat-pump installations runs nearer three, which means no fuel saving at all, but it does mean that electrical energy, with its convenience and cleanliness, can be used without penalty for the losses incurred in making and distributing electricity.

In spite of the minor effect of the heat pump on ultimate fuel consumption, the heat pump is an important and rapidly growing energy development for the simple reasons that electrical heating has such a powerful appeal, and air conditioning is becoming so widespread.

The COP varies with the temperature of the substance to be cooled (evaporator) and the temperature to which the space-heating medium is to be raised (condenser). For example, to go from 50 to 96 degrees F gives a typical COP of 5.8, whereas to carry the temperature up to 117 degrees gives about 4.8. To go from 34 up to 117 degrees F gives a COP of about 4. The advantage of carrying the temperature high is that less radiation area is required for the building. The advantage of providing a reasonably high temperature source of heat is that smaller heat-pump equipment is required. The cost of operation of any kind of heating system is made up not only of fuel cost but of interest on investment. Much serious engineering study is being devoted to the heat-pump device. Up to 1942, only 44 installations had been made in the United States. By 1950 installations had risen to 750. Of these, about 60 percent are residential. Few of these installations have brought about fuel economy. One residential installation, for example, is said to show costs equivalent to an oil furnace with oil at several cents per gallon above the market price. But this home is located where summer cooling is at least as important as winter warming.

Manufacturers of such equipment are trying to bring down the cost of installation by designing self-contained units adaptable to quantity production. Research organizations are experimenting with the use of solar-heat collectors to supply heat directly to the source material of the heat-pump cycles, and with the same sort of chemical-heat storage described for solar heating. Storage is of importance because it lowers peak demands for electric power by collecting heat in mild weather to deliver in extremely cold weather. This makes it possible to reduce the investment in heat-pump compressor and motor, the sizes of which are determined, naturally, by peak load.

About one-third of the fuel consumed in the United States for space heating is consumed in the northern belt of Fig. 1 where the solar climate is relatively unfavorable for solar heating. About a tenth is consumed in the southern region in which complete solar heating could be managed without difficulty. Nearly half of our population is in the intermediate zone where solar heating aided by the heat pump could (theoretically) reduce the consumption of fuel to one-twelfth of what it is now. The normal consumption of fuel for space heating in this zone is about 57 percent of all fuel so used in the United States. The heat pump would be used in the southernmost region primarily for air cooling in the summer. But the heat pump could be of greatest conservational importance in the northernmost region, where, unfortunately, its return is least. The time may come when solar-heat collectors will be used for the purpose of melting ice while water at the freezing point is used as a reservoir of low-level heat to be raised by means of the heat pump to comfort levels.

Use of solar energy for space heating definitely has practical limits.

The population of the earth is not nicely arranged for the purpose. We cannot all live in separate houses with correct exposures and with suitable plantings of vegetation. We cannot all live near bodies of water, or where deep wells can be drilled, or surrounded by adequate land. On the contrary, many of us must spend our time in city houses, apartments, hotels, tenements, office buildings, and factories. Such congested living presents many problems. If some of these problems can be solved so that we can bring the utilization of solar energy up to half of space heating demands, the world consumption of fuels for all purposes will be cut by almost a quarter. The chances are that we shall eventually do much better than this for the simple reason that we must. Progress is likely to be rapid—in geometric proportion to the rising cost of fuels. All of the ingredients of the formula for successful development are here. We have seen the glass industry come to a belated maturity. The plastics industry has made a promising beginning. Effective insulation of buildings has become commonplace. Space-heating engineers and architects have thrown off the shackles of precedent. The technology of heat storage has leaped suddenly ahead. The heat pump is no longer a device of purely academic interest.

No house has yet been built to employ all devices for optimum fuel economy. In fact there is no economic reason for building such a house, for the annual interest on the additional investment would now be somewhat higher than the annual fuel saving. But the separate strands of endeavor are being gradually woven together. The eventual depletion of fossil fuel will not be disastrous. On the contrary, the dream of our architects and engineers will some day come true—communities of people who live in comfort without combustion, without chimneys, free from atmospheric pollution, with no dark and hidden corners, but with windows everywhere.

16

How Much Vegetation

The lands and waters of the earth are quietly going about the business of storing solar energy. Millenniums ago the accumulation became coal and petroleum. The same processes today are what we see as forests, fields of grain, and beaches of seaweed. When driving by a field of corn it is just as reasonable to think of it as plain Btu energy as to regard it as food. How much of the current vegetation could be made available for the production of energy? To answer this question it is necessary to determine how much vegetation must be used for food, and how much of the potential energy of the vegetation would be lost by processes of conversion.

For food we depend upon cropland for edible plants, to some extent upon pasture land for meat, and upon the sea and inland waters for fish. In other words we eat portions of certain plants, portions of animals that depend upon terrestrial vegetation, and portions of fish that depend upon marine vegetation. Thus all of our food is derived from photosynthesis. Man has no capacity to use any solar energy directly to support life processes. He and all his fellow animals on the earth are dependent on the ability of plants to absorb radiant energy and store it in a form that becomes food.

The proportions of the three types of food vary widely in different countries. In the United States, on a calorie basis, the distribution is about as follows: plants (vegetables, fruits, and grains) 76 percent; meat (including poultry, butter, milk, and eggs) 22 percent; and fish 2 percent. Thus 98 percent of our food is dependent upon terrestrial vegetation which, in turn, is dependent upon suitable land. In the case of the world as a whole, including the United States, meat supplies only about 3 percent of the food calories.

Terrestrial Vegetation

About 500 million acres (about one-fourth of the land area) of the United States can be considered cropland. Of this about 10 million acres represents the minimum area of annual crop failure, 40 million acres is a reserve of idle and fallow land necessary to conserve moisture and fertility, and about 100 million acres is not well suited to sustained crop production. We can count on the remaining 350 million acres (20 million of which is under irrigation) to produce annually the vegetation required directly as food by man and two-thirds of the vegetation required as food by livestock. The other third of the livestock requirement comes from about 1000 million acres of pasture and grazing land. Much of this land is timbered, and perhaps 100 million acres of it could be converted to cropland.

Despite an increase of one-third in population between 1920 and 1950, our cropland acreage has remained almost stationary because of improved productivity. An especially interesting factor is the increased mechanization of farms, which has led to the substitution of fossil-fuel energy for animate energy. Land required to provide feed for horses and mules in this period fell off 65 million acres! Human population, on the other hand, is continuing to increase in the United States at the rate of around 4000 a day. It is believed that future improvement in productivity of the land can keep pace with population, at least until 1975. This can come about by the application of proven soil and fertilizer technologies; weed, insect, and disease control; plant breeding; and further mechanization. For example, the partial use of hybrid corn during the four years 1942–1945 gave the farmers two billion dollars more than they otherwise would have received. Since 1930, corn yields have gone up 36 percent; cotton, 58 percent; potatoes, 68 percent; soybeans, 59 percent; and oats, 17 percent. Insecticides alone have been highly effective. In Iowa in 1949, corn treated with DDT produced 17 bushels per acre more than untreated corn, and alfalfa seed in Utah was increased by 135 pounds per acre.

Additional cropland can be provided by suitable reclamation techniques. About 20 million additional acres can be reclaimed by drainage of overwet lands and by irrigation of overdry lands, and such reclamation could probably greatly increase the productivity of about 100 million acres now in use. Fortunately, much of the new or improved acreage can be obtained by drainage, which requires an average capital investment of only about a quarter as much per acre as irrigation.

Reclamation may increase national production to a point high enough to carry us safely to the end of this century.

The foregoing figures make clear that extension of the use of vegetation as fuel is not easy. Food must come first. The trend has been in the opposite direction—less wood is being used as fuel, less wood is being used for construction, motor fuel is being substituted for horses and mules, and the nonfood uses of crops are beginning to be supplemented by plastic materials made from coal and petroleum.

The relation between foods, fuels, and synthetic chemicals is not immediately apparent but it is very real. With few exceptions, synthetic chemicals are made from fuels. Chemicals are stepping stones to materials intended to replace those that have formerly been supplied only by nature. Processes of nature require extravagant areas of suitable land, and any project that competes with food for land is waging a losing battle. Things made from synthetic chemicals probably would not be developed if the materials with which they compete were abundant and low-priced. The fundamental cause of the present high pace of synthetic-chemicals progress is the world's agricultural dilemma. The trend is strongly toward substitution of fossil fuels, which are now abundant, for arable land which is already insufficient to provide the population of the earth with suitable food.

We are already beginning to feel the pinch in the production of nonfood items. Take wool, for example. The number of acres of pasture land in this country divided by the population of all farm animals is about five. Sheep require more land than cattle, and cattle are bad enough. The average annual yield of wool in this country is not above one pound per acre. In Australia, which is exporting wool to us, the yield is nearer one-half pound per acre. This is in startling contrast with cotton, which runs 150 pounds per acre or better. Our domestic production of cotton is about twenty-seven times our production of wool, but we use five times as much land for our wool. Naturally domestic wool production is declining. At the same time our agricultural experts are warning against the rapid depletion of soil quality by the repeated plantings of cotton.

The rising demand for textiles coupled with high prices has led to the development of all sorts of synthetic fibers—the United States nylon, the German Perlon, and the British Terylene, to name a few of the outstanding ones. New synthetic fibers are coming along rapidly. The most important ones are derived from fossil fuels.

The synthetic-fiber business is just beginning. Annually we consume around 5 billion pounds of textile fibers derived from vegetation. This includes cotton, wool (domestic and imported), rayon, and silk. But we consume only about 90 million pounds of synthetic fibers of all sorts. Fuel (especially petroleum) has reduced land requirements for fibers by only about 2 percent. If the synthetics were inferior this might be regarded as almost too much progress, but they are definitely superior in

Mechanized equipment has cut down hand and animal labor on many sugar-cane plantations. The substitution of fossil-fuel energy for animal power on farms of the United States since 1920 has contributed three times as much arable land for food for humans as the total reclaimed by irrigation. This is because 65 million acres are no longer required for food for horses and mules. (*U.S. Department of Agriculture.*)

many ways. The business should grow and the demand for synthetic chemicals should grow correspondingly.

Because natural rubber is not native to the United States an analysis of the effect of synthetic-rubber production on land requirements is of less interest. However, it may be remarked that the use of fermentation alcohol for butadiene manufacture is not rational from the standpoint of conservation of land. Fortunately, it is also not economically competitive with the production of butadiene from petroleum.

Fermentation ethyl alcohol (other than that from molasses) requires the use of about 90 000 acres of arable land. In 1950, 70 percent of our ethyl alcohol was synthetic. To have produced this alcohol by fermentation would have required nearly a million acres of the kind of cropland of the United States devoted to the production of food. If the total amount of ethylene (1.5 billion pounds) now derived from petroleum and utilized for the production of synthetic chemicals had to be obtained by the fermentation of vegetation, we would have to allocate at least 2 million acres of our best land to this purpose.

Until the advent of synthetic glycerine from petroleum, all glycerine was made from natural animal or vegetable fats. The average land requirement has been around five pounds of glycerine per acre—more for vegetable oils and much less for animal fats. Every pound of glycerine made per annum from petroleum liberates a fifth of an acre of fertile land. Natural glycerine is derived, for the most part, from the manufacture of soap. The synthetic detergents now made largely from petroleum are doing about half as much work as soap itself. The billion pounds of detergent are liberating over 2 million acres of cropland, enough to produce about 3½ million tons of corn.

With these few examples it should be clear that the interactions of the synthetic chemicals and agricultural industries are fundamental, and that the job of circumventing the dire prophecies of Malthus has only just begun.

The impact of synthetic-chemicals production upon the availability of fuels is negligible. About 3.5 billion pounds of petroleum are being diverted to synthetic chemicals every year. But half this much petroleum is being produced every day. So the synthetic-chemicals industry is in its very early stage not only with respect to ultimate demand but also with respect to ultimate supply. Even when demand for oil as such seriously exceeds domestic production, the petroleum industry will find it profitable to divert a portion of its oil to the many projects that will help keep our granaries filled. Continued development of synthetic chemicals is assured because projects that are sociologically correct have a way of eventually turning out to be commercially profitable.

All these trends have made our food supply more secure for a few decades ahead, but this improvement has been at the cost of utilizing our precious supply of fossil-fuel reserves. Because of population increase, demands upon agriculture for food are sure to increase, while productivity of the lands of the earth, after reaching some sort of peak from the application of various technologies, will show a steady decline. No one has offered a solution to the problem of soil depletion, for in the growth and consumption of vegetation we take essential elements from the soil of the cropland and deposit them in rivers that flush them to the sea. At the same time erosion takes its toll. Even now more than half the world's population is on a near-starvation diet.

The sugar beet is one of the most efficient energy-producing crops. One reason for this is the long tap roots. Another is the efficient earth coverage by foliage which traps the sunlight for photosynthesis. (*The Great Western Sugar Co.*)

Phosphates are more essential than petroleum to our survival because there are no substitutes for phosphates. Some of the virgin soils of the United States have been deficient in phosphates. About 80 percent of our soils are now deficient in phosphates. Estimates have been made that we lose about 2.5 million tons of phosphate annually by harvesting crops and shipping livestock to centers of consumption. Another 3 million tons are probably lost through erosion. The 5.5-million-ton loss is remedied to some extent by the application of 3.5 million tons of phosphate fertilizer, but the net annual loss has been about 2 million tons per annum. Some authorities believe the true figure may be closer to 6 million tons. We have in the United States enough phosphate deposits to last a very long time but, of course, not indefinitely. Most of the remainder of the world is in worse shape in this respect.

The phosphate picture for the world as a whole is not too cheerful for the long term. Some authorities believe that the phosphorous leached away from the rocks of the continents each year may amount to 20 million tons. This corresponds to perhaps 100 million tons of phosphate that is largely deposited upon the floors of the ocean—not to be regained for use unless or until some geologic accident should elevate the sea floor. The world's annual production of phosphate rock as fertilizer amounts to about 10 million tons. This also ultimately reaches the bottom of the ocean. No one has yet suggested a method of getting the phosphorous cycle in balance for the lands of the earth, but a solution to the problem will be necessary for the long-term survival of the human race. It is no comfort to know that what is lost to man is gained by fish and that the earth as a whole may be in satisfactory balance.

Production of meat from grain is one of many inefficient processes of nature. If we take arbitrarily the sugar beet as representing 100-percent efficiency in land utilization for calories of energy, the production of beef has only about a 2-percent efficiency (Table 1). In other words, for

TABLE 1. Efficiency of Use of Cropland

Edible Materials	Percent
Sugar beets	100
Sugar cane	82
Potatoes	37
Corn	35
Wheat	19
Tomatoes	19
Apples	12
Pork	9
Milk	7
Beef	2

a million calories we must use fifty times as much land for beef as for sugar beets. The high consumption of meat is concentrated in only a few countries containing a minority of the earth's population. The United States is one of these countries. The production of milk requires only about a third as much land as the production of beef. However, a pound of butter requires much more land than a pound of food fats from soybeans, peanuts, or corn.

To obtain a given number of food calories, the production of beef requires fifty times as much land as the production of sugar beets. This is why the substantial consumption of meat is concentrated in only a few countries containing a minority of the earth's population. (*U.S. Department of Agriculture.*)

About 54 percent of the annual production of vegetation in the United States is used for food for man and beast. About 16 percent is for lumber (Table 2). The calorific value of food is more than 10 percent of our

TABLE 2. United States Consumption of Vegetation in 1947

Use	Trillions of hphr	Percent
Lumber and wood products	0.46	16.0
Fuel	0.70	24.4
Paper pulp	0.11	3.7
Distillation and tanning	0.01	0.3
Food	1.53	54.0
Nonedible, other than wood	0.05	1.6
Total	2.86	100.0

total requirement of energy for heat and power, but the food that we bring into our kitchens is only one-ninth of this, and the calorie intake of food by man is even less. The reason for this is the loss inherent in the conversion of vegetation to meat, and the losses sustained in preparation of food. We do not ordinarily eat the skin of the grapefruit or the bones of the cow.

Only after the energy in food has been supplied can we think about use of vegetation for combustion. Here, again, alternatives are possible. Dried vegetation can be burned as such or it can be converted to more convenient forms such as alcohol or gasoline. Either conversion is wasteful of energy.

Statistical figures are inclined to be low because a farmer, for example, has no incentive to make a report when he burns a cord of wood or eats a bushel of corn. But it appears that not much more than 14 percent of our annual crop of vegetation is now consciously utilized. About 86 percent is "wasted" in the sense that it is allowed to rot and return to the earth to promote new growth, or is eaten by nonproductive animals or insects—in which case it also returns to the earth. "Wasted" is a poor word to use in this connection because biological balance must be maintained; and if a substantial proportion of vegetation is not allowed to return promptly to the earth in the right places, it is necessary to provide artificial fertilizers. The proportion of vegetation that can be utilized may depend, in the long run, upon availability and effectiveness of artificial fertilizer. But even this is doubtful for artificial fertilization on a very large scale might not be effective if continued indefinitely, and natural restoration of fertility is almost as slow a process as formation of coal and petroleum. Many questions with regard to soil maintenance over the long term cannot yet be answered. Future research will certainly lead to improved means for building up the productivity of the soil instead of merely retarding its depletion. Mankind cannot indefinitely "wage a losing battle with nature through a series of strategic retreats."

Of vegetation now utilized, about 25 percent is employed as fuel. Most of this, of course, is wood. The earth has a land area of about 55 million square miles. About 11 percent, or 6.2 million square miles, is regarded as arable, but not all this land is suitable for intensive farming. Only about 4 million square miles (2.6 billion acres) have favorable temperature, topography, rainfall, and soil quality. Nearly 8 percent of the good farm land is under irrigation. About 27 percent of the land area of the earth (15 million square miles) is forested. About two-thirds of the forested area is regarded as productive, and somewhat more than half the productive area is regarded as economically accessible. Of the productive area, about 36 percent is coniferous and 64 percent is broadleaf. If more than one cord of wood per acre per annum is removed from forested areas, on the average, productivity of the forest, even with good management, is likely to decline. The balanced production of forests varies widely, of course, with tree varieties, climate, terrain, and other factors and may run in some cases above two cords. On the slopes of hills the figure may be below half a cord. In some European countries an attempt has been made to limit the rate of removal of wood

The world's forests, prehistoric and historic, have provided man with fuel, food, shelter, structural materials, and been invaluable in conserving our precious bit of soil. Within the last few generations we have placed a new drain on forests, to supply our growing demand for paper. (*Kimberly-Clark Corp.*)

to the rate of growth. In 1950 it was decided that estimates of the permissible rate of removal had been too high and a cutback of 30 percent was ordered. Some years of experience will be required to prove the adequacy of the new reduced rate.

A cord of wood per acre corresponds to 640 cords per square mile or about 5 million hphr per square mile per annum. The energy requirements of the world could therefore be satisfied with about 8 million square miles of forest—an area nearly three times the area of the United States, and about one-half the total forested area of the world. And this assumes that no other demands upon this wood were made—no lumber or paper.

Forests are not divided equally between the nations of the earth, nor are they used similarly. Table 3 shows the estimated rate of growth

TABLE 3. Average Annual Growth and Removal of Wood in Certain Countries, 1947

In Billions of Horsepower-hours per Annum

Country	Growth	Removal	Difference
Europe (without Russia)	388	486	−94
Canada	131	146	−15
United States	710	727	−17
Alaska	13	1	+12
Japan	84	140	−56

and removal of wood for a few countries. The figures for rate of removal are undoubtedly too low because they are based on records of industrial or commercial operations. They do not include removal by individuals. If these countries alone are considered, we are consuming wood at the

In lands of fossil-fuel shortage, reliance must be placed on large-scale and efficient use of wood. These large piles of wood for fuel are in Finland. (*Finnish National Committee*).

rate of 170 billion hphr per annum faster than wood is growing, or nearly 13 percent faster than the rate of growth. In some other less industrialized areas of the earth, the rate of growth is undoubtedly higher than the rate of use.

Three hundred years ago we had in the United States and Alaska about 1.3 million square miles of dense forest. But our forests have been dwindling rapidly. Some experts say our forests may be practically wiped out before the end of the century unless a comprehensive pro-

Three hundred years ago we had in the United States and Alaska about 1.3 million square miles of dense forest. We now have less than 250 000 square miles that can be classified as "merchantable," and not all of this is virgin. Here one may see how timber can become over-ripe and hold down new growth on the forest floor. The size of these trees may be judged by man by the arrow. (*Weyerhaeuser Timber Co.*)

gram of replacement is adopted. For we now have only about 700 000 square miles of trees. Of this, one-third is "merchantable" although not all virgin; about 45 percent is cutover forest now growing; the remaining is cutover forest now dying. About half of the merchantable forest area is in small holdings and about 16 percent is government-owned, but this contains about 30 percent of our saw timber.

The peak of production of wood in the United States was reached in 1907, and production has been declining irregularly ever since. Soft wood has been disappearing about eight times as fast as it has been growing. Hardwood has been used up at about four times the rate of

The forest lands owned by the government contain about 30 percent of our saw timber. On the average only about 1 cord of wood per year can be removed from an acre of forest without impairing productivity. The peak of production of wood in the United States was reached in 1907, and production has been declining irregularly ever since. (*U.S. Department of Agriculture.*)

replacement. Such depletion is bringing about its own cure because scarcity of lumber has increased its price and encouraged substitution. For example, much of the production of synthetic chemicals from coal and petroleum is used for the manufacture of substances that might be called wood substitutes if they were not so superior to wood in certain respects. So far, the inroads made upon wood consumption by solid plastics is now only about 1 percent of our use of lumber. But solid-plastics production is growing rapidly. It is interesting to note that wood itself is a plastic. It is composed of hollow cellulose tubes impregnated with the natural resin, lignin. Since the volume of wood is roughly two-thirds air and one-third solid, it can be compressed, and because of the lignin it can be molded with heat and pressure. This fact was not fully understood until the technology of molding plastics was well along. Unknowing we have lived in an age of plastics for thousands of years.

In various other ways fossil fuels have retarded the depletion of our forests. For example, most methanol and acetic acid are now being made from coal and petroleum instead of by distillation of wood. On a replacement basis, an average acre of forest can yield each year from 200 to 250 pounds of these chemicals and about 500 pounds of charcoal. The 1950 production of around 800 million pounds of synthetic methanol and 300 million pounds of synthetic acetic acid would have required the use of about 6 million acres of forest land. About 35 million pounds a year of these chemicals are still produced by the destructive distillation of wood because charcoal is still needed for some industries —for example, in the manufacture of carbon disulfide essential for the conversion of cellulose to viscose.

Much of our wood has been used as fuel (427 billion hphr in 1947). About 45 percent of this fuel has been from living trees, 35 percent from industrial waste, and 20 percent deadwood. Some of the wood has been made into briquettes—which at $7.50 per ton have about the same heat value per dollar as bituminous coal at $11.25 per ton. About 200 000 tons of wood briquettes are being produced each year in Idaho, Montana, and the Pacific Coast. An estimated 60 percent of total fuel consumption of Seattle and Portland is satisfied by wood. Wood is not a negligible fuel even in the United States.

The world consumption of wood fuel is estimated at about 3 trillion hphr per annum—about 7 percent of the world's energy requirements. But wood is not the only suitable agricultural fuel. Associated with production of food is the creation of large quantities of cellulosic wastes such as corn stalks, cobs, straw, hulls, and shells. The amount for the United States is around 1.5 trillion hphr per annum—about 3.5 times the wood we burn. Much of this is now used as fuel on our seven million farms, but some of it is returned to the soil. The same general situation can be presumed to exist for the rest of the world. In terms of weight of crops of all sorts the average nonmarketable material runs about 14 percent. With corn the figure is nearer 50 percent.

Obviously, the best energy-system efficiency for the use of wood or other cellulosic wastes is to burn it directly without conversion to another form. Much of it is now being burned in stoves of very low efficiency but industrial steam plants for wood have been designed to operate with efficiencies of around 88 percent. Energy required for production of fuel wood—animate or mechanized energy for cutting and gathering—varies widely. No national average has been estimated. The transportation of wood has lower efficiency than the transportation of other more concentrated and conveniently formed fuels. In connection with some commercial projects, fifty miles has been suggested as the maximum land distance for economical transportation. This contrasts with the thousands of miles for oil and natural gas in pipe lines and the hundreds of miles for coal by railroad. Because it is so bulky and so variously shaped, wood, like other cellulosic wastes, can be utilized directly as fuel only in the general neighborhood of its formation except when logging operations involve the movement of logs down convenient streams. For widespread distribution of energy vegetation must be converted to liquid—*i.e.*, alcohol by fermentation or gasoline by the Fischer-Tropsch process.

Alcohol and Gasoline

Before 1940 the annual world production of fermentation alcohol was about 3 million tons. Of this less than one-fifth was used as fuel, or about 5 billion hphr per annum. This is about one-sixth of one percent of the energy represented by the world consumption of fuel wood. Most of the alcohol fuel was consumed in Europe. Since 1940 the world production of alcohol fuel has declined to an even lower figure because petroleum motor fuel has been so much cheaper. However, the situation is being constantly reexamined in the light of possible future requirements and a brief résumé is, therefore, offered here.

Reported yields of alcohol by fermentation are commonly based upon the portions of plants that are taken into the fermentation process —not upon the whole plant. For example, the thermal efficiency based upon corn (the relation between the heating value of corn and the heating value of the alcohol made from it) is about 34 percent. When the heat for processing is taken into account, the figure is 25 percent. Based, instead, upon the whole corn plant the thermal efficiency is about 14 percent. Intermediate efficiencies can be reached by processing agricultural wastes as well as corn to produce alcohol. This can bring the yield up to about 18 percent.

Plants vary widely in the proportion of unfermentable material. The predominant constituent of wood is cellulose, which is unfermentable. But cellulose can be converted in part by chemical processes to fermentable sugars, and alcohol and other liquid fuels can be obtained

Since 1930, corn yields per acre have gone up 36 percent. But processing of all good crops produced in the United States would give less than half enough motor fuel to operate our cars. And then we would have no food. (*U.S. Department of Agriculture.*)

from these sugars. Wood yields both dextrose and pentose sugars. Modern procedure calls for the separate production of the sugars and the separate fermentation of them. The combined total of liquid fuel amounts to about 70 gallons per ton of wood or 65 gallons per ton of agricultural residues. Research shows promise of raising these yields considerably. Table 4 gives some comparative figures from which it is possible to draw the rather interesting conclusion that alcohol from an acre of sugar beets would represent more energy than could be obtained by burning directly the wood from an acre of forest. This is, of course, upon a repeated annual basis.

Quite aside from economics, agricultural alcohol will not provide the

TABLE 4. Alcohol Yields from Certain Materials

Material	Gal per Ton	Gal per Acre
Wood	70	70
Corn	84	89
Potatoes	23	178
Sugar cane	15	268
Sugar beet	22	287

solution to our motor-fuel problem. Processing of all food crops produced in the United States would give less than half enough motor fuel to operate our cars. And then we would have no food. The more expensive processing of all agricultural wastes could yield about 30 percent of our needs but the cost of gathering and processing would be fantastic.

The cheapest alcohol now is that made from the ethylene of petroleum refinery gases. When such ethylene is no longer abundant, ethylene will be provided from conversion of coal and natural gas. With appropriate credits for by-products, the cheapest fermentation alcohol is from blackstrap molasses. The most expensive is from wood. Corn is intermediate. In general, fermentation alcohol cannot be made for less than twice the present cost of gasoline.

Alcohol used alone is an excellent motor fuel and, except for its tendency to separate from gasoline in the presence of moisture, it is an excellent addition agent for gasoline. The curve for octane-number improvement versus percent alcohol in motor-fuel blends rises rather steeply in a straight line up to 20 percent. Alcohol in a blend does not interfere with the effectiveness of tetraethyl lead on gasoline component. Alcohol and lead are independent and additive in their effects. Theoretically (because of its lower Btu value) alcohol should give less car mileage than gasoline. In practice the effects are not measurable with 10-percent blends, only slightly noticeable with 20-percent blends, and rather easily found with 30-percent blends.

A number of new power-alcohol plants were built in the late 1940's: 2.5 million gallons per annum in the Dominican Republic, 1 million gallons in Jamaica, 2 million gallons in India, 5 million gallons in Brazil, and a large plant is planned for Pakistan. In all of these countries petroleum products must be imported and sugar crops are locally available.

In the United States the production of agricultural wastes (stalks, cobs, straw, etc.) amounts to about 3.5 times the wood we burn. At Peoria, Ill., the U.S. Department of Agriculture is experimenting with the continuous conversion of corncobs, shown above, to motor fuel and chemicals in a modern plant as shown below. (*U.S. Department of Agriculture.*)

Gasoline is as easy (or as difficult) to make from wood or agricultural wastes as from coal. With oxygen and steam, wood can be converted to carbon monoxide and hydrogen, which can be passed through the conventional Fischer-Tropsch synthesis to make gasoline, light oils, and wax. The energy producible per square mile of land in the form of gasoline would be higher than in the form of alcohol. The thermal efficiency of the conversion is around 40 percent compared with around 25 percent for fermentation. Costs per gallon of the two

What pulp and paper mills once regarded as waste to be dumped into streams is now being converted into fuel alcohol by some progressive companies. Here is shown the loading of the first tank car of alcohol made from waste in paper-pulp mills at the plant of the Puget Sound Pulp and Timber Company in 1945.

products would be near enough to require rather careful process economics for comparison.

Costs per therm would be definitely lower for gasoline, for alcohol has only 84 000 Btu per gallon compared with 135 000 for gasoline. From both economic and conservational standpoints, if we are going to make liquid fuel from vegetation we had better make gasoline rather than alcohol.

The determination of the most efficient way to derive energy from terrestrial vegetation involves the sort of analysis of the land area of the earth that is not possible at this time. While reasonably accurate estimates have been made of forests, too little is known of the apportionment between cropland, pasture land, and desert in remote parts of the earth. In the United States where much serious study has been devoted to the subject we come out with 21 percent forest, 26 percent cropland, and 53 percent pasture land. Desert areas are included in

Less than 1 percent of the petroleum production is processed to make chemical intermediates such as ethyl alcohol, ethylene glycol, synthetic glycerine, detergents, and a host of others. These operations have liberated millions of acres of arable land for the production of food. (*Gulf Oil Corp.*)

cropland and pasture land. Some desert land can be converted to excellent cropland where adequate irrigation can be provided, but the problem is complicated by the fact that certain fertile areas will inevitably become arid and unproductive because of the loss of water. Agriculture and forestry are by no means static.

In the meantime certain generalizations can be made. It is clear, for example, that about three times as much energy can be obtained by burning corn directly as by burning alcohol or gasoline that can be made from corn. Burning of food offends our sense of sociological proprieties. Production of power alcohol from food seems more appealing perhaps because we are accustomed to the idea of consuming food to make beverage alcohol. Fermentation is a "natural" process in the sense that it involves the action of living organisms. The lifeless chemical reactions of combustion and synthesis sometimes seem "unnatural" except to the chemist. But we must not permit such emotional factors to obscure the fact that production of either alcohol or gasoline from vegetation is merely a way of burning up vegetation wastefully instead of efficiently, and that the only justification for such production on a large scale would be a rather desperate requirement for fuel in liquid form.

Another generalization is that any major dependence upon vegetation will put the industrial nations of the earth at a disadvantage, for the great forests of the earth are elsewhere—in Asia, in South America, in tropical latitudes, and in the far north.

Marine Vegetation

The relatively shallow borders of both fresh and salt waters contain large tonnages of marine plants of all sorts. The oceans contain even greater tonnages of freely suspended particles of vegetation. Most of this marine vegetable life is called "algae"—a name originally meaning "seaweed." Algae are interesting to botanists because they represent the simplest forms of life. Many different varieties of algae have been identified. They exist in many forms ranging from complex structures resembling land plants to unicellular motile particles. Algae are now being used on a small scale for the production of agar, algin, alginic acid, alginates, potassium, and iodine, and British experiments are under way for the manufacture of a synthetic fiber. Some kelp is collected, dried, and ground for use as animal food. But almost no seaweed has been harvested for fuel. In our present economy such fuel would be expensive. A project for mechanized recovery would be seriously handicapped by the migratory characteristics of growth and by the vagaries of weather.

This is unfortunate because nearly 90 percent of the production of vegetation of the earth is believed to be in the 300 million cubic miles of water of the oceans. Inconceivably large amounts of solids can be suspended in such a vast volume of water and still the suspension can be extremely dilute.

The freely floating particles of vegetation are called "phytoplankton," to distinguish them from "zooplankton," which are microscopic animals. The latter feed on the former, and fish feed on the latter. Thus all animal life of the sea is derived from phytoplankton, which contains chlorophyll and is formed by photosynthesis from carbon dioxide and water.

Since phytoplankton depends upon sunlight, it is not formed at great depths but only in the top layer of the ocean—from the surface down to about 300 feet. This is only about 2 percent of the average ocean depth. The growth would not extend down even this far if it were not that phytoplankton is adapted to optimum growth in dim rather than intense light. The rate of production is highly variable because replenishment of the necessary nutrient salts depends upon the complex system of ocean currents for distribution from continents and from the depths of the ocean where phosphates and nitrates are particularly abundant.

It seems rather unlikely that we shall be able to develop ways of recovering net energy directly from the abundant phytoplankton. To do so would obviously involve the investment of less energy than that represented by gross recovery. However, we now recover a little of this energy indirectly in the form of fish, and there has been much speculation as to whether fish recovery cannot be greatly increased. If fish could be counted upon to provide a larger share of the world's food, the drain upon arable land would be at least less serious than it is now. Unfortunately, those who have studied the matter have concluded that while the yield of fish can be increased, we must not expect any substantial contribution to the total food of the world. The average annual yield of sea food for the world is 0.5 pound per acre of ocean, but the yield varies all the way from 40 pounds for the Azov Sea to 0.3 pound for the open waters of the Pacific Ocean.

Productivity of shallow waters can be increased enormously by cultivation. Oyster bottoms have been made to yield up to 750 pounds per annum of oyster meat per acre, and yields of sea-mussel meat can be even 6000 pounds. Table 5 shows the great range of production of a number of selected items.

An analysis of the present state of knowledge of marine vegetation brings one to the rather surprising conclusion that the most practical program for the 1950's is fundamental academic research. A little of this

TABLE 5. Comparative Yields from 1 Acre

Materials	Lb per Annum
Chlorella, predicted	200 000
Chlorella (experimental)	30 000
Potatoes, rich land	15 000
Sea mussel meat (maximum)	6 000
Wood, average	2 600
Milk (dehydrated)	2 400
Gasoline from potatoes (Fischer-Tropsch)	2 000
Alcohol from potatoes, rich land	1 300
Beef (good pasture)	800
Oyster meat (maximum)	750
Methanol and acetic acid from wood	250
United States cotton, average	150
Glycerine, average	5
United States wool, average	1
Australian wool, average	0.5
Fish (world average)	0.5

sort of research is now going on, but there is need for much more. Fundamental projects of this general nature are ideal for government agencies, but almost nothing is being done by government. In university laboratories special emphasis has been placed on studies of the single-celled alga, *Chlorella pyrenoidosa*. This elemental life is handled in the form of a suspension in water. All conditions for growth can be conveniently controlled—nutrient salts, carbon dioxide concentration, incident light, illumination cycles, temperature, and cell concentration. Study of chlorella has greatly accelerated our understanding of photosynthesis. Production of such algae in trays of water about 6 inches deep is said to be capable of absorbing up to 2 percent of solar energy falling upon the area of operation as compared with less than 0.1 percent for average agriculture. Experimental yields have been as high as 15 dry tons per acre per annum (much higher than typical land growth), and some investigators believe this yield can be made nearer 100 tons per acre. Thus technology appears to have already shown the way to a manyfold increase in the efficiency of utilization of sunlight through the agency of chlorophyll.

A part of this improvement comes from the smaller proportion of solar energy reflected into space by algae suspensions. Under a summer sun a stagnant pool becomes much warmer than a tree. This is a consequence not only of difference in reflection but also of difference in ratio of absorption area to evaporation area, and difference in effective air circulation. Water can be evaporated more rapidly from leaves than from the surface of a pool, and energy used for evaporation is not used for photosynthesis.

A part of the improvement comes from the controllable concentration of carbon dioxide. The optimum concentration (for chlorella) appears to be near 5 percent. The rate of ordinary land growth is limited by the rate at which nutrient salts in aqueous solution can diffuse through the earth to the roots, as well as by the identity and concentration of the salts. Natural land growth is subject to wide variations in temperature, humidity, and light intensity.

In spite of the wide variation of protein and fat content that has been found possible, it is not certain that chlorella can be made into suitable food. It is not good for fish production. The matter is being studied. R. L. Meier, of the University of Chicago, has made the interesting suggestion that algae be fermented to alcohol to provide motor fuel. This could certainly be done, although the relatively high protein content of optimum yields of chlorella might be a problem. Either alcohol or gasoline (by Fischer-Tropsch) could be made, but at costs several times as high as the cost of petroleum gasoline. Meier proposes that carbon dioxide from fermentation be used to maintain optimum concentrations for photosynthesis.

Internal-combustion engines in the United States consume about a billion barrels of gasoline per annum. To make this volume of motor fuel by the application of the Fischer-Tropsch process to chlorella would require an area of about 35 000 square miles—nearly the size of the state of Louisiana. This is assuming an intermediate predicted yield of 35 dry tons per acre per annum. Such an operation would be located preferentially on level land in a southern climate with rivers ample to ensure a supply of fresh water. The investment would be fantastic. Our scientists will probably come up with something much better than this, but here is one conceivable solution to the motor-fuel problem for the far-distant future. Perhaps by that time motor fuel as we know it will be obsolete.

A variety of blue-green algae has the property of causing "fixation" of atmospheric nitrogen. This may some day compete with the cheaper conventional processes of nitrogen fixation through consumption of fossil fuels. It is of some interest to note that terrestrial forms of algae (such as the green films on trunks of trees) have the extraordinary property of living through extended periods of drought. Cultivation of terrestrial algae may some day lead to unexpected values.

Industrial Photosynthesis

In much of the foregoing discussion the hazards and uncertainties of agriculture and aquiculture have been stressed. Present large-scale agriculture represents a tremendous step ahead of wild growth. More than two thousand "tree farms" dotting the United States represent a marked advance over the wild forest. Greenhouse culture is another step, and hydroponics is still another. The experimental production of chlorella, however, is as far ahead of anything done before as hydroponics is ahead of wild growth. Chlorella culture can be carried out as a perfectly continuous industrial process, in which the irradiated suspension is filtered to remove developed algae, the mother liquor is fortified with make-up nutrient salts, the rate of flow of the suspension is controlled by the amount of available solar energy and the concentration of carbon dioxide, and temperatures are maintained at optimum points. In this case a farm is a factory. The reason such ideal controls can be maintained is that chlorella is rootless—merely particles of freely suspended vegetation. The varieties of phytoplankton are legion. Our marine botanists have an immense and important task in the investigation of these varieties. Perhaps some are composed predominantly of carbohydrates.

Until more fundamental information has been garnered industrialization will have to wait.

To Sum Up

Those who know most about vegetation are inclined to believe that the best that technology will be able to do in the decades ahead will be to provide a sufficient amount of food for the 2⅓ billion people of the earth. The rate of increase as of 1950 is about 60 000 every day, and we are starting this race well behind the mark. Tremendous progress will have to be made to catch up with events, and until this essential problem is solved we can have no peace on earth. For energy we shall have to be content with the "scraps" unless, indeed, photosynthesis can be industrialized.

17

Rain

About one-third of the sun's radiation falling on the earth is used to evaporate and lift 16 million tons per second of water from the hydrosphere to the atmosphere. This is about 20 000 times the present energy requirements of the world. But the prospect of capturing more than a tiny fraction of this ocean of energy that continually surrounds us is as remote as this figure is large.

Of the total amount of sun energy expended on the hydrosphere, all but one-third of one percent is spent evaporating water from the surface of oceans, lakes, streams, and perspiring vegetation. None of this is controllable by man, as it remains locked in the water vapor until, upon condensation to rain or snow, it reappears as low-grade heat, reradiated into stellar space.

Only 0.33 percent is used to lift water vapor above the earth. While this percentage is tiny, the absolute amount is enormous. Assuming that precipitation falls an average of 10 000 feet, the falling of rain and snow the world over continuously liberates energy at the rate of 600 billion horsepower.

An appreciable portion of it can be captured, in the form of water power of streams. About 2 percent of this part of the solar energy absorbed by the waters of the earth is potentially recoverable. The amount actually recovered by existing water-power installations is only about 0.11 percent.

The theoretical total of the water power of the streams of the earth has been computed from figures on mean rainfall and mean elevation of land areas. The annual rainfall is taken at 36 inches per year average over all land areas. This is 80 million cubic feet per square mile of land area per annum. This area is about 51 million square miles. The mean elevation of the land (excluding Antarctica) is about 2400 feet. If all flow of water could be utilized, we would have at our disposal some 360 trillion hphr yearly. This would be about eight times our 1947 energy requirement.

Actually but little of this can be put to work. Nor would we, if we could. Much of the precipitation goes directly into the earth, becoming an essential part of the agricultural cycle. The greater part of the loss

The Grand Coulee Dam is the largest hydroelectric power producer in the world. Three times as big as the largest Egyptian pyramid, it utilizes only 27 percent of the practically available power of the Columbia River. This dam backs a lake 150 miles long, extending into Canada. The lake will serve to irrigate an area about the size of the state of Delaware. (*U.S. Bureau of Reclamation.*)

comes in the fall in rivulets and streams too small in size or too gradual in descent to be useful. This energy loss reappears as low-grade heat that simply adds to the total earth reradiation.

The flow of water cannot be harnessed as a practical matter until it forms large rivers or until the drop is large or both. In fact only where water can be impounded with sizable head is development practical. Of the commercial water-power plants in the United States only 20 have heads of less than 10 feet. About 560, or two-thirds of the total, are of heads less than 100 feet. The average head of all United States hydroplants is 89 feet. The highest head water-power plant in the United States is a 40 000-kw California plant where the water drops almost exactly one-half mile.

It seems unlikely that more than 5 percent of the maximum power of streams can ever be realized. This would be about 18 trillion hphr per year. As a matter of fact, the present best estimates of potential water power that seems to be practically possible of development throughout

An appreciable portion of the energy of rain can be captured in the form of water power of streams. The amount actually recovered by existing water-power installations is only about 0.11 percent. (*U.S. Weather Bureau.*)

the world stand at 6.54 trillion kwhr (8.72 trillion hphr). This assumes a normal (mean) stream flow three times the low-water or minimum flow and a use factor of 0.5. However, the estimates of undeveloped water power for Africa, much of Asia, and South America are little better than guesses. Some streams have scarcely been seen; much less evaluated. This figure, if correct, is less than one-fifth of the total world energy needs in 1947. The capacity of water-power plants installed throughout the world at the end of 1947 stood at 86.9 million horsepower (Table 1). Assuming a world-wide use factor of 50 percent and an over-all efficiency (from lake level to the station electrical bus) of

80 percent, hydraulic plants produced 300 billion kwhr of energy. Thus water power accounts for a little less than 1 percent of the total energy requirements.

The North American continent possesses not quite 13 percent of the present estimated world's potential water power, but contains about two-fifths of the total installed hydraulic power plant, as shown in Table 1. Europe, with about 10 percent of world's potential, also has 40 percent of the world's total water-power development. The remaining one-fifth developed water power is divided by Asia, Africa, South America, and island countries—but which between them hold the lion's share of the potential—77 percent. Africa particularly is rich in water-power possibilities, having at least 40 percent of the world's potential, more than three times that in North America. Essentially none of Africa's water power has been put to work. Africa, with her extensive deserts and great store of minerals, can be expected eventually to find good use for the power from her rivers.

The United States Water-power Heritage

When nature arranged the river systems of the United States she did not have convenience of water-power utilization in mind. Geographically the availability of hydroelectric energy and the need for it are out of phase. The more populous areas that need it most have comparatively much less than the more thinly settled Far West, which enjoys the greatest abundance of water power. From a water-power point of view, the Mayflower should have landed on the coast of the Pacific Northwest. The three Pacific Coast states have the preponderant amount of the nation's potential water power—34 percent of the total. The Mountain states are not far behind with 24 percent. Thus the 11 Western states with but 14 percent of the population have about three-fifths of the potentially available water power. Regionwise, the South Atlantic and East South Central states with the great Tennessee River system, are next best blest, with 17 percent. The Northern states from the Atlantic through Illinois and Wisconsin with almost half of the people and an even higher proportion of industry possess but 15 percent of the nation's water power. The remaining 10 percent lies in the tier of prairie states from North Dakota down through Texas.

The nation as a whole, however, has substantial quantities of water power. According to Federal Power Commission estimates this water power would support an additional 88 million kilowatts in generators,

TABLE 1. Installed Capacity of Water-power Plants of the World and Potential Power,* December, 1948

In Millions of Horsepower

Continent and Country	Installed Capacity of Water-power Plants	Potential Water Power	
		Based on Ordinary Minimum Flow	Based on Mean Flow (100% eff.)
North America	35.85	84.40	
United States	24.21	34.70	113.0
Canada	10.49	32.00	72.0
Mexico	0.65	8.50	
Guatemala	0.035	2.10	
Costa Rica	0.031	1.40	
Alaska	0.035	1.40	
Honduras	0.007	1.40	
Nicaragua	0.001	1.10	
South America	2.39	66.60	
Brazil	1.52	28.00	
Peru	0.27	6.40	
Argentina	0.07	5.40	27.0
Colombia	0.03	5.40	
Venezuela	0.015	4.30	
Bolivia	0.044	3.60	
British Guiana	0.001	3.60	
Chile	0.03	3.60	
Paraguay	0	2.80	
Ecuador	0.021	1.30	
Dutch Guiana	0.001	1.10	
Europe	34.94	67.86	
U.S.S.R.	1.90	14.00	50.00
Norway	3.80	10.00	27.00
France	6.10	6.00	12.00
Italy	6.25	6.00	
Spain	1.98	5.70	
Sweden	3.82	4.00	21.00
Yugoslavia	0.25	4.00	
Switzerland	3.70	3.60	
Rumania	0.127	3.00	8.00
Finland	0.82	2.50	
Germany	2.60	2.00	
Austria	2.00	1.55	4.00
Poland	0.128	1.35	3.60
Great Britain and North Ireland	0.49	0.70	
Africa	0.368	273.89	
Belgian Congo and Mandate	0.070	130.00	
French Congo	0	50.00	
French Mandate in Cameroons	0	18.50	
Nigeria and British Mandate in Cameroons	0.001	13.00	

* From U.S. Geological Survey, 1948.

TABLE 1. Installed Capacity of Water-power Plants of the World and Potential Power,* December, 1948.—(Continued)

In Millions of Horsepower

Continent and Country	Installed Capacity of Water-power Plants	Potential Water Power	
		Based on Ordinary Minimum Flow	Based on Mean Flow (100% eff.)
Africa—(Continued)			
Madagascar	0.001	7.00	
British East Africa	0.010	6.70	
Portuguese West Africa	0.004	5.70	
Ethiopia	0.001	5.70	
Liberia	0.007	5.70	
Portuguese East Africa	0	5.00	
Tanganyika	0.018	4.00	
Ivory Coast, Dahomey, and French Mandate in Togo	0	4.00	
Rhodesia	0.040	3.50	
French Guinea	0	3.00	
Sierra Leone	0	2.50	
Union of South Africa	0.004	2.30	
Gold Coast of British Mandate in Togo	0	2.00	
British Central Africa	0	1.70	
French Sudan	0	1.40	
Asia	12.059	150.60	
U.S.S.R.	0.342	64.00	325.00
India and Ceylon	0.767	39.00	
Chinese Republic	0.004	22.00	41.00
Japan	8.600	7.200	
French Indo-China	0.001	6.000	
Siam and Malay States	0.050	5.700	
Kovo	1.800	3.000	
Manchuria	0.208	1.000	
Formosa	0.237	1.000	
Oceania	1.283	20.150	
Borneo, New Guinea, and Papua	0.005	10.500	
New Zealand	0.670	2.000	3.6
Philippine Islands	0.065	2.000	
Sumatra	0.020	2.000	
Celebes	0.001	1.400	
Java	0.140	1.100	
Australia and Tasmania	0.352	1.000	
Hawaii	0.032	0.150	
World total	86.900	664	
Africa	0.368	274	
Asia	12.059	151	
North America	35.849	84	
Europe	34.937	68	
South America	2.392	67	
Oceania	1.284	20	

or five times the amount actually installed (17⅔ million kilowatts). Water power is only 17 percent developed in the United States as shown in Table 2.

TABLE 2. Potential and Developed Water-power Resources in the United States by Drainage Basins

Drainage Basin	Generating Capacity, thousands of kw			Generation, millions of kwhr		
	Potential	Installed Jan. 1, 1950	Ratio, Percent	Average Annual Potential	Actual, 1949	Ratio, Percent
1. North Atlantic	9 625	2 178	23	29 830	8 569	35
2. South Atlantic and Eastern Gulf	8 847	1 988	22	31 763	9 918	31
3. Ohio River	9 903	3 050	31	42 438	18 857	45
4. St. Lawrence—Great Lakes	4 783	1 539	32	26 743	8 480	32
5. Upper Mississippi River—Red River of the North	1 362	549	40	5 062	2 488	49
6. Missouri River	9 257	647	7	44 558	3 667	8
7. Lower Mississippi River	4 634	278	6	13 693	1 029	8
8. Rio Grande and Western Gulf of Mexico	1 100	200	18	3 671	538	15
9. Colorado River	7 047	1 314	19	35 839	7 344	20
10. Great Basin	1 040	369	35	4 071	1 322	33
11. Pacific Slope in California	9 427	2 114	21	50 305	10 100	20
12. Columbia River and Pacific Slope in Oregon and Washington	38 709	3 436	9	192 486	22 461	12
Total for United States	105 734	17 662	17	480 459	94 773	20

If all potential water power in this country, based on the Federal Power Commission estimates, were developed it would provide 480 billion kwhr annually on the average, or about five times more than is being obtained from water power. In other words, if water power were fully developed in the United States it could carry more than one and a half times the entire 1950 electrical load (329 billion kwhr).

The gradual development of water-power resources can be counted on. The cost of fuel-generated electricity is rising and probably will continue to rise faster than that produced from streams. In spite of the acrimonious discussion of public-produced power the sentiment of the people favors development of this natural resource, particularly when it is accompanied by other public benefits, such as flood control, land reclamation, improvement to navigation, and recreational facilities.

The dream, held by some, of the transmission of large blocks of hydroelectric energy from the Rocky Mountain regions to the industrialized East is not likely to materialize. Electric-power transmission over such distances simply costs too much. Some future reductions in power-transmission costs will undoubtedly be possible, but the savings are not likely to raise the economic distance limits from the present 300 to 500 miles to, say, 2500 miles.

The Hoover Dam on the Colorado River between Nevada and Arizona is the highest in the world—about as high as the Woolworth Building. The water from this dam flows through immense turbine-generators to produce electric power. (*U.S. Bureau of Reclamation.*)

A great increase in the economic distance of electric-power transmission does not seem to be in the cards. To get it by pushing the voltage up much above the present maximum of 287 kilovolts, where it has been for nearly twenty years, does not seem likely. There is no foreseeable prospect for transmission lines operating in this country above about 315 kilovolts and certainly not above 380 kilovolts.

The problems of high-voltage, direct-current transmission appear no nearer solution than they did two decades ago. The recent introduction of series capacitors for transmission lines will result in somewhat lower costs but not by any large percentage. The fact is, the energy of our rivers will likely continue to be used within 200 or 300 miles—and mostly less—of its generation. History has shown that where low-cost power is, there energy-consuming industries go.

Is Water Power Perpetual?

A hydroelectric development is thought of as being a permanent source of energy; one that, unlike fossil-fuel energy, can be counted upon for

Irrigation, flood control, and navigation factors of hydroelectric-power developments are threatened by the deposit of silt in the lakes behind the dams. The V-shaped line indicates where the muddy Colorado plunges down and under the clear water of Lake Mead, 93 miles above Boulder Dam. (*U.S. Bureau of Reclamation.*)

all time. But is it? What about the heavy load of soil and sand annually carried by flood waters into the lakes behind the dams, there to be dropped to rob the reservoirs of their storage capacity? Perhaps we should apply some discount to the consideration of reservoirs as endless sources of energy.

The answer is both yes and no. Obviously given enough years even the clearest of rivers will carry enough silt into a reservoir to fill it up—not to mention the notoriously muddy ones. When that happens the water storage will be lost, with all that it means to irrigation, flood control, and navigation. As to power generation, on the other hand, the full head would remain. The amount of power generated would depend on the run of the river and, on the average, might be 75 percent as much as before the lake became filled with mud.

The question is, how fast do reservoirs fill with sediment? Is the storage life of dams to be measured in decades or in centuries? The answer depends on the particular stream. The silt load of streams varies enormously. The Columbia River, for example, carries relatively little silt. Hence the dams at Grand Coulee and Bonneville will have extremely long lives—as far as storage capacity is concerned—certainly well beyond a thousand years.

But other rivers are not so kind. The Colorado River as it enters the canyon country brings in an average year 105 500 acre-feet of silt. This is equivalent to the top 2 inches of soil from 1000 square miles each twelve months. In its first thirteen years Lake Mead, behind Hoover Dam, had acquired nearly 1½ million acre-feet of silt, reducing its capacity from an original 31 250 000 acre-feet to 29 827 000 acre-feet, or 4.5 percent.

The rates at which reservoirs are filling with silt are not definitely known. The original storage capacity of the older reservoirs, which should give the best clues, was not too accurately determined. Also, only recently have methods of silt calculation been standardized. Newer methods, such as supersonic soundings, and better coordination of measurement technique between all reservoir owners or agencies are bringing some order to this question.

The best that can be said at present is that silting is a highly variable factor in reservoir life, and that it cannot be ignored. Experts of the U.S. Geological Survey believe that Lake Mead is good until at least the year 2225 or, taking into account probable compacting effect, 2380. This assumes no change in rate of silt influx, as would be caused by construction of dams above it, or alteration in the rate of erosion in the Colorado River basin, effected either by nature or man.

Indicative of the high variability of silting rates is the Guernsey Reservoir, on the North Platte River in Wyoming. It has the worst record of any Federal reclamation project. In twenty years it has lost one-third of its capacity. In a little over another generation, assuming no change in conditions, this reservoir will be filled with mud. On the other hand, the Elephant Butte Dam, on the Rio Grande in southern New Mexico, has lost one-sixth of its capacity in thirty-two years. It should, with unchanged conditions, have a total useful life of two hundred years.

The filling of reservoirs with sand and mud can thus be taken as having no early effect in the energy supply. However, it does underscore another problem that is in dire need of attention—control of soil erosion.

18

Wind and Tide

Ever since it was discovered that the sun does not revolve around the earth and that the earth is round instead of flat, man has been distrustful of intuitions. When we consider the inexorable rise and fall of the mighty ocean and the irresistible forces of the hurricane, we are inclined to think of these sources of energy as infinite. They have even been called that. But in these cases, as in so many others, our intuitions are faulty. Even the theoretical maxima are not impressive. The wind has been historically important, as it provided means for getting about on the water, but is now of more romantic than practical importance. The tide has at no time been important energywise. The amounts of energy practicably obtainable from either are little more than traces of what we need.

Wind

Cervantes in his creation of Don Quixote was sensitive to the romantic appeal of the wind. Perhaps one reason for the universality of this appeal is that wind is such an unpredictable manifestation of nature. For thousands of years, the wind carried sailing vessels to their destinations, or tossed them upon rocky coasts, or left them becalmed.

Wind has had a value to its users out of all proportion to the modest power developed. To the Dutch, wind-powered pumps literally meant their land, for these slow-moving mills enabled them to push back the sea from their earth. To uncounted farmers of our agricultural regions, windmills have spelled water pumped without effort of man or beast, and reception of radio programs.

The use of wind energy to drive sailing vessels, touched on in Chap. 2, now has little more than historical and recreational value. On the contrary, thousands of the familiar multibladed windmills are still in service on our farms. Between 1940 and 1950 about 40 000 pumping windmills were being sold annually in the United States, with about 300 000 in service. In addition, an estimated 50 000 wind-driven electric plants dotted the rural areas. These wind chargers, with an average

The wind is an unpredictable manifestation of nature, varying from almost perfect calm to the tornado. The maximum energy available from the wind is only about one-twentieth of the world's present requirements. (*U.S. Weather Bureau.*)

rating of almost 2 kilowatts, developed power from winds beginning at about 6 miles per hour, reaching rated capacity at about 20 miles per hour. Varying with the season, they charge from 150 to 400 kwhr per month into storage batteries. The annual output of these rural wind-powered generators amounts to about 150 million kwhr. This satisfies the yearning of farmers and others isolated from public-utility power for electric energy for radio.

The 300 000 wind pumpers average about ¼ horsepower each, and therefore represent an installed capacity of about 75 000 horsepower. Because of the variable nature of wind velocity, the horsepower-hours amount to about 250 million per annum. When this is added to the horsepower-hour equivalent of the 150 million kwhr obtained from the

To the Dutch, wind-powered pumps have literally meant their land, for these slow-moving mills have enabled them to push back the sea from their earth. (*Netherlands Information Bureau.*)

wind chargers, we have about 450 million hphr per annum as the total output of wind power for the United States in recent years.

Is this a lot of energy or only a little? Perhaps a useful comparison is with electric fans, which consume power to create wind instead of using wind to create power. There are about 30 million fans installed in the United States. The horsepower output of the average fan is about 0.02, giving an installed total of 600 000 horsepower. If these fans operate only a third of the time they consume more than three times as much power to produce little individual winds as the total power generated by the wind.

The trend of windmill capacity is downward because of the steady expansion of the network of public-utility power lines.

Commercial development of wind power has been almost nil. But not quite. For many years wind-powered generators in Denmark have

England is exploring every means of extending her declining coal supplies. An experimental wind turbine is planned for erection on Costa Hill on the coast of Orkney—one of the windiest spots on earth. (*North of Scotland Hydroelectric Board.*)

been operating in parallel with oil engines to serve rural communities. During World War II the number of these 30- to 50-kilowatt Danish units rose to 88 and in seven and one-half years they generated 18 million kwhr. If reports can be believed, Russia has had a 5000-kilowatt wind turbine operating for some time.

Commercial harnessing of the wind is being given serious and official consideration in the British Isles. The British Electrical and Allied Industries Research Association has for several years made extensive studies of the possibilities. Late in 1949 the North of Scotland Hydro-electric Board ordered the erection of an experimental unit on Costa Hill on the coast of Orkney, one of the windiest spots on earth. While

In the United States the only notable commercial wind-power experiment was the Smith-Putnam wind turbine installed on Grandpa's Knob, Vt., in 1941. This has since been dismantled. (S. *Morgan Smith*.)

this is but a 100-kw unit on a 75-foot tower, its main purpose is to provide data for much larger structures. It is expected that this experimental turbine will feed 400 000 kwhr annually into a neighboring 11-kilovolt diesel-supplied network.

Several factors support this serious interest in wind power. The western shores of England and Scotland, with fairly constant winds of 18 miles per hour mean annual wind velocity, are particularly suited to wind-energy capture. Water-power resources are insufficient and fuel is rising in cost and definitely limited in amount. England is, of necessity, looking to every means to extend her declining coal supplies. It is a case again of values determined by need and supply.

Numerous interesting facts appear in the reports of the British Electrical and Allied Industries Research Association. The amount of energy in the wind passing through a rectangle 10 miles long and 150 feet high is reckoned to be 2.5 billion kwhr yearly at velocities prevalent along the western coast of Britain and Scotland. (This is an academic figure, of course, because if sails were put up to catch all of it there would be no wind and hence no energy recovery.) It is believed that several hundred sites are suitable for installation of 2000-kilowatt units, providing an installed capacity of between 1 and 2 million kilowatts. The studies also indicate that about 4000 kwhr annually per kilowatt installed can be expected (45-percent use factor). Thus some 4 billion kwhr annually might be provided to be integrated with the hydroelectric systems to provide firm power. Scotland's present electricity requirements run to about 3.5 billion kwhr per year. The total potential water power of Scotland is 8 billion kwhr.

In the United States the only notable commercial wind-power experiment was the Smith-Putnam wind turbine installed on Grandpa's Knob, Vermont, in 1941. It was a single, 175-foot wheel with two blades on a 125-foot tower that could turn automatically to face the wind. It demonstrated its ability to develop 1000 kilowatts at the rated wind velocity and up to 1400 kilowatts in favorable winds. After an extensive experimental period, it ran in routine commercial service for several weeks, delivering power to the local power system. However, a structural failure developed, which, with the difficulty of obtaining repairs during the war, led to its being dismantled.

The most complete studies of wind turbines on a commercial scale in the United States have been made by Percy H. Thomas, engineer (now retired) of the Federal Power Commission. Utilizing the experience at Grandpa's Knob, he has created detailed designs of two essentially similar units but of different ratings. One is a two-blade turbine planned to develop 7500 kilowatts at wind velocities of 23 to 25 miles per hour and the other 6500 kilowatts with three-bladed turbines in winds of 18 to 20 miles per hour. Each design consists of two turbines mounted on the ends of a 235-foot bridge that swings on a turntable atop a 475-foot tower.

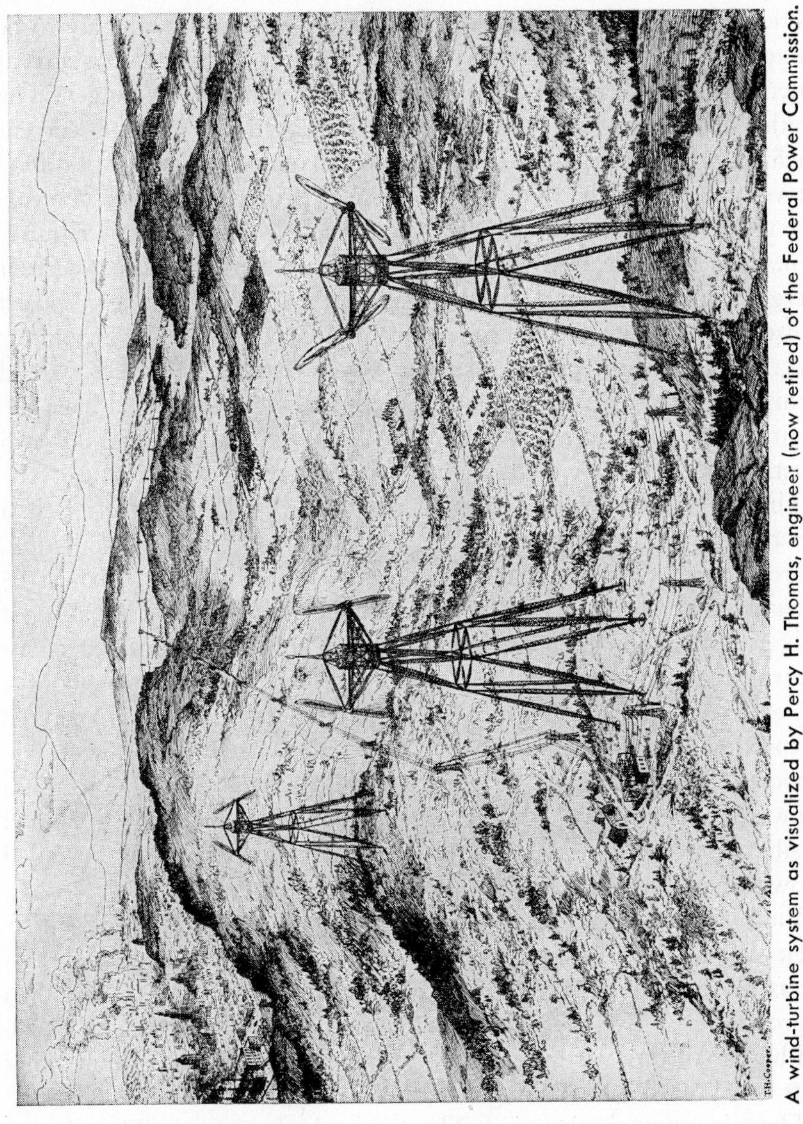

A wind-turbine system as visualized by Percy H. Thomas, engineer (now retired) of the Federal Power Commission. (*Federal Power Commission.*)

Each pair of wheels of either of Thomas' proposed plants are to be connected by shaft and step-up gearing to a single direct-current generator located at the center of the bridge on top the tower. The Smith-Putnam turbine was a constant-speed, alternating-current machine, which introduced limitations to accommodate winds of different velocities. On the other hand, Thomas proposes to allow the turbine to run at speeds best suited to the particular wind and load requirements and without need for feathering. To convert this direct-current energy to fixed-frequency, fixed-voltage alternating current he proposed to use a synchronous converter mounted adjacent to the d-c generator. Inverters of the mercury-pool type, being stationary devices, would seem more practical, but that is a detail. His turbines would have the merit of running at a speed suitable to the wind and load and not at a constant speed fixed by the frequency of the system it feeds.

Thomas estimated the costs of erection per kilowatt of such a generator as about a quarter of the cost of a hydroelectric installation. More recent British estimates are relatively much higher. It must be remembered, however, that hydroelectric stations are capable of delivering firm power, which wind turbines are not. Thomas envisions a battery of, say, ten of these wind turbines, located throughout a power system—scattered to capitalize on wind diversity—and operated in coordination with hydroelectric plants to achieve firm power. He proposes that experience be gathered with wheels of 6500 to 7500 kilowatts, but believes that larger units would probably be found feasible. Obviously the larger units would be cheaper per installed kilowatt and per kilowatt-hour.

Wind velocity increases about 40 percent in the first 500-foot rise in elevation, which means that the energy content of the wind, increasing as the cube of the velocity, is 275 percent greater at 500 feet than at ground level. By going to higher masts, by increasing turbine speed, and by use of three or even four wheels per mast, Thomas thinks that units of 25 000 kilowatts might be technically feasible.

There is energy in the wind. There is no doubt about it. That energy is lean, but the volume of moving air is enormous. Furthermore, this energy stock, although intermittent, is everlasting. Most of it comes from the sun, which heats the air in the tropics to start world-wide convection currents. Some have estimated that as much as 2 percent of the earth's receipt of solar radiation goes to create winds. The remainder of the wind energy arises out of the friction effect of the atmosphere as it is dragged along by the spinning earth, thus slightly diminishing the earth's speed of rotation.

It is easier to compute the energy required to create winds than to compute the energy that can be generated from winds. In contrast to water power, wind energy is kinetic energy—the kind of energy that disappears if you try to recover it all. We sometimes get the impression that wind energy is almost infinite, but the total recoverable amount cannot be very large. An assumption of an hourly deceleration of 0.1 foot per second from an average over-all velocity of 10 miles per hour of the portion of the atmosphere within 500 feet of the surface of the land area of the earth (the weight of this portion of the atmosphere is 3×10^{13} tons) would represent less than 15 percent of the world's present total energy requirements. The assumptions seem reasonable, but this method of evaluation is admittedly controversial.

There seems no reason, engineeringwise, why practical aeroturbines in commercial sizes could not be set to work. Like any energy development, utilization of the wind has its own characteristic set of problems. These include, in particular, its variability, both periods of calm and periods of excess. Windmills of sufficiently rugged construction to withstand high winds are not capable of yielding net power from moderate winds. Low velocities are useless, and high velocities are dangerous. Wind much under 20 miles per hour is not considered practical, and much above 30 miles per hour is unmanageable. Also the presence of very high towers in this air age is not desirable. It seems that the only part of the wind accessible to us is the part rather close to the surface of the earth. And in practice an exceedingly small fraction of this part of the wind could conceivably be approached as a maximum, because the earth's entire land area would have to be covered with wind machines of high efficiency—leaving no space for growing of food or utilizing the power developed.

Some wind-energy plants will probably be erected for special purposes or where the combination of factors are particularly favorable. But the wind must compete with many other sources of energy which seem to be more bountiful and attractive. Energy from the winds is not likely to supply more than a trifling part of the world's future energy stock.

Tide

The earth was endowed with an enormous fund of energy at the time of its creation. One form of this dowry was its enormous kinetic energy of rotation. A portion of the energy of spin reappears in recognizable form as part of the earth's winds and as ocean tides. The gravitational effect of the moon, principally, but to some extent the sun, causes the movement of the ocean but the energy dissipated comes from the kinetic energy of the earth, not from a distant body. The effect is a slowing down of the earth—about one second in a thousand years. This seems insignificant, but represents a lot of energy. The loss of kinetic energy of the earth as it slows down is equivalent to the continuous dissipation of 2.1 billion horsepower, or a rate equivalent to about one-half the present total consumption of energy. This energy appears as an infinitesimal warming of the oceans and shore line and is finally lost as radiation to space. Since the birth of Christ the day on earth has become about two seconds longer and the heavens have been enriched by 36 500 trillion hphr because of it.

In total amount tide energy is vast. If it were accessible, tide energy could supply about one-half of the world's needs. But the figure is of academic interest only. Essentially none is utilized at present, and the prospect in the foreseeable future is for capture of but a microscopic amount—perhaps 0.3 percent of the potential at most.

Tide energy has long been of tantalizing interest to engineers. The energy is there. You can see it, even hear it. It is perpetual; it is free. It seems so close at hand. Yet for all practical account it is of little use to us.

Actually many small tide mills have been built. At least one is still operating in Maine, furnishing, for two periods daily, some 35 horsepower to drive a wood saw. The first water-pumping system for the city of London was operated by energy from a tide wheel installed in old London Bridge. It remained in service until the bridge was replaced in 1824.

Numerous schemes have been devised for capturing tide energy. They have been of four types: lifting a weight, compressing air, moving paddle wheels by the tide stream, and the filling of basins during flow tide and operating turbines on the basis of difference in head on ebb tide (or vice versa). Except for the basin principle all schemes have been more ingenious than practical.

The basin scheme comes in three varieties. The single-basin plan is simplest. An estuary is closed from the ocean by a dam with gates. The basin thus formed is filled during rising tide. When the maximum level in the basin is reached the gates are closed. The water is held at this level until on ebb tide the difference in head reaches some chosen amount—usually 5 to 8 feet. The entrapped sea water is then allowed to flow through hydraulic turbines, generating power until, on the next rising tide, the head becomes less than the minimum practical for turbine operation. The power plant is then shut down, the gates opened, and the basin refilled. The reverse scheme, of course, is possible—*i.e.*, operating the turbine during flow tide instead of ebb tide, but the energy profit comes out about the same.

Clearly, the one-basin plan provides generation of power for several hours, followed by a period of no power in each tide cycle (12 hours and 25 minutes in most parts of the world where the cycles are about equal), or almost—but not exactly—two power-generation periods every day. Thus the time of occurrence of the peaks and absences of power shifts from day to day. Also, the peak amount of power varies from maximum to minimum every 14½ days in step with spring and neap tides.

The variability of tide energy, and with the single-basin scheme the complete absence of any continuity in power flow ("firm power"), are its greatest handicaps. The power available from a given tide plant would, however, be precisely predictable as to time and amount.

A second class of development is the two-basin system. Here two basins are separated from each other by a dam with gates and are closed off by gates from the sea. One is operated as a high-level basin and the second as a low-level basin. The power plant is placed between the two basins and arranged to discharge at will either into the low-level basin or directly into the sea. By proper timing of the gates, operation of the power plant can be made continuous, but at a sacrifice in peak power and total power. With the two-basin arrangement, some firm power can be developed, but it would vary in amount with neap tides.

Another way around the dilemma of no firm power is the addition of pumped storage to either a single- or two-basin tide project. During periods of maximum power generation, water is pumped into a storage basin for reuse through the turbines in that interval of each tide when the head is insufficient for energy generation. In this way, depending on circumstance, continuous power is guaranteed. However, this requires a suitable storage area, which is not always handy. Also it increases the cost of the development, and greatly reduces the total power developed.

A successful basin scheme requires two things: (1) a large mean difference between high and low tide, and (2) a shore line of suitable geography for establishment of one or more storage basins. At least a 10-foot tide would be required for an economical installation, and very likely few installations, if any, of less than 20 feet would be practical. Places about the earth where tides average 20 feet or more are not many. In the continental United States the only places where tides are adequate are the Hudson River and the Maine shore above Penobscot Bay. On the Pacific side there are essentially no suitable tides except in Alaska.

Only about a half dozen of the world's major potential tide-power sites have received serious attention. These are the Severn River in southern England, the Rance River and Mont St. Michel on the shores of Brittany in northern France, the San José and Deseado Rivers of Argentina, the Petitcodiac and Memramcook Estuaries in the Bay of Fundy, Canada, and Passamaquoddy where Maine joins New Brunswick. If all of these sites were utilized to their fullest capacity we might obtain about 0.2 percent of the world's present energy requirement.

The Severn project seems most likely of realization. Since World War II, with power short and with coal dwindling in availability and rising in cost, the possibility of tide energy has had increasing appeal to the British government. This is in spite of its twice-a-day variability because the Severn is a one-basin project. The Bristol Channel narrows to a point so that tide waters are driven up into a narrow channel causing a maximum (spring) tide of 47 feet and a minimum (neap) tide of 22 feet. It is proposed to place a dam across this channel just above the confluence of the Severn and Wye Rivers. The basin above the dam would fill during rising tide, whereupon the gates would be closed. When the head, on ebb tide, reaches 5 feet, the water would be released through thirty-two 25 000-kilowatt generating units until the head, after the start of the next flow tide, again becomes less than about 5 feet. The generators would then be shut down, the gates opened, and the basin refilled for the next cycle.

Estimates place the energy obtainable from the Severn project at 2 billion kwhr per year, which Britishers visualize as saving almost a million tons of coal per year. The energy would either be absorbed into the British electrical system or used for hot-water house heating in southern England.

No firm energy would be available from Severn. Studies indicate that pumped storage, while possible, would increase the cost by 40 percent and decrease the energy output by 27 percent, and is deemed not practical. There has been some conversation about laying power cables across the English Channel and operating the Severn River tide plant in coordination with French water-power plants to provide firm energy.

The Rance project of France is a single-basin scheme which would use a tide variation of 38 to 11 feet, in a plant containing 300 000 to 400 000 kilowatts in generators to produce 700 million kwhr annually. The Mont St. Michel project, where the tide variation is 42 to 12 feet, is much the larger of the two French tide-power possibilities but involves a dam 14½ miles long. It would have a barrier down its middle dividing it into two basins. With a 3-million-kilowatt power plant it would produce some 25 billion kwhr. As it is a two-basin scheme the two daily periods of complete shutdown would be briefer than with a single-basin development, but even so this unregulated energy is too much for the present French system to absorb.

The Bay of Fundy, New Brunswick, has the highest tides on earth. The spring tides reach 52.2 feet, and neap tides 21.1 feet. Furthermore, the Petitcodiac and Memramcook estuaries that converge into the bay are separated by a narrow ridge of rock—forming an excellent natural dam between them. Thus a two-basin system could be readily created. The power plant would probably consist of 250 000 kilowatts in generators. These two basins could be operated in different ways, depending on whether maximum kilowatt-hours or maximum firm energy is desired. The plant could develop a maximum of 1.3 billion kwhr per year of unregulated energy or 0.3 billion kwhr per year of firm energy. Estimates prior to World War II placed firm-energy operation as competitive with coal at seven dollars per ton.

The only tide project of importance to the United States is the much discussed Passamaquoddy, a bay that separates Maine from New Brunswick. Here tides vary from 26 feet at spring tide to 13 feet at neap tide, with an average of 18 feet. The Passamaquoddy tide project has had a long, turbulent, and expensive history.

The first large-scale investigation of Passamaquoddy tide power was made by Dexter P. Cooper in the early 1920's. His original plan was international in character. He proposed using Passamaquoddy Bay as a high-level pool and Cobscook Bay as a low-level pool. Canadian approval for this plan was later withdrawn because of anticipated adverse effects on the herring fisheries. His plan was later modified to employ areas wholly within American boundaries and with the addition of pumped storage to increase the firm-power output.

For economic and other reasons his plans failed of development and the project was taken over by the United States government in 1935. Interest in the project was renewed during the depression and on other occasions since, but it always failed to receive the essential Congressional support.

Because of the numerous islands and extremely irregular shore line several different tide-power development schemes are possible at Passamaquoddy. The two most recent all-American schemes, as re-

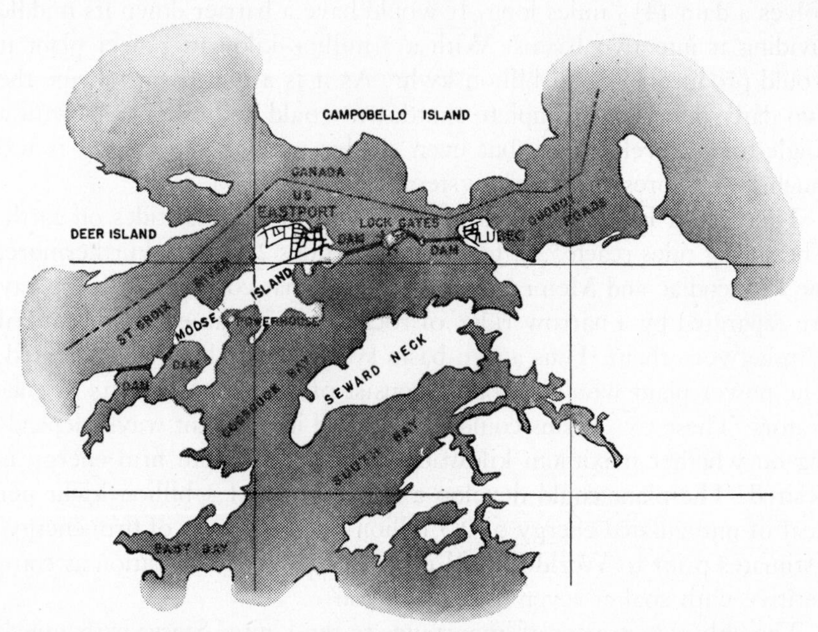

FIG. 1. A possible one-pool all-American scheme of trapping tidal energy at Passamaquoddy Bay.

ported on by the Federal Power Commission in 1941, suffice to illustrate the possibilities. One is a one-pool plan, shown in Fig. 1, and the other a two-pool plan, shown in Fig. 2.

In the two-pool plan the power plant would consist of ten 10 000-kilowatt generators, or 100 000 kilowatts total. A pumped-storage plant with turbine capacity of 180 000 horsepower and generator capacity of 135 000 kilowatts would be used as an auxiliary to the tide plant to provide firm power.

The firm-power output of the two-pool, all-American scheme was estimated at 578 million kwhr. The cost of the development in 1941 was placed at 90 million dollars. Including 5 percent interest and taxes, the cost of energy developed was figured to be 10.47 mills per kilowatt-hour. Not cheap power this—and 1951 costs would be much higher.

The one-pool, all-American scheme with a 62 500-kilowatt power plant comprising five 12 500-kw generators would be expected to produce 175 million kwhr. The cost (at 1941 prices) of this unregulated energy was estimated to be 7.38 mills per kilowatt-hour. If a larger powerhouse, of ten machines instead of five, were installed the output would be 340 million kwhr, at a unit cost of 5.44 mills (again 1941 costs). Certainly not bargain prices for power with twice-daily periods of zero availability.

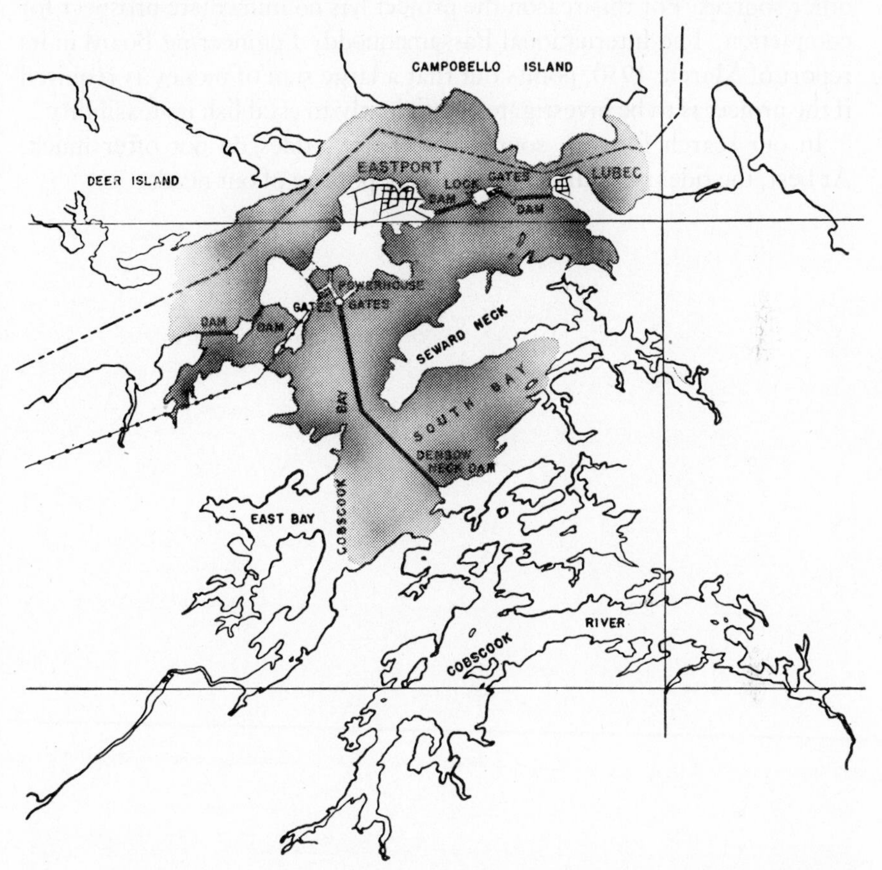

FIG. 2. A possible two-pool all-American scheme of trapping tidal energy at Passamaquoddy Bay.

The large blocks of energy that undoubtedly can be taken from the exceptional tides at Passamaquoddy Bay would scarcely make an impression on United States demand for power. Many millions of private and public money have been spent in the making of studies and preparation of plans. But the energy cannot now compete in cost with other sources. For this reason the project has no immediate prospect for completion. The International Passamaquoddy Engineering Board in its report of March, 1950, points out that a large sum of money is required if the project is to be investigated sufficiently to establish its feasibility.

In our search for new sources of energy, tides do not offer much. At best, the tides will fill but a minuscule portion of our needs.

19

Miscellanea

All of the energy available to us is derived from the sun and the earth. The land of the earth provides terrestrial vegetation—but also internal heat. The atmosphere of the earth provides wind power—but also an electrical potential difference. The sea provides marine vegetation and tide power—but also a temperature differential between the surface and the deep. In this chapter these additional sources of energy will be briefly described.

The earth is radiating more energy than it receives from the sun. The phenomenon is not clearly understood, but the major part of this energy is believed to come from radioactive substances in a skin of surface rock not more than 20 miles deep. While it has been traditional to think of the center of the earth as consisting of molten material, mostly iron, under great pressure and temperatures of 2000 to 3000 degrees C, there is no proof that the earth is really hot inside. What indirect evidence exists points in the opposite direction and suggests that the center may be no warmer than a wood fire.

Whatever the earth's interior be like, an enormous amount of heat is working its way to the surface and radiating to space. If the earth had no atmosphere, and if there were no sun or stars to send heat our way, the supply of heat from the interior alone would keep up the surface temperature to about 60 degrees absolute, or −400 degrees F. The flow of heat through the earth's crust is estimated to be in the neighborhood of 250 trillion hphr per annum—about six times our 1947 energy requirement.

Unfortunately, no practical plan is in sight for the utilization of more than a trifling proportion of this energy. A few power plants have been based upon local occurrences of volcanic steam. The largest development of earth heat has been the Larderello steam wells, in the valley of the river Possera about 50 miles from Florence, Italy. Here, unlike most volcanic outlets, the output is a continuous flow of steam. This development began, in a small way, in 1904. By 1944 six electric power plants with 135 800-kilowatt installed capacity were delivering 900 million kwhr per year. These plants became a casualty of the war in 1944 but have since been rebuilt. Two new plants are being added, which will bring the number of turbine generators to 32 with a combined capacity of 254 500 kilowatts.

The steam wells of Larderello, Italy, have been harnessed for the production of electricity for many years. This represents the world's largest scale utilization of earth heat. (G. Donato.)

The depth of the wells varies from 1000 to almost 2000 feet. Superheated steam emerges at pressures from 71 to 390 pounds per square inch gauge and at temperatures between 290 and 400 degrees F. Even before the drilling of new wells for the current expansion of generating capacity the steam production ran to 4 400 000 pounds per hour from 140 wells and there has never been any indication of diminution of volume or pressure.

The volcanic steam at Larderello brings with it more than heat. It contains many valuable chemicals such as pure borax, carbonic acid, ammonia, and boric acid. By 1950 about 8 000 000 tons of these had been recovered as a valuable adjunct to power development.

While the chemicals are desirable they are corrosive to normal turbine steels. Consequently, prior to the two new plants, it was the practice not to pass the earth steam directly through the turbines but through a heat exchanger which delivered steam to the turbines. This involves a heat loss—and very seriously a pressure loss—which has led to the development of turbines with special alloys not corroded by the chemicals of the earth steam. The Larderello turbines develop 1 kwhr from about 20 pounds of steam.

In numerous other parts of the world, natural steam or hot water emerges from the earth, but few such sources are employed for their energy content. An interesting exception is Iceland. This fuelless volcanic island has numerous "heat fields" where steam or hot water naturally issue from fissures in the rock. One such field is about ten miles from the capital city of Reykjavik. Between 1933 and 1945 some 45 wells were drilled to depths of from 450 to 2400 feet, from which is provided a constant flow of 4200 gallons per minute of water at 188 degrees F. This serves all the space-heating requirements of the city of 30 000 people.

Altogether it is estimated that the several heat fields about Iceland produce 25 000 gallons per minute of water at a mean temperature of 167 degrees F and 300 to 500 tons of steam per hour at 5 to 10 pounds per square inch gauge. Measurements of underground temperatures have indicated 400 degrees F at 600 feet and 600 degrees probable at 1000 feet. The total amount of heat available is, naturally, unknown but experts have estimated that it is equivalent to the yearly combustion of between 6 and 12 billion barrels of petroleum—say three times the total production to date from the East Texas oil field. The heat, of course, lacks the grade and portability of petroleum. One would expect the source of the heat undoubtedly to be volcanic but some geological experts insist there is no such relationship.

The Oregon State Highway Department is experimenting with heat taken from hot springs to keep two hazardous grades on short sections of automobile road free of ice and snow. By drilling 12-inch wells to 420 feet, water is obtained at 190 degrees F. This water, like the steam in Italy, contains corrosive agents. Heat from it is absorbed in a heat exchanger by a mixture of pure water with an antifreeze, which is circulated through pipes embedded in the sections of highway.

Japan has about 800 hot springs, some of them considerably more than a mile above sea level. Use of these is confined to therapeutic purposes, and a small amount of house and greenhouse heating.

Near Lake Talbot in New Zealand, superheated steam at 12 atmospheres emerges continually from a natural vent. Unfortunately this natural steam jet is in uninhabited, inaccessible regions. Just the same the New Zealand government is interested and may employ the experience in Italy for a power development. The steam emission in New Zealand is similar to that in Italy except that the wells to reach it must be much deeper.

Any large-scale utilization of earth heat is hampered by the random locations of the vents. While individual volcanoes deliver large volumes of heat they are not inviting prospects for energy development. The total volcanic escape of heat from the earth has been figured as not more than 1 percent of the heat lost by conduction through the crust. If all of the volcanic heat of the earth could be captured it would meet only about one-tenth of our total energy requirement, and much of this supply would be in remote islands of the Pacific.

Various schemes have been proposed to tap the heat of the earth, but, except for a few steam wells, the schemes have brought no net power or absurdly expensive power. It appears that a shaft about 6 miles deep and 300 yards in diameter would produce only 15 horsepower! At the greatest depth at which temperatures have been recorded —at the bottom of a 3-mile hole in Texas—the temperature was but 120 degrees C. The earth crust has extremely low thermal conductivity. That it is a good heat insulator is, incidentally, fortunate for us, but puts out of reach any easy capture of its heat.

Engineers in the future may get some better ideas. The energy is there if we can only get hold of it.

Atmospheric Electricity

We are living, literally, in a medium of subtle energy. We become suddenly and often unpleasantly aware of this when lightning strikes. On other occasions wire and radio communication systems misbehave for brief periods because of disturbing atmospheric effects. These are the conspicuous manifestations of the sea of electricity surrounding us, to which we are otherwise insensible.

In general there are four varieties of atmospheric electricity. Lightning is the one type of which we have visual and audible evidence. A lightning stroke is the heavy rush of current that follows when the difference in electric potential between two oppositely charged regions is sufficient to break down or "ionize" a path between them. This may be between a cloud and earth, between a pair of clouds, or between different regions within one cloud. The path is formed, and current surges through it with explosive violence until the two charges are equalized or the path disrupted.

The amount of noise and light created by lightning is considerable. But for all the great havoc a lightning stroke can cause the total amount of energy in the average flash isn't so much. To be sure, within the brief

Around the world, lightning strikes about 100 times every second. But if all of this energy could be harnessed, it would not be enough to supply the power required by the city of Pittsburgh. The violence of lightning disguises its weakness. (*U.S. Weather Bureau.*)

life of a stroke, which may be from a few millionths to nearly a second, the energy dissipation may reach the enormous rate of 1 billion kilowatts. But this lasts for only a very few millionths of a second. The total energy in strokes to earth on the average runs to only about 1 kwhr—two evenings burning of a 100-watt lamp. Even if all of the lightning strokes going on all around the world—estimated at 100 per second or about 300 million per year, of which perhaps one-tenth are strokes to earth—could be coordinated to make a unified flow of electric energy we would have only about 30 million kwhr—about one-hundredth enough to supply a single big city such as Pittsburgh.

Furthermore this form of atmospheric electricity is not very inviting as a source of energy. Quite the contrary. Engineers are put to great expense and trouble to protect apparatus from it. Even so lightning takes an enormous toll yearly in damage to structures, in human life, and in destruction of forests.

The other three forms of atmospheric electricity are completely unobtrusive. Only by laboratory-type investigations can they be found at all. But they are there.

One is precipitation currents due to falling of charged raindrops, snow, hail, etc. During periods of precipitation without thunderstorms it has been measured at 0.002 ampere per square mile. Not much current, and very small energy transfer. During thunderstorms it is more—about 20 amperes per square mile.

Then there are convection currents resulting from mechanical transfer of ions in the atmosphere from one place to another by winds, both horizontal and vertical. Through much of the atmosphere this convection current is about 2½ millionths of an ampere for each square mile of a 20-mile-per-hour wind.

Most mystifying of all is a continuous flow of conduction current of approximately 1000 amperes from the earth. The current varies, being somewhat less during the day than at night, less in summer than winter. On the average it is 5 microamperes per square mile for the whole surface of the earth. The puzzle is, what keeps this current flowing? If the normal earth charge were left to itself it would all leak off to the ionosphere in less than 10 minutes. How it is replenished is not known. There are theories involving radioactive elements within the earth, cosmic rays, and so on, but none fully explain the continuous replenishment of the earth's charge.

However, if we could harness all the energy represented by the whole of the earth and the atmosphere, we would have only about a third of the present world consumption of electricity. But from an energy standpoint it does not much matter. We are not likely to capture any of it anyway.

The Claude Process

Find a sizable body of something with an appreciable temperature difference and you have a potential energy source. The ocean provides us exactly that. The drawback is that while the volume is enormous the heat is low grade and the temperature difference is small. But it cannot be wholly ignored.

Largely through the efforts of the French inventor, Georges Claude —the same man who is principally responsible for the neon lamp—it is not being ignored. Although he is at present serving a life sentence in prison for collaboration with the Nazis, the French government is backing an experimental installation of his design at Abidjan on the coast of West Africa to extract energy from the ocean. The plan, scheduled for completion in 1953, is to create steam, with vacuum pumps, from lagoon surface water whose mean annual temperature is 86 degrees F, pass this steam through steam turbines and condense it with cold water—44 degrees F—sucked up from 1600 feet below the ocean surface. Using 9000 gallons per minute of warm surface water and 3000 gallons per minute of cold water and two large turbine generators, the expectation is to develop 11 000 kilowatts, with a net of 7000 kilowatts after deducting auxiliary and pumping requirements. By-products will be—perhaps—several thousand tons of fish annually sucked up with the cold water, and a quantity of salt.

The scheme is not a new one. Claude experimented on the shores of Brazil and Cuba in 1929 and 1930. Difficulty was experienced with the rigid ocean tube used. It could not withstand the stresses from the waves. The cold water at Abidjan will be drawn up through a flexible rubber pipe two meters (78 inches) in diameter reinforced with steel hoops and floated 3 miles offshore.

One other big problem is the air entrapped in the cold sea water, which on reaching the condenser expands and destroys the vacuum. It is hoped that new centrifugal air extractors may solve that difficulty.

The ultimate hope is to raise the temperature of the "hot" water source by spreading oil on the lagoon, thus increasing the ability to capture sun's heat. It is the experimenter's hope that by this trick the temperature will be raised to 100 degrees F, which would give a 56-degree temperature difference instead of 42, with a very large increase in heat recovery.

It has been estimated that there are 20 000 miles of ocean shore line where the sun heats water amply (40 degrees F difference is believed to be a minimum) to operate a condensing turbine. In addition there are tropical islands and the possibility of man-made floating islands. Assuming, for rough estimation purposes, that it might be feasible to construct a 10 000-kilowatt (net) power plant at 1-mile intervals operating at a 50-percent load factor, we would have 1⅓ trillion hphr of energy per year. This is equal to 5 percent of the world's present energy requirements.

One difficulty with this—granted the engineering practicality of such energy capture—is the fact that most of this energy would be made available to areas that—now at least—have comparatively little use for it. Certainly but little of it could be transported to the present heavy energy-consuming areas located not only in the temperate zone, but also often far back from the ocean's edge. This, however, does not minimize its possible future importance to tropical areas, which can be counted on to increase in energy requirements, and which, it so happens, are only meagerly supplied with fossil fuels.

20

Roundup

From the discussions in the earlier chapters of this book, it is clear that the problem of energy for the United States is not one of the dim future. It is upon us now. Our imports of petroleum are small but each year they become larger. By 1960 they are likely to be quite substantial. By 1970 they will almost certainly be huge—if foreign oil is still available then in sufficient quantity.

Coal will not "last for thousands of years." This bubble of hope has disappeared. Because coal will have to be converted to electric power and to liquid and gaseous fuels, less than a century is likely to see the beginning of coal's decline as king of energy sources.

Despite our great resources of oil shale, exploitation of all of it will delay the final accounting only a few years. Domestic tar sands are almost nil. Nuclear energy for heat and industrial power is finite and insufficient, if available, to postpone more than a few years the time of accounting when we can no longer depend upon our store of concentrated energy.

The problem for the world as a whole is a little worse than for the United States.

If there were no alternatives the outlook for our descendents would be dismal. This tiny period of earth's life, when we are consuming its stored riches, is nearly over. But man's resourcefulness continues on and becomes more potent with each passing decade. Because of this the future is bright.

We cannot know what the solutions to the energy problem *will* be, but we do know what some of the solutions *could* be. A characteristic of all proposals is high capital investment. But most of the plans have so far been "paper plans." Engineers have not seriously undertaken the job of putting the plans into practice. Such a job will become gradually more timely within this century, and who can tell what new technologies will appear to cut down some of the cost estimates.

Solar radiation is more than ample to supply our maximum energy requirement in the future. There are many different ways of capturing some of this energy—from desert areas, peat bogs, fertile valleys, forests, ocean. If photosynthesis can be manipulated to take care of the world's food requirements, similar industrialized techniques may be applied to the growth of fuel. Superior photochemical reactions will probably be found. We are only at the threshold of knowledge of such phenomena.

Before consciously engineered plans are worked out we should have fundamental understanding in many fields. Otherwise development will be unduly empirical. Fortunately for us, there is still time for fundamental research. But not too much time.

Our children's children may be puzzled when they read that in 1951 nearly two billion dollars was spent for scientific research under United States government auspices, but less than one-hundredth of one percent of this sum was devoted to solar-energy problems.

An ideal blueprint for future development would be the use on a substantial scale of the most economical projects for solar-energy utilization within the next decade, to be followed by other projects as they can be developed. The most obvious "first project" is heating of domestic water supplies, even now widely practiced. The next project is solar space heating, which is regarded as competitive now in certain sections of the country. The area of profitability will expand as more is learned about solar-energy collectors, heat storage, the heat pump, and architectural treatment. By the time these projects are well under way, we may know enough about photogalvanic phenomena to begin the generation of electric power by solar radiation without the mediation of the steam cycle. If this is a poor guess, some other line of endeavor will be successful.

Step by step, as determined by economics, solar energy will supplement the combustion of fuels. The net effect of the development of continuous sources will be that we shall finally reach the point where it will be no longer necessary to deplete our fuel resources at an accelerating rate. It is unlikely that energy can be obtained from continuous sources at costs lower than the costs of producing fossil fuels—at least not until the fossil fuels are nearing their end. The effect of new developments upon prices of fuels should be to retard the abnormal price increases stimulated by scarcity—the sort of price increases that would inevitably result in decreased demand.

As of 1950 we have already made a start on the use of solar energy. Table 1 lists eight different ways with predictions (based on our text) of

TABLE 1. World Utilization of Solar Energy
In Trillions of Horsepower-hours per Annum

	Maximum Energy Available	Energy Used in 1950	Energy Possible in 100 years
Land vegetation	60	3	10
Waterfalls	360	1	6
Solar collectors for power	17 000	Trace	20
Solar collectors for space heating	9*	Trace	3
Peat	5	Trace	1.0
Wind	2	Trace	Trace
Heat pumps	2	Trace	0.2
Tropical waters	20	....	Trace
Total	....	....	40

* This is the amount of energy now required for space heating. More than this amount is, of course theoretically available.

the amounts of energy that might be obtained in each way within one hundred years. The world is now using as fuel about 5 percent of its annual growth of vegetation. Even this may be too much when other necessary uses of vegetation are considered. However, the development of industrial photosynthesis seems assured and a considerable expansion of supply of such fuel seems certain. We are using only 0.3 percent of the world's water power. A tenfold expansion is probably possible when we consider the locations, like Africa, which have yet to be developed.

The conversion of solar energy to power is being practiced on a tiny experimental scale, but the possibilities are limited almost only by competitive investment. This is likely to be the largest energy development of the future for the simple reason that here is our greatest energy reservoir. Another trace of solar energy is being used for heat. Expansion of this use should also be considerable.

The use of wind power is not likely to exceed "trace" proportions, but the use of the heat pump is sure to grow. Not much energy increment is practically available from the heat pump. An increase to 10 percent of the practical maximum seems about as far as such a project could go. The temperature differential of tropical waters represents a more substantial energy reservoir, but engineering difficulties are vast. Peat is included in this table on the assumption (possibly not valid) that peat bogs can be made to form repeatedly after removal of peat.

Aside from these various ways of utilizing solar energy, a few other sources of energy are known. These are listed in Table 2. Not much can be obtained here.

TABLE 2. World Utilization of Other Constant Energy Sources
In Trillions of Horsepower-hours per Annum

	Maximum Energy Available	Energy Used in 1950	Energy Possible in 100 years
Earth heat	200	Trace	Trace
Tides	13	....	0.05
Atmospheric electricity	10		

Estimates of what may be possible in the way of energy development during the next century are, of course, matters of personal judgment. No two men would guess the same figures, but there is likely to be fairly general agreement on orders of magnitude. For example, it does not seem improbable that we should find it possible during the next century to use better than 0.1 percent of solar radiation by one means or another. By the year 2050 the world may well be able to obtain a substantial part of its energy requirement from current solar radiation. The 40 trillion hphr per annum from Table 1 happens to be the amount assumed for present world requirements.

At the present time current solar energy accounts for about 10 percent of our energy (wood and hydroelectric power). This has come about within the framework of natural economic compulsions. Additional supplemental supplies will be stimulated by the growth and spread of industrialism. The predictions (for what they may be worth) assume competitive projects in the market for energy. If economics could be ignored the predicted amounts could be made indefinitely larger.

Some day our appetite for energy will probably be satiated, and energy production will remain about constant. We shall have become a nation of philosophers. Most of us like to feel that improvement in our physical environment and facilities has just begun and that, just as long as we have inventiveness and enterprise, we shall continue to create new demands for energy, and to find ways of meeting these demands. We cannot believe that this fossil-fuel era in which we live, an era which may soon start its climactic approach to exhaustion, will be regarded by historians of the future as a period in which energy has been uniquely abundant. Instead, there is every reason to expect that succeeding eras will provide still greater abundance of energy from our constant sources. In the meantime, there is a lot of work to be done. Within a few decades a good start must have been made toward the new systems of energy production and consumption; and, while this goes on, our technological rear guard will be engaged in retarding in every possible way the corrosive growth of our energy losses.

21

*Energy Balance Sheet**

Now comes the less palatable portion of this book. Accounting systems are always dull to those unfamiliar with them and this is no exception. Dull though they appear, accounting systems are the basis of many of the important decisions that affect our present and future. The energy balance sheet presented here reveals much of the complexity of the energy picture, each part of which has some bearing on our daily lives. While many of the important conclusions and nuggets of information have been discussed in earlier chapters, others are still hidden within the mass of figures.

We are blessed with supplies of energy in fuel of several forms. In our complex industrial civilization, these forms are used as such or in the production of many other fuel forms. In some cases the secondary fuels are derived from other secondary fuels. A summary of the energy situation in which crude petroleum is added to gasoline or coal added to coal gas has no meaning, as certain energy supplies are being counted twice. Electric power, plus the coal used in its production, plus hydroelectric power gives a figure having no relation to any actual use of fuel.

As in any business, a balance sheet that actually does balance can be drawn up for the over-all business of obtaining and using fuel. The sum of the energy amounts of each fuel form used can be made to balance the sum of the energy amounts consumed in all applications.

A balance sheet can represent only a past period. The production of an energy balance sheet for the United States requires a vast amount of statistical information. Much of this information is not available until several years after the energy has been consumed. Because of this an energy balance sheet must always be out of date—it cannot be com-

*This chapter was written by Rolande C. Widgery.

pleted until about three years after the period in question. If we know accurately what was going on three years ago, however, we are less likely to form a confused or misleading picture of what is going on now.

Distribution among Energy Sources

Table 1 lists the production of mineral fuels, water power, and wood between 1800 and 1949. It shows that wood provided over 94 percent

TABLE 1. Production of Mineral Fuels, Water Power, and Wood

	Billions of Horsepower-hours								
Year	Crude-petroleum and Natural-gas Liquids	Natural Gas	Bituminous Coal	Anthracite	Water Power*	Fuel Wood	Total Energy	Thousands of hphr Per Capita	Population of United States
	Annual Average								
1800–1809	0	0	1.4	Neg	11.8	220.9	234.1	38.0	6 161 977
1810–1819	0	0	2.6	Neg	13.6	294.1	310.3	37.4	8 299 639
1820–1829	0	0	4.6	0.5	16.3	395.2	416.6	37.6	11 088 859
1830–1839	0	Neg	9.7	7.1	20.7	537.3	574.6	38.8	14 792 594
1840–1849	0	Neg	21.9	25.1	29.6	723.5	800.1	40.0	19 875 563
1850–1859	0	Neg	71.3	75.8	43.3	951.0	1 141.4	42.3	26 973 788
1860–1869	6.8	Neg	128.1	136.5	58.0	1 116.1	1 445.5	41.0	35 281 921
1870–1879	24.0	Neg	317.7	237.2	69.5	1 158.6	1 807.0	40.1	44 556 394
1880–1889	62.2	61.9	752.4	382.3	77.2	1 073.7	2 409.7	43.0	56 018 751
1890–1899	122.0	94.8	1 424.2	533.4	92.8	895.9	3 163.1	45.9	68 927 525
1900–1909	279.9	143.3	3 113.7	711.8	149.0	698.6	5 096.3	61.3	83 109 358
1910–1919	647.2	264.2	4 855.3	903.4	254.3	696.2	7 620.6	76.7	99 349 140
1920–1929	1 704.0	487.0	5 252.0	790.2	322.4	569.2	9 124.6	79.6	114 566 640
1930–1939	2 403.9	815.9	3 966.0	540.9	309.2	533.8	8 569.7	67.1	126 874 229
1940–1949	3 951.7	1 612.3	5 707.0	564.4	515.8	478.1	12 829.3	92.0	139 504 904
	Cumulative Total								
1800–1849	0	0	401.9	326.9	919.6	21 710.0	2 335.7		
1849–1899	2 149.9	1 567.7	26 938.0	13 652.3	3 408.5	51 952.3	9 966.7		
1900–1949	89 863.7	33 226.3	228 938.7	35 107.9	15 511.5	29 757.1	43 240.5		
1800–1949	92 013.8	34 793.9	256 278.6	49 087.1	19 839.6	103 419.4	55 543.0		

* Includes hydroelectric and direct drive. Amount shown is equivalent of fuel required.

Source: Tables 1–4 inclusive were prepared by Rolande C. Widgery of the Gulf Research & Development Company in collaboration with Walter L. Slifer and John Degnan of the Bituminous Coal Institute. The underlying data and advice concerning them were obtained from the Bureau of Mines, Bureau of the Census, Federal Power Commission, Forest Service, Bureau of Public Roads, American Gas Association, American Petroleum Institute, and the American Coke and Coal Chemicals Institute.

of the energy at the beginning of this period and remained the major supplier of energy over the first half. Not only did wood supply the energy necessary for space heating and cooking but also for most of the river boats, the early railroads, the industrial steam plants remote from coal supplies, and, as charcoal, for metallurgical operations. Even in recent years, wood has remained of great importance in certain regions. For instance, figures collected during the 1940 census of housing show that in 19 states wood was used in heating more homes than any other fuel. As late as 1944, more homes continued to be heated by wood than gas and oil together, and almost one-fourth of the dwelling units in this country were equipped with cooking devices in which wood was being used.

TABLE 2. Production of Mineral Fuels, Water Power, and Wood

Year	Bituminous	Anthracite	Crude-petroleum and Natural-gas Liquids	Natural Gas	Water Power*	Fuel Wood
	Percentage of Annual Average Formed by Each Fuel					
1800–1809	0.6	Neg	0	0	5.0	94.4
1810–1819	0.8	Neg	0	0	4.4	94.8
1820–1829	1.1	0.1	0	Neg	3.9	94.9
1830–1839	1.7	1.2	0	Neg	3.6	93.5
1840–1849	2.7	3.2	0	Neg	3.7	90.4
1850–1859	6.3	6.6	0	Neg	3.8	83.3
1860–1869	8.9	9.4	0.5	Neg	4.0	77.2
1870–1879	17.6	13.1	1.3	Neg	3.9	64.1
1880–1889	31.2	15.9	2.6	2.6	3.2	44.5
1890–1899	45.0	16.9	3.9	3.0	2.9	28.3
1900–1909	61.1	14.0	5.5	2.8	2.9	13.7
1910–1919	63.7	11.9	8.5	3.5	3.3	9.1
1920–1929	57.6	8.7	18.7	5.3	3.5	6.2
1930–1939	46.3	6.3	28.1	9.5	3.6	6.2
1940–1949	44.5	4.4	30.8	12.6	4.0	3.7
	Cumulative Total					
1800–1849	1.7	1.4	0	0	3.9	93.0
1850–1899	27.0	13.7	2.2	1.6	3.4	52.1
1900–1949	52.9	8.1	20.8	7.7	3.6	6.9
1800–1949	46.1	8.8	16.6	6.3	3.6	18.6

* Includes hydroelectric and direct drive. Amount shown is equivalent fuel which would have been required.

Percentagewise, however, wood has declined to some 4.0 percent (Table 2) of our energy supply, and it has become fashionable to ignore its past and present contribution. As more and more wood is displaced by natural gas, fuel oil, liquefied petroleum gas, kerosene, etc., the cycle of one major fuel will be almost complete.

The machine age brought a demand for large quantities of concentrated fuels. Bituminous coal was in such demand that its production almost doubled every decade during the last century and its relative importance continued to increase until the 1910–1919 period. By 1920, the year of coal's maximum percentage contribution to our energy supply, it provided about 64 percent of the total energy consumed. Since then, though some annual production figures have passed earlier peaks, the percentage of our energy supply from bituminous coal has declined and in the last decade was only about 44 percent.

Anthracite production also grew rapidly during the nineteenth century, reaching a peak of about 17 percent of the total energy consumed in the 1890–1900 decade. Although tonnage figures continued to rise until the 1910–1919 period, anthracite's importance as a percentage of the total fuel picture has consistently declined until it provides less than 5 percent of our total energy needs. While the total energy of anthracite used in this country is about the same as that of the fuel wood, more useful heat is obtained per pound from the anthracite because the latter is usually burned much more efficiently.

Petroleum and natural gas are still enjoying the upward surge of increasing annual consumption. Prophets differ in their guesses as to when the peak will be reached, but all agree that eventually there will be a curtailment in the supply and that again the trends of these fuels in the make-up of our energy supplies will change.

At the right of Table 1, the total heat value of the fuels and water power are shown divided by the population. Instead of indicating the approximately 140-fold increase that we would have had if mineral fuels and water power had been our only sources of fuel energy, we find that, because of the large consumption of wood during the early days, per capita consumption has increased by almost two and one-half times during the period. The benefits we obtain from our fuel, however, have increased much more than this factor of two and one-half times. This is because we are using less fuel wood, which we nearly always use inefficiently, and our ability to get more heat from all our fuels has greatly increased. Taking these improvements into consideration, it is probable that the actual utilizable energy per person has increased four or five times, while making only a two and one-half times increase in the per capita drain on the energy supply.

TABLE 3. Amounts of Primary and Secondary Fuels Entering the Various

	Primary Fuels and Power					
	Crude-petroleum and Natural-gas Liquids, thousands of bbl	Natural Gas, millions of cu ft	Bituminous Coal, thousands of tons	Penna. Anthracite, thousands of tons	Water Power, millions of kwhr	Wood, thousands of cords
For mining of fuels:						
Bituminous coal[a]	....	....	2 051	......	......	......
Anthracite	....	....	......	1 639	......	......
Petroleum and natural gas	27 020[b]	933 761	......	......	......	......
Total	27 020	933 761	2 051	1 639	......	......
For transportation of fuels—all fuels	....	269 105	35 000	14	......	......
For conversion:						
Coke ovens	....	2 594	99 864	218	......	......
Blast-furnace gas	....	....	......	......	......	......
Manufactured gas	4 103[d]	....	7 515	470	......	......
Mixed gas	....	124 265	......	......	......	......
Briquettes and packaged fuel	....	39	1 956	1 096	......	......
Generation of electricity	....	472 199	108 872	4 458	88 343[i]	265
Petroleum refining	1 934 363[e]	407 686	1 707	......	......	......
Total	1 938 466	1 006 783	219 914	6 242	88 343	265
For end uses:						
Primary-metals industries[c]	....	192 504	9 745	451	......	......
Other manufacturing	4 133[b]	603 847	74 151	4 141	......	......
Railroads	....	....	79 640	913	......	......
Water transportation	....	....	3 500	......	......	......
Highway and air transportation	2 376[b]	....	......	......	......	......
Tractor	....	....	......	......	......	......
Residential and commercial[g]	27 394[b]	991 430	99 163	34 800	......	40 000
Miscellaneous[h]	18	76 054	34 241	......	600[i]	15 735
Total end uses	33 921	1 863 835	300 440	40 305	600	55 735
Total fuel uses	1 999 407	4 073 484	557 405	48 200	88 943	56 000
Nonfuel uses[j]	14 662[b]	499 016	......	......	......	70 000
Total all uses	2 014 069	4 572 500	557 405	48 200	88 943	126 000

[a] *Bituminous coal* includes all coal and lignite except Pennsylvania anthracite, which is shown in the adjacent column.

[b] Data all refer to consumption of natural-gas liquids.

[c] *Primary-metal industries* includes iron and steel, aluminum, copper, lead, zinc, and other metallics industries.

[d] Includes 4 032 000 barrels of natural-gas liquids.

[e] Includes 81 874 000 barrels of natural-gas liquids.

[f] *Other manufacturing* Includes all the industries covered by the 1947 Census of Manufacturing except primary metal industries.

[g] *Residential and commercial* is necessarily a somewhat general category owing to the limitations in the definition of the available data. It is based primarily on retail deliveries of coal and oil and domestic and commercial accounts of natural gas and electricity. Undoubtedly some small manufacturers such as bakeries, tool shops, etc., are included. The detailed applications are, of course, too numerous to specify, but the ultimate breakdown is probably 60–75 percent space heating, 15–25 percent lighting, 10–15 percent miscellaneous—radios, small motors such as are used in operating washing machines, vacuum cleaners, refrigerators, etc.

Fuel-converting and Energy-consuming Operations in the United States, 1947

Secondary Fuels and Power													
Refinery Gas, millions of cu ft	Motor Fuel, thousands of bbl	Kerosene, thousands of bbl	Distillate Fuel Oil, thousands of bbl	Residual Fuel Oil, thousands of bbl	Petroleum Coke, thousands of tons	Blast-furnace Gas, millions of cu ft	Coke-oven Gas, millions of cu ft	Manufactured Gas Sold by Utilities, millions of cu ft	Mixed Gas Sold by Utilities, millions of cu ft	Tar and Pitch, thousands of bbl	Coke, thousands of tons	Briquettes and Packaged Fuel, thousands of tons	Electricity, millions of kwhr
......	......	......	......	......	....	....	......	......	......	......	......	....	5 423
......	......	......	......	......	....	....	......	......	......	......	......	....	1 028
......	......	......	......	......	....	....	......	......	......	......	......	....	800
......	......	......	......	......	....	....	......	......	......	......	......	....	7 251
......	98 662	......	12 830	88 900	....	....	......	22 409	6 198	......	......	....	33 869
5 600	......	......	......	601	....	276	404 215	......	......	......	333	....	958
......	......	......	......	......	....	....	......	......	......	......	32 189		
6 381	......	......	8 476	21 398	....	....	184 825	11 808	......	1 786	3 881		
......	......	......	......	......	....	....	......	59 253	1 515				
......	......	......	......	17	168	....	......	......	1	966	......	24	32
......	......	......	7 266	50 087	....	2 257	17	......	......	......	......	....	12 045
322 493	......	......	2 191	45 310	721	....	......	200	......	......	....	......	5 340
334 474	......	......	17 933	117 413	889	2 533	589 057	71 261	1 516	2 572	36 403	24	18 375
......	......	......	......	61 530	350	4 181	341 588	13 545	9 183	6 336	32 811	....	40 645
3 435	21 897	32 007	33 299	59 711	....	36	28 558	52 986	24 140	......	3 666	....	93 972
......	1 073	......	19 619	70 404	....	....	......	......	......	......	......	....	9 088
......	1 005	......	5 645	40 000									
......	621 565	......	14 579	......	....	....	......	......	......	......	......	....	6 799
......	50 736	8 209	4 118										
......	77	62 482	189 991	79 565	617	....	......	359 840	138 747	......	4 146	3 330	86 570
5 000	......	......	......	8 830	....	....	......	7 939	......	......	......	....	24 829
8 435	696 353	102 698	267 251	320 040	967	4 217	370 146	434 310	172 070	6 336	40 641	3 330	261 903
342 909	795 015	102 698	298 014	526 353	1 856	6 750	959 335	527 980	179 784	9 088	77 044	3 354	321 398
......	......	5	39 959	54 090	160	....	9 960[k]	......	......	21 208[l]	2 000		
342 909	795 015	102 703	337 973	580 443	2 016	6 750	969 295	527 980	179 784	30 296	79 044	3 354	321 398

[h] *Miscellaneous* is mainly a balance item including distribution not adequately covered by available statistics, such as the use of wood as an industrial fuel and the fuel consumed by the armed forces.

[i] Includes the energy of the falling water as calculated from the 83 926 million kwhr of electricity produced, assuming a 95 percent efficiency.

[j] *Nonfuel uses* include applications such as those of petroleum products as lubricants, solvents, and chemical raw materials, wood used as lumber and wood pulp. A large part of this is eventually burned after being used

[k] Represents the ammonia included in coke-oven gas. It is equivalent to 228 000 tons of ammonia. Most of it was recovered as ammonium sulfate.

[l] Includes tar and light oils; the light oils containing naphthalene and other important coal chemicals.

Probably the most important conclusions from Tables 1 and 2 are:

1. The long-term trend is toward increased energy consumption per capita.

2. The demand for individual fuels fluctuates irregularly.

3. The effects of these fluctuations are greater than the long-term increase, and the trends of consumption for individual fuels can be opposite to that for all fuels.

In order that the extent and direction of such changes can be gauged and their effects on the energy supply properly understood, it is necessary to set forth the relationships of fuels to each other and to their application.

Distribution among Applications

The data presented in Table 3 are for 1947, the last year for which complete statistical information was available as this balance sheet was prepared (1950). The titles at the left of the tables indicate the applications or using industries by which most of the fuel consumed in this country is utilized. These fall into four main categories. They are (1) *Mining*—which means the recovery of fuels from the coal mines and oil and gas wells; (2) *Transportation*—which includes all the fuel used in moving fuels from these mines and wells to the ultimate consumer; (3) *Conversion*—which includes the fuels used in the production of secondary fuels and power; (4) *End Uses*—which include all applications in which the heat values of the fuels are completely utilized or lost to accomplish some purpose; and (5) *Nonfuel Uses*—which include all those materials such as lubricating oil, road tar, lumber, etc., which, while of the same origin as fuel materials, are primarily used for other purposes.

Directly above the columns of the tables are listed the principal forms of fuel currently being utilized. The amount of each fuel used for each application is listed in the commercial unit of measurement in which it is usually considered.

The same data are given in Table 4 as percentages of each fuel consumed in each use. For example, the bituminous coal used in 1947 for *Residential and Commercial* applications was 99,163,000 tons (Table 3), which represented 17.8 percent (Table 4) of the bituminous coal produced in the United States in that year.

The first six columns of Tables 3 and 4 cover the five basic fuels and water power which are obtained from the ground, forests, or hydro-

TABLE 4. Amounts of Primary and Secondary Fuels Entering the Various Fuel-converting and Energy-consuming Operations in the United States, 1947

Percent of Fuel Consumed in Each Use

	Primary Fuels and Power						Secondary Fuels and Power													
	Crude Petroleum	Natural Gas	Bituminous Coal	Penna. Anthracite	Water Power	Wood	Refinery Gas	Motor Fuel	Kerosene	Distillate Fuel Oil	Residual Fuel Oil	Petroleum Coke	Blast-furnace Gas	Coke-oven Gas	Manufactured Gas Sold By Utilities	Mixed Gas Sold By Utilities	Tar and Pitch	Coke	Briquettes and Packaged Fuel	Electricity
For mining of fuels:																				
Bituminous coal			0.4																	1.7
Anthracite				3.4																0.3
Petroleum and natural gas	1.3	20.4																		0.3
Total	1.3	20.4	0.4	3.4																2.3
For transportation of fuels—all fuels		5.9	6.3					12.4		3.8	15.3				4.2	3.5				10.5
For conversion:																				
Coke ovens		0.1	17.9	0.5			1.6				0.1		4.1	42.1				0.4		0.3
Blast-furnace gas																		40.8		
Manufactured gas	0.2		1.3	1.0			1.9			2.5	3.7			19.3	2.3		5.9	4.9		
Mixed gas		2.7													11.2	0.8				
Briquettes			0.4	2.3								8.3					3.2		0.7	Neg
Generation of electricity		10.3	19.5	9.2	99.3	0.2				2.2	8.6		33.4		Neg					3.7
Petroleum refining	96.1	8.9	0.3				94.0			0.6	7.8	35.8								1.7
Total	96.3	22.0	39.4	13.0	99.3	0.2	97.5			5.3	20.2	44.1	37.5	61.4	13.5	0.8	9.1	46.1	0.7	5.7
For end uses:																				
Primary-metals industries		4.2	1.7	0.9							10.6	17.4	62.0	35.6	2.6	5.1	20.9	41.5		12.7
Other manufacturing	0.2	13.2	13.4	8.6			1.0	2.8	31.2	9.9	10.3		0.5	3.0	10.0	13.4		4.6		29.2
Railroads			14.3	1.9				0.1		5.8	12.1									2.8
Water transportation			0.6					0.1		1.7	6.9									
Highway and air transportation	0.1							78.2		4.3										2.1
Tractor								6.4	8.0	1.2										
Residential and commercial	1.4	21.7	17.8	72.2		31.7			60.8	56.2	13.7	30.6			68.2	77.2		5.3	99.3	27.0
Miscellaneous		1.7	6.1		0.7	12.5	1.5				1.5				1.5					7.7
Total	1.7	40.8	53.9	83.6	0.7	44.2	2.5	87.6	100.0	79.1	55.1	48.0	62.5	38.6	82.3	95.7	20.9	51.4	99.3	81.5
Total fuel uses	99.3	89.1	100.0	100.0	100.0	44.4	100.0	100.0	100.0	88.2	90.7	92.1	100.0	100.0	100.0	100.0	30.0	97.5	100.0	100.0
Nonfuel uses	0.7	10.9				55.6				11.8	9.3	7.9					70.0	2.5		
Grand total	100.0	100.0	100.0	100.0	100.0	100.0	100.0	100.0	100.0	100.0	100.0	100.0	100.0	100.0	100.0	100.0	100.0	100.0	100.0	100.0

electric sites. The remaining columns are concerned with fuel products and power made from these basic fuels and power. To differentiate these from the basic or primary fuels we call them secondary fuels.

The fuels as shown in Table 3 are not comparable. In order that a clearer picture of the relationships between fuel sources and applications can be obtained, all data must be presented in the terms of the same unit. The horsepower-hour has been chosen as this unit, and in Tables 5 and 6 the data are shown converted on the basis of the thermal equivalents of the fuels as shown in Appendix 2.

In Table 5 are shown the energy equivalents of the primary fuel and power sources. Since all forms of fuel and power of present commercial significance are derived from these primary sources, their total heat value is equivalent to the total consumed in the United States in 1947. This is shown in the lower right-hand corner of the table as 13.7952 trillion hphr. Of this we find that bituminous coal provided 41.6 percent, crude petroleum 33.1 percent, natural gas 14.0 percent, wood 7.0 percent (its importance here due largely to nonfuel uses), anthracite 3.5 percent, and water power 0.9 percent. In some studies, as in Tables 1 and 2, the contribution of water power seems more important because it is expressed in terms of the fuel that would be required to produce an equivalent amount of electric power.

Perhaps the most interesting conclusion reached by totaling the fuels used in each application is that, of our total fuel and power supply, 52.8 percent enters conversion processes. Only 34.5 percent is used in its "as-is" form for various fuel end uses, 5.6 percent is used in the production of nonfuel items, while 3.6 and 3.4 percent, respectively, are used in their primary forms in the mining and transportation of fuels.

Conversion Losses

The conversion processes as discussed here not only include the generation of electricity and the production of manufactured gas, in which case the form of the fuel is entirely changed, but also processes such as the production of petroleum products from crude oil or the manufacture of briquetted fuel, in which some of the original materials appear unchanged. The criterion used has been whether the process results in a different commercial entity.

Since more than half of our primary fuel and power is channeled into conversion processes, it is natural to inquire what becomes of the energy in this fuel. In Table 6 an attempt has been made to show the

TABLE 5. Amounts of Primary Fuels Entering the Various Fuel Converting and Energy Consuming Operations in the United States, 1947

In Trillions of Horsepower-hours

	Crude Petroleum	Natural Gas	Bituminous Coal	Anthracite	Water Power	Wood	Total Primary Fuels	Percent Used in Each Application
For mining of fuels:								
Bituminous	......	......	0.0211	......	......	......	0.0211	0.2
Anthracite	......	......	....	0.0164	......	......	0.0164	0.1
Petroleum and natural gas	0.0613	0.3940	....	......	......	......	0.4553	3.3
Total	0.0613	0.3940	0.0211	0.0164	......	......	0.4928	3.6
For transportation of fuels—all fuels	......	0.1135	0.3604	0.0001	......	......	0.4740	3.4
For Conversion:								
Coke ovens	......	0.0011	1.0283	0.0022	......	......	..1.0316	7.5
Blast-furnace gas								
Manufactured gas	0.0065	....	0.0774	0.0047	......	......	0.0912	0.7
Mixed gas	......	0.0524	....	......	......	......	0.0524	0.4
Briquettes	......	....	0.0201	0.0110	......	......	0.0311	0.2
Generation of electricity	....	0.1950	1.1211	0.0447	0.1185	0.0020	1.4813	10.7
Petroleum refining	4.4084	0.1720	0.0176	......	......	......	4.5980	33.3
Total	4.4175	0.4205	2.2645	0.0626	0.1185	0.0020	7.2856	52.8
For end uses								
Primary-metals industries	....	0.0812	0.1003	0.0045	......	......	0.1860	1.3
Other manufacturing	0.0065	0.2548	0.7936	0.0415	......	......	1.0964	7.9
Railroads	......	....	0.8200	0.0091	......	......	0.8291	6.0
Water transportation	......	....	0.0360	......	......	......	0.0360	0.3
Highway and air transportation	0.0037	....	....	......	......	......	0.0037	
Tractor								
Residential and commercial	0.0432	0.4184	1.0211	0.3470	......	0.3051	2.1348	15.5
Miscellaneous	......	0.0321	0.3262	......	0.0007	0.1200	0.4790	3.5
Total end uses	0.0534	0.7865	3.0972	0.4021	0.0007	0.4251	4.7650	34.5
Total fuel uses	4.5322	1.7145	5.7432	0.4812	0.1192	0.4271	13.0174	94.4
Nonfuel uses	0.0333	0.2106	....	......	......	0.5339	0.7778	5.6
Total primary fuels for all uses	4.5655	1.9251	5.7432	0.4812	0.1192	0.9610	13.7952	100.0
Percent from each source	33.0	14.0	41.6	3.5	0.9	7.0	100.0	

distribution of this energy between the uses of secondary fuels and conversion losses. The totals in the right-hand column in this table indicate the sum of both the primary and secondary fuels used in each application, and the total of this column is equal to the total consumption, 13.7952 trillion hphr, shown in Table 5.

TABLE 6. Energy Equivalents of Different Primary and Secondary Fuels Operations in the United States, 1947*

In Trillions of Horsepower-hours

	Primary Fuels Used as Such								
	Crude Petroleum	Natural Gas	Bituminous Coal	Penna. Anthracite	Water Power	Wood	Total Primary Fuels	Refinery Gas	Motor Fuel
For mining of fuels:									
Bituminous	.....	.....	0.0211	.....	.....	.....	0.0211	.....	.....
Anthracite	.....	.....	.....	0.0164	.....	.....	0.0164	.....	.....
Petroleum and natural gas	0.0613	0.3940	.....	.....	.....	.....	0.4553	.....	.....
Total	0.0613	0.3940	0.0211	0.0164	.....	.....	0.4928	.....	.....
For transportation of fuels—all fuels	.....	0.1135	0.3604	0.0001	.....	.....	0.4740	.....	0.2024
Conversion losses:									
Coke ovens	.....	0.0011	0.0572	0.0001	.....	.....	0.0584	0.0033	.....
Blast-furnace gas	.....	.....	.....	.....	.....	.....	.....	.....	.....
Manufactured gas	0.0001	.....	0.0542	0.0032	.....	.....	0.0575	.....	.....
Mixed gas	.....	0.0008	.....	.....	.....	.....	0.0008	.....	.....
Briquettes	.....	.....	0.0020	0.0011	.....	.....	0.0031	.....	.....
Generation of electricity	.....	0.1557	0.8859	0.0352	0.0059	0.0016	1.0843	.....	.....
Petroleum refining	0.1210	0.1720	0.0176	.....	.....	.....	0.3106	0.1899	.....
Total	0.1211	0.3296	1.0169	0.0396	0.0059	0.0016	1.5147	0.1932	.....
For end uses									
Primary-metals industries	.....	0.0812	0.1003	0.0045	.....	.....	0.1860	0.0020	.....
Other manufacturing	0.0065	0.2548	0.7936	0.0415	.....	.....	1.0964	.....	0.0449
Railroads	.....	.....	0.8200	0.0091	.....	.....	0.8291	.....	0.0022
Water transporation	.....	.....	0.0360	.....	.....	.....	0.0360	.....	0.0021
Highway and air transportation	0.0037	.....	.....	.....	.....	.....	0.0037	.....	1.2748
Tractor	.....	.....	.....	.....	.....	.....	.....	.....	0.1041
Residential and commercial	0.0432	0.4184	1.0211	0.3470	.....	0.3051	2.1348	.....	0.0002
Miscellaneous	.....	0.0321	0.3262	.....	0.0007	0.1200	0.4790	0.0030	.....
Total end uses	0.0534	0.7865	3.0972	0.4021	0.0007	0.4251	4.7650	0.0050	1.4283
Total fuel uses	0.2358	1.6236	4.4956	0.4582	0.0066	0.4267	7.2465	0.1982	1.6307
Nonfuel uses	0.0333	0.2106	.....	.....	.....	0.5339	0.7778	.....	.....
Total all fuels for all uses as such	0.2691	1.8342	4.4956	0.4582	0.0066	0.9606	8.0243	0.1982	1.6307
Heat value of primary fuels which reappears in secondary fuels	4.2964	0.0909	1.2476	0.0230	0.1126	0.0004	5.7709		
Total energy (as shown in Table 5)	4.5655	1.9251	5.7432	0.4812	0.1192	0.9610	13.7952		

* The data in this table are fundamentally the same as in Tables 3, 4, and (as concerns primary fuel) 5, except for
the earlier tables, and appears in the secondary-fuels section in the form in which finally consumed. See fuller explanation

The data of Table 6 are shown in percentage form in Table 7. Here we find that 65.6 percent of our present fuel and power supply is consumed in end uses for its energy content. An analysis of the *Fuel End Uses* indicates that the largest use we make of this energy after we have gone to such lengths to prepare it is in the *Residential and Commercial*

Used within the Various Fuel Converting and Other Energy Consuming

In Trillions of Horsepower-hours

Secondary Fuels Used as Such

Kerosene	Distillate Fuel Oil	Residual Fuel Oil	Petroleum Coke	Blast-furnace Gas	Coke-oven Gas	Manufactured Gas Sold by Utilities	Mixed Gas Sold by Utilities	Tar and Pitch	Coke	Briquettes and Packaged Fuel	Electricity	Total Secondary Fuels	Total All Fuels
......	......	......	......	......	......	......	......	......	......	......	0.0073	0.0073	0.0284
......	......	......	......	......	......	......	......	......	......	......	0.0014	0.0014	0.0178
......	......	......	......	......	......	......	......	......	......	......	0.0010	0.0010	0.4563
......	......	......	......	......	......	......	......	......	......	......	0.0097	0.0097	0.5025
......	0.0294	0.2196	......	......	......	0.0048	0.0022	......	......	......	0.0458	0.5042	0.9782
......	......	0.0001	......	0.0108	0.0873	......	......	......	0.0002	......	0.0013	0.1030	0.1614
......	......	......	......	......	......	......	......	......	0.0485	......	......	0.0485	0.0485
......	0.0135	0.0370	......	......	......	0.0025	......	0.0032	0.0265	......	......	0.0827	0.1402
......	......	......	......	......	......	0.0002	0.0005	......	......	......	......	0.0007	0.0015
......	......	......	0.0002	......	......	......	......	0.0002	......	......	......	0.0004	0.0035
......	0.0148	0.0995	......	0.0007	......	......	......	......	......	......	0.0161	0.1311	1.2154
......	0.0050	0.1119	0.0081	......	......	......	......	......	......	......	0.0072	0.3221	0.6327
......	0.0333	0.2485	0.0083	0.0115	0.0873	0.0027	0.0005	0.0034	0.0752	......	0.0246	0.6885	2.2032
......	......	0.1520	0.0039	0.1643	0.0738	0.0029	0.0033	0.0167	0.3198	......	0.0544	0.7931	0.9791
0.0700	0.0762	0.1475	......	0.0014	0.0062	0.0112	0.0086	......	0.0357	......	0.1259	0.5276	1.6240
......	0.0449	0.1739	......	......	......	......	......	......	......	......	0.0122	0.2332	1.0623
......	0.0129	0.0988	......	......	......	......	......	......	......	......	......	0.1138	0.1498
......	0.0333	......	......	......	......	......	......	......	......	......	0.0091	1.3172	1.3209
0.0180	0.0094	......	......	......	......	......	......	......	......	......	......	0.1315	0.1315
0.1368	0.4350	0.1965	0.0069	......	......	0.0763	0.0494	......	0.0406	0.0322	0.1144	1.0883	3.2231
......	......	0.0218	......	......	......	0.0017	......	......	......	......	0.0349	0.0614	0.5404
0.2248	0.6117	0.7905	0.0108	0.1657	0.0800	0.0921	0.0613	0.0167	0.3961	0.0322	0.3509	4.2661	9.0311
0.2248	0.6744	1.2586	0.0191	0.1772	0.1673	0.0996	0.0640	0.0201	0.4713	0.0322	0.4310	5.4685	12.7150
......	0.0915	0.1336	0.0017	......	0.0001	......	......	0.0560	0.0195	......	......	0.3024	1.0802
0.2248	0.7659	1.3922	0.0208	0.1772	0.1674	0.0996	0.0640	0.0761	0.4908	0.0322	0.4310	5.7709	13.7952

the fact that the heat value of the secondary fuels has been removed from the conversion section, in which it appeared in in text.

category, equivalent to 23 percent of the total, which consists mainly of applications in space heating, lighting, cooking, refrigerating, air conditioning, cleaning, and the like. The *Primary Metals Industries* and *Other Manufacturing Industries* show the consumption of the country for manufacturing is 18.9 percent of the total consumption. *Transportation*, which includes *Railway*, *Highway and Air*, and *Water Transportation*, consumes 18.4 percent. Thus, fuel needs of transportation are about equal to those of manufacturing. *Tractor Fuel* and *Miscellaneous* uses such as the armed forces and many minor applications account for the remaining 3.9 percent.

Next in order of magnitude of the applications of our resources is the loss of energy in the processing of primary fuels to secondary fuels. In considering the production of secondary fuels, it must be understood that the energy of the secondary fuels is obtained from that of the primary fuels (as shown in Table 5) and that losses occur in this conversion to secondary fuels. What has been done in Table 6 is to indicate the energy equivalent of each type of fuel in the form in which it is consumed. This has meant subtracting, in the section *Conversion*, the energy equivalent of the secondary fuel or power. This energy is shown on the table in the form of the secondary fuels to which it has been converted, opposite the use in which it is finally consumed.

To make the table more easily comparable with Table 5, these energy equivalents are shown in a line directly below the main body of the table. There it can be seen that the total consumed as *Primary Fuels* plus the total consumed as *Secondary Fuels* equals the total consumed as shown in Table 5. By having subtracted this energy of the secondary fuel from that of the primary fuel entering conversion processes, we have made sure that it will not be counted twice. *The amounts that remain in the section* Conversion Losses, *therefore, are only those amounts that are lost or "disappear" in the production of secondary fuel and power.* In the *Generation of Electricity*, for example, the 1.2154 trillion hphr lost in *Conversion* plus the 0.4310 trillion hphr distributed as *Electricity* equal the total heat value of the primary and secondary fuels and the water power used in the *Generation of Electricity*.

Since the energy of the secondary fuels and power has been subtracted from the total energy of the primary fuels used, these totals are, as we would expect, considerably smaller. It can be seen, for example, that the total of the column *Crude Petroleum* is small. This is because we burn a very small amount of crude oil. The large amount of energy contained in *Crude Petroleum* as seen in Table 5 is distributed and applied in the form of refined petroleum products. In Table 6, however, it can be seen that some of the energy from the crude eventually appears in other columns such as *Electricity* and *Manufactured Gas* since some of the energy in these categories comes from refined petroleum products.

Since the energy indicated in the section *Conversion Losses* is equal to that used in the production of secondary fuels, less the energy of the fuels produced, it can represent only the energy lost in the conversion process. In 1947 the total "loss" or use of energy incurred in "conversion" or in giving "form utility" amounted to 15.9 percent of our total energy supply.

Production and Transportation Losses

Extraction of our fossil fuels from their native locations, the mining of coal and the pumping of oil and gas, consume about 3.6 percent of the fuel supply. Transportation of fuels to preparation plants and refineries, to dealers and jobbers, and finally to the ultimate consumers requires 7.1 percent of the total. These two endeavors contribute "place utility" to the fuels. The combined task of giving "form" and "place utility" to fuels, therefore, requires the expenditure of 26.6 percent of the total energy supply. Remember that 65.6 percent was used for its energy content, and the remaining 7.8 percent constitutes the energy remaining in fuels now being used for nonfuel purposes.

Nonfuel Uses of Fuels

The problem of nonfuel uses is an interesting one because of its importance, from a supply standpoint, as constituting a part of the fuel demand, and yet there is really no clear dividing line between some fuels used for nonfuel purposes and other materials, such as vegetable oils, which could conceivably be used for heat or power. Thus the future of nonfuel use of fuel materials is dependent upon the relative cost of what we consider fuel-based products compared to the cost of equivalent materials from other sources. Since the synthetics industry is at present based mainly on petroleum and coal chemicals, it would seem that the magnitude of nonfuel uses will grow larger or at least remain of its present order. Since the fuel value of the materials going into these nonfuel uses is almost 8 percent of the total fuel used, it may be expected that greater attention will be paid to the subsequent use of some of these materials for fuel purposes after the nonfuel applications have been served. A few indications of the directions these steps may take are the use of waste wood for the generation of steam for power in lumber mills, etc., of burnable refuse in municipal steam plants, and of reclaimed lubricating oil in heavy-oil burners.

TABLE 7. Energy Equivalents of Different Primary and Secondary Fuels Operations in the United States, 1947

Percent of Energy Uses Supplied By Each Fuel

	Primary Fuels Used as Such								
	Crude-petroleum and Natural-gas Liquids	Natural Gas	Bituminous Coal	Penna. Anthracite	Water Power	Wood	Total Primary Fuels	Refinery Gas	Motor Fuel
For mining of fuels:									
Bituminous coal	....	....	74.3	....	...	....	74.3	....	....
Anthracite	....	....	....	92.1	...	....	92.1	....	....
Petroleum and natural gas	13.4	86.3	....	....	...	....	99.7	....	....
Total	12.2	78.4	4.2	3.2	...	....	98.0	....	....
For transportation of fuels—all fuels	....	11.6	36.9	Neg	...	....	48.5	....	20.7
Conversion losses:									
Coke ovens	....	0.7	35.4	0.1	...	....	36.2	2.0	....
Blast-furnace gas	....	....	....	....	...	....	....	....	....
Manufactured gas	0.1	....	38.6	2.3	...	....	41.0	....	....
Mixed gas	....	53.4	....	....	...	....	53.4	....	....
Briquettes	....	....	57.2	31.4	...	....	88.6	....	....
Generation of electricity	....	12.7	72.9	2.9	0.5	0.2	89.2	....	....
Petroleum refining	19.1	27.2	2.8	....	...	....	49.1	30.0	....
Total	5.5	14.9	46.2	1.8	0.3	0.1	68.8	8.8	....
For end uses									
Primary-metals industries	....	8.3	10.3	0.4	...	....	19.0	0.2	....
Other manufacturing	0.4	15.7	48.8	2.6	...	....	6.5	....	2.8
Railroads	....	....	77.2	0.8	...	....	78.0	....	0.2
Water transportation	....	....	24.0	....	...	....	24.0	....	1.4
Highway and air transportation	0.3	....	....	....	...	....	0.3	....	96.5
Tractor	....	....	....	....	...	....	....	....	79.2
Residential and commercial	1.3	13.0	31.7	10.8	...	9.5	66.3	....	....
Miscellaneous	....	5.9	60.5	....	Neg	22.2	88.6	0.6	....
Total end uses	0.6	8.7	34.3	4.5	Neg	4.7	52.8	0.1	15.8
Total fuel uses	1.9	12.8	35.2	3.6	0.1	3.4	57.0	1.6	12.7
Nonfuel uses	3.1	19.5	....	....	...	49.4	72.0	....	....
Total all fuels for all uses as such	2.0	13.3	32.5	3.3	0.1	7.0	58.2	1.4	11.8

Having gone over Table 7 in detail, let us look at it as a whole. A framework has been presented on which many of the important current fuel statistics have been related to one another, to their sources, and to the ultimate disposition of the energy involved. Any fuel-consumption figure which has not been listed can be placed on the framework and its relation to the secondary and primary fuels and to all fuel uses readily determined.

Used within the Various Fuel Converting and Other Energy Consuming

Percent of Energy Uses Supplied by Each Fuel															
Secondary Fuels Used as Such															
Kerosene	Distillate Fuel Oil	Residual Fuel Oil	Petroleum Coke	Blast-furnace Gas	Coke-oven Gas	Manufactured Gas Sold by Utilities	Mixed Gas Sold by Utilities	Tar and Pitch	Coke	Briquettes and Packaged Fuel	Electricity	Total Secondary Fuels	Total All Fuels	Total Energy Consumed	Per Cent of Total
....	....	....	...	....	....	....	....	...	.....	...	25.7	25.7	100.0	0.0284	0.2
....	....	....	...	....	....	....	....	...	.....	...	7.9	7.9	100.0	0.0178	0.1
....	....	....	...	....	....	....	....	...	.....	...	0.3	0.3	100.0	0.4563	3.3
....	....	....	...	....	....	....	....	...	.....	...	2.0	2.0	100.0	0.5025	3.6
....	3.0	22.4	...	....	....	0.5	0.2	...	.....	...	46.8	51.5	100.0	0.9782	7.1
....	....	0.1	...	6.7	54.1	....	....	...	0.1	...	0.8	63.8	100.0	0.1614	1.2
....	....	....	...	....	....	....	....	...	100.0	...	....	100.0	100.0	0.0485	0.4
....	9.6	26.3	...	....	....	2.0	....	2.3	18.8	...	....	59.0	100.0	0.1402	1.0
....	....	....	...	....	....	13.3	33.3	...	.....	...	....	49.6	100.0	0.0015	Neg
....	....	....	5.7	....	....	....	....	5.7	.....	...	....	11.4	100.0	0.0035	Neg
....	1.2	8.2	...	0.1	....	....	....	...	.....	...	1.3	10.8	100.0	1.2154	8.7
....	0.8	17.7	1.3	....	....	....	....	...	.....	...	1.1	50.9	100.0	0.6327	4.6
....	1.4	11.3	0.4	0.5	4.0	0.1	....	0.2	3.4	...	1.1	31.2	100.0	2.2032	15.9
....	....	15.5	0.4	16.8	7.5	0.3	0.3	1.7	32.7	...	5.6	91.0	100.0	0.9791	7.1
4.3	4.7	9.0	...	0.1	0.4	0.7	0.5	...	2.2	...	7.8	32.5	100.0	1.6240	11.8
....	4.2	16.4	...	....	....	....	....	...	.....	...	1.1	22.0	100.0	1.0623	7.7
....	8.6	65.9	...	....	....	....	....	...	.....	...	....	76.0	100.0	0.1498	1.1
....	2.5	....	...	....	....	....	....	...	.....	...	0.7	99.7	100.0	1.3209	9.6
13.7	7.1	....	...	....	....	....	....	...	.....	...	....	100.0	100.0	0.1315	1.0
4.2	13.5	6.1	0.2	....	....	2.4	1.5	...	1.3	1.0	3.5	33.7	100.0	3.2231	23.4
....	....	4.0	...	....	....	0.3	....	...	.....	...	6.5	11.4	100.0	0.5404	3.9
2.5	6.8	8.7	0.1	1.8	0.9	1.0	0.7	0.2	4.3	0.4	3.9	47.2	100.0	9.0311	65.6
1.8	5.3	9.8	0.2	1.4	1.3	0.8	0.5	0.2	3.7	0.3	3.4	43.0	100.0	12.7150	92.2
....	8.5	12.4	0.2	....	Neg	....	....	5.1	1.8	...	....	28.0	100.0	1.0802	7.8
1.6	5.5	10.1	0.2	1.3	1.2	0.7	0.5	0.6	3.6	0.2	3.1	41.8	100.0	13.7952	100.0

It is in Table 6 that the analogy to the accounting balance sheet is most apparent. The assets (more specifically, income)—the total of the various fuels that entered our possession during the year—are indicated by the subtotals across the bottom of the table. The debits (more specifically, expenditures)—the total of the amounts of fuel we expended during 1947—are indicated by the totals in the right-hand column of the table. As in any balance sheet the assets and debits are equal and in this case both are represented by the grand total of 13.7952 trillion hphr shown in the lower right-hand corner of the table.

Distribution of Energy Losses among End Uses

Table 6 indicates that the disposition of energy in the United States fell in five main categories: *Mining Losses*, *Transportation Losses*, *Conversion Losses*, *End Uses*, and *Nonfuel Uses*. Since the losses would not have occurred had not fuel been required for the last two categories, the energy lost can be charged against the applications whose fuel requirements caused its loss.

This has been done with the results shown in Table 8. In section (1), *Net Energy Consumed by End Uses*, the total *End Use* and *Nonfuel* data are shown as they occur in Table 6. In section (2), the *Losses* incurred in *Mining*, *Transportation*, and *Conversion* are listed opposite the *End Uses* in the preparation of fuel for which they were incurred. The totals of these losses are shown at the left of the section.

The Net Energy Consumed plus *Losses* equals the *Gross Energy Consumed by End Uses* shown in section (3). This section gives the disposition of our entire energy supply divided among the nine major categories of fuel needs.

In an ideal situation the net energy consumed for any end use would approximate the gross energy consumed in that use. Since this is not the case, it is interesting to discover what percentage of our gross-energy supply for each use is available for the net energy requirements. This percentage figure is the yield of the combined mining, transportation, and conversion processes that are necessary to prepare fuels for their end uses.

Changes Since 1947

Many of the statistics in the tables are obtainable only several years after the period to which they refer. Statistics are available, however, for several important industries for more recent years. To indicate the extent of changes in fuel preference some figures indicating the types of fuel used are shown in Table 9 as percentages of energy requirements supplied by each fuel. The principal conclusion that can be drawn from these figures is that the relative importance of coal has decreased, while the consumption of diesel oil by the railroads and natural gas by other industries has shown substantial gains. The use of oil shows mixed trends—its residential and commercial use growing, while its impor-

TABLE 8. Distribution of Mining, Transportation, and Conversion Losses among End Uses in the United States, 1947

In Trillions of Horsepower-hours

End Use	(1) Net Energy Consumed by End Uses†	(2) Losses*											(1) + (2) (3) Gross Energy Consumed by End Uses‡		$\frac{(1)}{(3)} \times 100$ (4) Yield,§ Percent
		Total Losses	Production Total	Transportation Total	Conversion										
					Total	Coke Ovens	Blast-furnace Gas	Manufactured Gas	Mixed Gas	Briquettes	Electricity	Petroleum Refining		Percent	
Primary metals	0.9791	0.5247	0.0487	0.0570	0.4190	0.1274	0.0485	0.0042	0.0001	.....	0.1945	0.0443	1.5038	10.9	65.1
Other manufacturing	1.6240	0.7271	0.0809	0.1260	0.5202	0.0146	.....	0.0168	0.0002	.....	0.4253	0.0633	2.3511	17.0	69.1
Railroads	1.0623	0.2523	0.0527	0.1130	0.0866	.....	.....	.....	.....	.....	0.0486	0.0380	1.3146	9.5	80.8
Water transportation	0.1498	0.0447	0.0081	0.0176	0.0190	.....	.....	.....	.....	.....	.....	0.0190	0.1945	1.4	77.0
Highway and air transportation	1.3209	0.4964	0.0658	0.1537	0.2769	.....	.....	.....	.....	.....	0.0365	0.2404	1.8173	13.2	72.7
Tractors	0.1315	0.0456	0.0064	0.0139	0.0253	.....	.....	.....	.....	.....	.....	0.0253	0.1771	1.3	74.3
Residential and commercial	3.2231	1.1824	0.1596	0.3359	0.6869	0.0129	.....	0.1164	0.0012	0.0035	0.4011	0.1518	4.4055	32.0	73.2
Miscellaneous	0.5404	0.1920	0.0266	0.0532	0.1122	.....	.....	0.0028	.....	.....	0.1094	.....	0.7324	5.3	73.8
Total fuel‖	9.0311	3.4652	0.4488	0.8703	2.1461	0.1549	0.0485	0.1402	0.0015	0.0035	1.2154	0.5821	12.4963	90.6	72.3
Nonfuel	1.0802	0.2187	0.0537	0.1079	0.0571	0.0065	.....	.....	.....	.....	.....	0.0506	1.2989	9.4	83.2
Total	10.1113	3.6839	0.5025	0.9782	2.2032	0.1614	0.0485	0.1402	0.0015	0.0035	1.2154	0.6327	13.7952	100.0	73.3
Percent of total	73.3	26.7	3.6	7.1	15.9	1.2	0.4	1.0	Neg	Neg	8.7	4.6	100.0		

* *Losses* equals energy consumed in giving place and form utility to fuels and power required for end uses.

† *Net energy consumed by end uses* equals energy of prepared fuels and power at point of use.

‡ *Gross energy consumed by end uses* equals energy of fuel in the ground, forest, or of falling water at hydroelectric site.

§ *Yield* equals Percentage *net energy* of *gross energy.*

‖ *Total fuel* is less than *total fuel* figure in Table 6 because in this table it does not include the fuels used in the mining, transportation, and conversion of fuels used for nonfuel applications.

tance in the iron and steel industry and the cement industry declines. The consumption of oil by electric utilities has fluctuated considerably due to changes in the oil-to-coal price ratio. The completion of several new long-distance gas pipe lines to major consuming centers indicates that subsequent data probably will show a continuation of the trend toward natural gas. However, although coal and oil may decline percentagewise, the volume consumed increased in 1950 and this rise is expected to continue for several years.

TABLE 9. Changes in the Fuel Picture, 1947–1949
Percent of Requirement Supplied by Each Fuel

	1947	1948	1949
Coal:			
Railroads*,†	62	55	45
Electric power	77	77	67
Residential and commercial†	54	51	48
Iron and steel†	80	79	75
Cement production	69	69	65
Oil:			
Railroads*†:			
Residual	19	17	14
Diesel oil	19	28	41
Electric power	10	8	14
Residential and commercial†	28	30	30
Iron and steel†	11	11	10
Cement production	10	9	9
Natural gas:			
Electric power	13	15	19
Residential and commercial†	18	19	22
Iron and steel†	9	10	15
Cement production	21	22	26

* Fuel for locomotive use.
† Includes purchased electricity distributed by source of fuel.

While changes for particular fuels and particular industries during the last few years have been considerable, these changes have probably had relatively little effect on the various major categories of the tables—*For Mining*, *For Transportation*, *For Conversion*, and *For End Uses of Fuels*.

No large changes have occurred in the mining of fuels. Any decrease in fuels used for transportation of fuels due to increasing efficiency brought about by dieselization of most railroads has probably been counteracted by increased consumption of natural gas for pumping of new pipe lines.

In the section on conversion, a steady growth in production of electric power, increase in petroleum refining, and a current expansion of coking capacity have undoubtedly counteracted the effect of a decrease in the conversion loss encountered in the production of manufactured gas.

Increases in fuel consumption of highway and air transportation and residential and commercial applications have occurred each year. The *Primary Metals Industries* and *Other Manufacturing*—both of which showed a lower level in 1949—are expected to show large gains in 1951 and continued growth is expected to take place in the fuel requirements of the armed forces.

Sources of Error

Any table that brings together widely divergent figures of different orders of magnitude and reliability is subject to error. Probably the most important errors in these tables are those introduced by the estimates it has been necessary to make for such items as the transportation of fuels, nonutility generation of electricity, the production of mixed gas, wood used as fuel, and nonfuel uses for natural gas and coke. In transportation of fuels, for instance, the figure for natural gas used in transportation is undoubtedly high because gas used in transmission and that lost in leakage are not separated in the available statistics. The figures for the other fuels used in the transportation of fuels are based on statistics as to the percentage of railroad freight and switching formed by fuel, the number of trucks hauling fuel, etc., the use of which required a number of assumptions.

One small error is related to the inclusion of the fuels required for the processing of the net exports of refined fuels taking place in 1947. Another is the net importation of 2120 million kwhr of electricity which was included in the electricity distributed although no fuel for its production is shown. Both of these errors, however, are by the size of the quantities concerned limited to factors of less than 1 percent and can be considered negligible.

Further errors are introduced by the lag that necessarily occurs between purchase of primary fuels by converters, their conversion into secondary fuels, and their consumption as such. To some degree the extent of these can be estimated by a study of the change in consumer stocks in the United States. Total consumer stocks of all petroleum oils at the end of 1947 differed by less than 1.0 percent from those reported at the end of 1946. The total stocks of bituminous coal in the hands of consumers also differed by less than 1.0 percent at the beginning and end of the period. It would appear, therefore, that the errors from this source are relatively small.

Though the conversion factors used are for the most part the latest official figures released by the Bureau of Mines, in common with all factors of this sort, they cannot adequately represent the actual fuels being produced and used in thousands of areas throughout the country. This is particularly true in the case of natural gas, since some is used "wet" and some has practically all of the higher hydrocarbons removed.

Another source of error lies in the fact that no attempt has been made to distribute conversion losses on the basis of individual efficiencies of conversion of the fuels involved. The procedure followed has been to obtain the energy difference between a secondary fuel and the fuels used in its production and distribute the loss on the basis of the fuels used. Allowances have been made for fuels completely consumed in the process (such as coal in petroleum production) and fuels unchanged in form (such as natural gas in the production of mixed gas). For example, in the production of manufactured gas

Total input = 0.2522 trillion hphr per annum
Total output = 0.1120 trillion hphr per annum
Lost in conversion = 0.1402 trillion hphr per annum

None of the loss can be attributed to gaseous fuels contributing 0.046 and, therefore, this should be subtracted from input and output.

0.2522 trillion hphr per annum
0.0462 trillion hphr per annum
0.2060 input of fuels for which change of form is necessary

0.1120 trillion hphr per annum
0.0462 trillion hphr per annum
0.0658 output of fuels for which change of form of raw material is necessary

The difference, however, remains the same:

$$0.2060 - 0.0658 = 0.1402 \text{ trillion hphr per annum}$$

We have, therefore, a loss of 0.1402×10^9 hphr distributed among 0.206×10^9 hphr, or loss equals 68.06 percent of those fuels in which a loss is incurred.

One possible source of disagreement in the disposition of fuels to conversion is the inclusion of the equivalent of residual fuel oil. This, although it is passed through the stills, is not improved, and any loss incurred should not, therefore, from some viewpoints, be attributed to the production of this material. Since it is part of the primary material that must be processed to obtain motor fuel, etc., and has markets for use as fuel, it is difficult to classify it in any other category. This is particularly true in view of the fact that for any short increment of time it becomes as essential as many of the highly refined secondary fuels.

Undoubtedly in many instances some of the fuel sold for a certain use is used in some other application. The operation of the Consolidated Edison Company in New York City, which sells steam from its electric power plants to many hundreds of apartments, office buildings, and stores, is representative of an instance in which fuel charged to *Generation of Electricity* was in reality used for *Residential and Commercial* purposes. This type of error is common to many manufacturing industries, railroads, etc., in which process fuel is used for heating, lighting, and miscellaneous applications.

In view of the sources of possible error, the totals of the lines and columns of the tables are not to be regarded as accurate to the numbers of figures shown. All available data indicating amounts greater than 1 billion hphr per annum have been included to show the energy picture in the greatest detail commensurate with the space available.

APPENDIX 1

A Few Numbers

If you have made your way through even a part of this book, you will have observed that numbers abound. You may want to refer back to certain quantitative statements that you can locate only with difficulty. Accordingly a few of the more interesting or useful numbers have been assembled here for your convenient reference. Page numbers are given to provide ready access to the context. Numbers from tables and charts are not included.

Petroleum

As of Jan. 1, 1950, the proved reserve of liquid hydrocarbons of the United States was about 29 billion barrels; of the world about 80 billion barrels (p. 29). The United States has so far produced about 40 billion barrels (p. 44) and may eventually produce from 20 to 60 billion barrels more than the 1950 proved reserve; the world perhaps 530 billion (p. 32). A part of this will come from secondary recovery methods which over the next few decades may give the United States around 10 billion barrels (p. 44).

The additional petroleum gained at Bradford by waterflooding was sufficient for only 30 days of United States consumption, and that gained at Spindletop by deep drilling was sufficient for only 12 days (p. 35).

The United States production in 1950 was almost as much as the entire proved reserve in 1900 (p. 30), but United States production in 1970 is expected to be not more than 1 billion barrels per year—only one-half our 1950 requirement (p. 40). In 9 states the peak of production has been passed (p. 42). About 110 fields as large as 100 million barrels have been found in the United States but only 4 of these since 1936 (p. 44). The production of 2.5 billion barrels from the East Texas field has been spread over 20 years (p. 40).

In 1950 a total of 5290 new-field wildcat wells were drilled in the United States but only 592 of these wells were successful. Even the new-field wildcat wells whose locations were determined by the best of modern technology averaged 5 failures for each success (p. 32).

The present annual production of petroleum in the United States depletes about 150 square miles of petroleum-producing territory. The maximum recovery of oil with water drive is usually 75 percent although occasionally we reach 85 percent. For gas drive 25 to 30 percent is normal (p. 43). The highest practicable average rate of production is about 12 percent of the proved reserve per annum. In recent years annual production has not exceeded 9 percent (p. 32).

Brazil's estimated total oil reserves would last only 3 days in the United States (p. 71).

The recoverable sulfur now being wasted by the petroleum industry amounts to about one-fifth of the United States sulfur consumption (p. 72).

The "topping" of crude petroleum has a thermal efficiency of about 98 percent. Complete refineries, prior to 1930, ran about 92 percent. The present average thermal efficiency is about 87 percent. Catalytic cracking has a thermal efficiency of about 82 percent (p. 100).

In 1946 the transportation of petroleum in pipe lines was about 430 billion barrel-miles. Motor trucks transport about 25 million barrel-miles per annum consuming about 5 million barrels of gasoline in the process (p. 124).

About 3.5 billion pounds of petroleum are being diverted to synthetic chemicals each year (p. 223).

Gas

The proved reserve of natural gas in 1950 was about 180 trillion cubic feet, about 50 times the rate of use in 1950 (p. 45). The total amount of gas produced since 1900 is probably of the order of magnitude of 115 trillion cubic feet, of which 8 trillion have been used for repressuring and will be available for reuse (p. 47). Ultimate gas reserves may be between 200 and 400 trillion cubic feet (p. 46).

Use of gas has increased enormously. About 120 miles of coal-gas pipe line had been laid in London by 1812, and by 1817 some 300 000 cubic feet of coal gas were being produced daily—sufficient to operate 76 000 Argand burners at 6 candle power each (p. 23). For natural gas in 1950 we had about 152 000 miles of pipe line in the United States of which 108 000 were trunk lines carrying almost 5 trillion cubic feet per annum (p. 95). It is predicted that by 1960 the volume of natural gas transmitted through pipe lines will have doubled. We will then require about 50 000 miles of additional pipe line and nearly 10 million additional horsepower for pumping the gas (p. 45). For 1947 the energy equivalent of about 130 million cubic feet of gas were required to transport each trillion cubic foot-miles (p. 125).

About 40 percent of natural-gas production is marketed by public utilities, repressuring accounts for about 15 percent, and about 20 percent is used to generate power for production of both oil and gas (p. 47). In 1945 the amount of natural gas used for carbon black was almost one-half the total amount of gas used as a domestic and commercial fuel. But carbon black is beginning to be made from oil with about one-sixteenth the waste of fuel (p. 152).

Natural gas at 6 cents per thousand cubic feet corresponds to residual fuel oil at 35.6 cents per barrel, and to coal at $1.52 per ton (p. 95).

Of the gas consumed in the United States 80 percent is natural and 20 percent manufactured. But only 40 percent of the heating value of manufactured gas comes from coal, the balance coming from various forms of petroleum (p. 117).

Coal

Of the total world reserves (7.2 trillion tons plus or minus several trillion) 53 percent is bituminous, 40 percent is subbituminous and lignite, and 7 percent is anthracite. More than half the bituminous coal of the earth is in the United States. America has about 93 percent of the subbituminous and lignite. But more than 80 percent of the anthracite is in Asia (p. 50). The United States reserves of *recoverable* coal may be between 0.2 and 1.6 trillion tons (p. 55). In 1924 coal reserves of Great Britain were given as 150 billion tons. This has recently been pared down to 48 billion tons for the portion likely to be produced (p. 51).

Production of anthracite in the United States in 1814 was only 22 tons, and only 300 tons of bituminous coal were mined in 1820 (p. 23). 1920 was the year of coal's maximum percentage contribution to our energy supply (64 percent). It has now dropped to around 44 percent. Anthracite reached a peak of 17 percent of the total energy demand in the 1890–1900 decade. It now provides less than 5 percent (p. 287).

Fuel production (essentially all coal) in the Soviet Union has been doubling approximately once in 5 years (p. 49). Within the next century British production can be made about 24 billion tons, and of this only 6 percent would be suitable for metallurgical coke. Over the next century the United States will need 10 billion tons for coke (p. 52). The production of coal in Brazil is only 0.3 percent of that of the United States (p. 71). One year's production of coal in the United States "exhausts" about 120 square miles of coal field (p. 57).

The probable life of the coal fields of the Eastern Province (the source of our bituminous) is estimated at between 90 and 150 years (p. 58). About 20 percent of this coal is used to make coke for steelmaking (p. 62). Eighty-five percent of the coal used in steelmaking is for coke (p. 63). About 1.4 tons of coal are required for the manufacture of each ton of steel, but nearly 15 tons are required for aluminum (p. 96).

Transportation of coal in 1948 was about 200 billion ton-miles, and about a half million tons of coal (as gasoline equivalent) was required for the retail delivery of around 100 million tons of coal to points of use (p. 122).

Other Fossil Fuels

About 1.25 trillion tons of oil shale have been reported for the earth, but the combustible portion is less than 10 percent. Thus the potential energy from oil shale is less than one-fiftieth of the potential energy from coal (p. 65). Nearly 55 percent of the known reserve of oil shale is in the United States and nearly 43 percent in Brazil (p. 66).

In 1950 the world's production of shale oil was about 2 million barrels—0.05 percent of petroleum production (p. 74). The yield of oil from oil shale varies from 10 to 60 gallons per ton (p. 67). Each barrel of oil means over a ton of ash (p. 70). Most oil shale contains less than 0.03 percent uranium (p. 68).

The world may have around 800 billion barrels of tar in deposits of various sorts, but almost none of this can be recovered (p. 76). Canadian deposits are estimated at 500 billion barrels while the United States has perhaps 5 billion barrels (p. 75).

The peat reserves of the world are believed to amount to about 136 billion tons which corresponds to 68 billion tons of coal—about 1 percent of the supposed coal reserves of the earth (p. 80). Nearly 60 percent of known peat reserves are in Russia (p. 79).

The production of peat in Russia is around 30 million tons per annum; in Denmark, 47 million tons; in Ireland, 6 million tons (p. 80). The rate of accumulation of peat beds is from 0.5 to 4 inches per year. Peat beds may grow at the rate of about 7000 tons per square mile per annum. This is more than 3 times as fast as wood can be taken from the average forest in balanced production (p. 77). Peat accumulation might be made to yield the equivalent of around half a billion tons of coal annually (p. 80).

Electricity

In 1949 the United States produced about 43 percent of all the electric-power generation in the world. Russia was a poor second with only about a fifth as much (p. 88). About 70 percent of our electric power was from fuel combustion and 30 percent was hydroelectric. Of the new generating capacity under construction in 1950, 84 percent was in steam units, 15 percent in hydroelectric units, and 1 percent in internal-combustion units (p. 103). By 1980 our generating capacity may be 5 times what it was in 1950. In 40 years installed industrial power for each worker has risen from 2.9 horsepower (31 percent electrical) to 7.2 (93 percent electrical) (p. 88).

Of the total energy requirement of the United States about 9 percent represents loss from generation of electric power. If there were no losses 1 kwhr would require the combustion of 0.26 pound of coal. The average coal consumption of the United States for electric-power generation in 1949 was 1.22 pound per kwhr—an efficiency of 21 percent (p. 102).

Under average conditions the transmission efficiency of electric power is about 80 percent (p. 127). The energy-system efficiency for electric power has risen from 3.4 percent in 1900 to 16.7 percent in 1950, and is likely to reach 20 percent (p. 138).

Use of Energy

Locomotive purchases in 1950 included 3653 diesel-electric, 15 steam, 6 electric, and 10 gas turbine (p. 93). It is from 5 to 10 times as profitable to spend money for the substitution of diesel-electric for steam locomotives than to retire a like amount of bonded indebtedness, for compared with fuel for generating steam, diesel oil can do 10 times as much useful work in switching service, 5 times as much in freight service, and more than 3 times as much in passenger service (p. 92). About 40 million tons of coal per annum are being saved by the use of the diesel-electric locomotive (p. 146).

In 1950 about three-quarters of the world's cars and half of all trucks were operated within the United States. The 6 million cars, trucks, and buses made in the United States in 1950 was more than 3 times the output of all other countries combined. Automotive businesses accounted for about a fifth of all United States retail trade, which used a billion barrels of motor fuel (p. 94).

The fermentation to alcohol of all food crops in the United States would give less than half enough fuel to operate our cars (p. 235). To make enough motor fuel by industrial photosynthesis would require, for the United States, an area of about 35 000 square miles of land (p. 242). The thermal efficiency of conversion of vegetation to gasoline is 40 percent compared with 25 percent for alcohol (p. 237).

During the 4 years after World War II we consumed 28 percent more gasoline than during the 4 years of the war (p. 166).

The aggregate horsepower of registered motor vehicles in the United States is about 4 billion, but the energy actually generated by these vehicles is less than 0.2 percent of this (p. 136). One reason for this is that the energy-system efficiency of the motor car with petroleum motor fuel is only 5 percent. With synthetic motor fuel the efficiency would drop to about 2.5 percent (p. 135). Automotive engines are made to last (under favorable conditions) from 200 to 400 hours under full load at 4000 rpm (p. 130).

In 1950 the ratio of gas ranges to electric ranges sold was about 3:2 while in 1935 the ratio was 16:1. The ratio of gas to electric ranges in service has declined from 20:1 in 1935 to 4:1 in 1950 (p. 86).

Electrical space heating aided by a heat pump with COP of 3.33 is thermally equivalent to heating with coal (p. 216). From 1942 to 1950 the number of heat-pump installations rose from 44 to 750 (p. 217).

About 30 percent of the 279 billion kwhr produced in the United States in 1950 was consumed by lamps (p. 140). But the coal-to-light efficiency is low and is not expected to become higher than 5 percent (p. 144).

Synthetic Fuel

The national average efficiency in the manufacture of fuel gas in the United States appears to be about 54 percent (p. 117), and the efficiency of conversion of coal to liquid or gaseous fuel is between 40 and 45 percent (p. 113). The loss from the manufacture of one-half of our present production of petroleum by conversion of coal would be nearly 40 percent of the total United States energy requirement for 1950 (p. 113).

The Fischer-Tropsch process involves the production of water gas. All the water gas now manufactured in the United States for fuel, methanol, and synthetic ammonia would not make more than 16 000 barrels a day of motor fuel (p. 109).

Coke-oven capacity in the United States has less than doubled between 1935 and 1950 whereas the demand for benzene has been multiplied in the same period by almost 5 (p. 107).

Solar Energy

To provide the earth with the average amount of energy showered upon us by the sun it would be necessary to burn up our entire stock of combustibles in 3 days (p. 187). But present schemes of utilization of solar energy are inefficient. About 50 horsepower per acre might be obtained as an average from sunlight in Arizona (p. 199) so that to produce by optical means all the heat and power now consumed by the United States would require an area of about 50 000 square miles (p. 200). Special thermocouples have obtained a 7-percent useful conversion of heat to electricity (p. 202). In a test of the M.I.T. solar-heated house, one-third of the total heating load was contributed by the south windows and about one-half by the roof collector (p. 211).

Vegetation

By wasteful "slash-and-burn" method of agriculture, used in certain places in earlier times, it probably required about 200 acres of forest land to maintain one person (p. 10). The United States now has, including Alaska, only about 3 acres of forest per person (p. 230). About 27 percent of the land area of the earth is forested (p. 227). About one cord of wood per acre per annum can be removed from the average forest in balanced production. Thus the energy requirement of the world could be satisfied with about 8 million square miles of forest if the wood were used for fuel alone (p. 228).

Improvements in agricultural methods are not being applied rapidly enough to take proper care of the growing population—4000 a day increase in the United States (p. 220) and 60 000 a day for the world (p. 243). However, nearly 8 percent of the good farm land of the earth is under irrigation (p. 227) and this can be extended. Between 1920 and 1950, land required in the United States to provide feed for horses and mules fell off 65 million acres—nearly 20 percent of our useful cropland (p. 220). Synthetic fibers from fuels have reduced land requirements for fibers about 2 percent (p. 222). If the 1.5 billion pounds per annum of ethylene now being obtained from petroleum had to come from the fermentation of vegetation we would have to use over 2 million acres of our best land for the purpose. The billion pounds of detergent now made largely from petroleum are liberating over 2 million acres of cropland (p. 223). The 1950 production of synthetic methanol and acetic acid would have required the balanced production of wood from 6 million acres of forest (p. 232).

Each acre of land has about 15 tons of carbon dioxide in the atmosphere above it (p. 197). Thus the total carbon of the atmosphere is about 1000 times the carbon in the annual coal production of the United States (p. 196). The carbon dioxide is essential for photosynthesis, but the actual utilization of sunlight in photosynthesis ranges from 0.1 to 0.5 percent of the radiation falling upon the land (p. 197). This low efficiency has been improved manyfold by development of industrial types of photosynthesis in which yields of chlorella have been as high as 15 dry tons per acre per annum, and may eventually reach 100 tons (p. 241).

Nearly 90 percent of the earth's vegetation is in the 300 million cubic miles of ocean (p. 239).

On a calorie basis we must use 50 times as much land for beef as for sugar beets (p. 225).

Wood

Ancient peoples used wood extravagantly. They probably required at least 150 cubic feet of wood (as fuel) to make 1 cubic foot of burnt brick (p. 9). A ton of lime required about 10 tons of wood fuel (p. 12).

As late as 1800 over 94 percent of the energy in the United States was provided by wood, and taking this into account the per capita consumption of total energy in the early nineteenth century was as high as 40 percent of what it is now (p. 287).

In 1900 the energy utilized from waterfalls was probably not more than 1 percent of the energy from the burning of wood. Today the two sources are about equal (p. 26) and the energy value of the wood fuel and the anthracite coal used in the United States are about equal (p. 287).

Wood is still an important fuel. In Brazil today wood provides about 85 percent of all energy used (p. 26) and the per capita consumption of fuel in Brazil is more than one-third that of the United States (p. 72). More than 80 percent of the fuel in the agricultural areas of Canada is wood (p. 26).

The 1940 census showed that in 19 states wood was used more than any other fuel for heating homes, and as late as 1944 more homes in the United States were heated with wood than with oil and gas together. Almost one-fourth of our homes were equipped with cooking devices in which wood was being used (p. 286).

Wood satisfies at least 7 percent of the world's energy requirements, and an additional amount comes from agricultural wastes that amount to about 3.5

times the wood used as fuel (p. 232). An estimated 60 percent of total fuel consumption of Seattle and Portland is wood, mostly in the form of briquettes which at $7.50 per ton have about the same heat value per dollar as bituminous coal at $11.25 per ton (p. 232).

Other Constant Sources

Water power is only 17 percent developed in the United States (p. 250). The 11 Western states with only 14 percent of our population have about 60 percent of the potential available water power of the United States (p. 247). The average head of all United States hydroplants is 89 feet (p. 245).

The theoretical maximum wind power is about 15 percent of the world's total energy requirements (p. 263). Electric fans in the United States consume more than 3 times as much power as the 450 million hphr per annum now obtained from windmills (p. 257).

Theoretically tidal energy could supply about half of the world's needs, but we are unlikely to obtain more than 0.3 percent of the potential (p. 266).

The volcanic escape of heat from the earth is only about 10 percent of our energy requirement. The total heat being generated in the crust of the earth is about 6 times our energy requirement, but only a trace is recoverable (p. 247).

About 300 million lightning strokes per year occur around the earth. About a tenth are strokes to earth. But if the energy of all the lightning could be brought together in one place and controlled, it would amount to only about 1 percent of the electric power consumed by Pittsburgh (p. 275).

General

A hundred years ago about 16 times as much work was done by man and beast as by fossil fuels, whereas today it happens that the relationship is almost exactly reversed (p. 27).

All the fossil fuel produced in the world up to 1900 would satisfy the present world economy only about 5 years (p. 27).

The peak of fossil-fuel production in the United States may come between the years 2025 and 2110 (p. 163). The rate of increase of the use of energy in the United States is assumed to be 50 percent in 50 years (p. 157).

In 1947, 53 percent of our fossil fuel went into one sort of conversion or another (p. 99).

APPENDIX 2:

Conversion Factors for Fuel and Power

HEAT VALUE OF REPRESENTATIVE SOLID FUELS

State	County	Mine	Btu per Pound	Hphr per Ton
COAL				
General Average: *Bituminous*			13 100*	10 297
Alabama	Jefferson	Bessemer	14 620	11 491
Alaska	Moose Creek		12 150	9 550
Arkansas	Hartford		13 270	10 430
Colorado	Gunnison	Somerset	12 630	9 927
Illinois	Christian	Pana	10 860	8 536
Indiana	Green	Jasonville	11 540	9 070
Iowa	Lucas	Chariton	10 240	8 049
Kansas	Crawford	Edison	12 500	9 825
Kentucky	Webster		12 500	9 825
New Mexico	San Juan	Farmington	11 630	9 141
Ohio	Jefferson	Yellow Creek	12 720	9 998
Oklahoma	Pittsburgh	Ridgway	13 280	10 438
Pennsylvania	Armstrong	W. Kittaning	13 040	10 249
Virginia	Wise	Josephine	13 270	10 430
Washington	Kittitas	Ellenburg	11 010	8 654
West Virginia	Brook	Collier	12 940	10 171
Wyoming	Lincoln	Green River	13 310	10 462
COAL				
General Average: *Anthracite*			12 700*	9 982
Pennsylvania	Schuylkill		13 351	10 494
Rhode Island	Providence	Cranston	11 620	9 133
Semianthracite:				
Virginia	Pulaski	Guntan Park	10 960	8 614
COAL				
General Average: *Semi-bituminous*			12 900*	10 139
Arkansas	Huntington	No. 6 Central	13 700	10 768
Maryland	Allegany	Frostburg	13 430	10 556
Pennsylvania	Cambria	Bakerton	14 460	11 366
Virginia	Montgomery	Blacksburg	12 740	10 014
West Virginia	Grant	Bismark	13 590	10 682
COAL				
General Average: *Subbituminous*			9 500*	7 467
Colorado	Weld	Erie	9 520	7 483
Montana	Carbon	Washoe	10 550	8 292
Oregon	Coos	Beaverhill	9 030	7 098
Washington	Thurston	Tono	8 700	6 838
Wyoming	Lincoln	Ebkol	10 080	7 923
CANNEL COAL				
General Average: *Cannel*			11 000	8 646
Kentucky	Johnson		13 748	10 806
Pennsylvania	Armstrong	Montgomery	10 460	8 222
Texas	Webb	Dolores	11 070	8 701

* U.S. Bureau of Mines Official Conversion Factors adopted Jan. 3, 1950.

HEAT VALUE OF REPRESENTATIVE SOLID FUELS.—(Continued)

	Btu per Pound	Hphr per Ton
LIGNITE		
General Average: *Lignite*	7 000*	5 502
Colorado, El Paso	6 055	4 759
North Dakota, Ward	6 010	4 724
Texas, Wood	7 348	5 776
PEAT		
General Average: *Peat (Air-dried)*	7 030	5 525
Connecticut, Kent	7 684	6 040
Connecticut, Westport	7 691	6 045
Maine, Kittery	7 319	5 753
Michigan, Hamburg	9 909	7 144
New Hampshire, Fremont	9 290	7 302
New Hampshire, Greenland	7 186	5 648
New York, Black Lake	7 522	5 912
New York, Cicero	7 576	5 955
Wisconsin, Madison	6 943	5 457
Peat (As Cut)		
Wisconsin, Fond du Lac	1 879	1 477
COKE		
General Average: *Coal Coke*	12 400	9 747
By-product coke	12 690	9 974
Beehive coke	12 527	9 846
Coke breeze	10 050	7 899
Gas-works coke	12 820	10 077
Low-temperature coke	14 030	11 028
Pitch coke	14 097	11 080
Vertical retorts	12 550	9 864
SOLID PRODUCTS OF PETROLEUM REFINING		
Asphalt	17 158	13 486
Briquettes and Packaged Fuel	12 271	9 645
Petroleum coke	15 060*	11 184
Wax (paraffin)	18 612	14 629
MISCELLANEOUS SOLIDS		
Guncotton	1 901	1 494
Dynamite (75 percent)	2 322	1 825

* U.S. Bureau of Mines Official Conversion Factors adopted Jan. 3, 1950.

HEAT VALUE OF REPRESENTATIVE SOLID FUELS.—(Continued)

	Btu per Pound	Hphr per Ton
MISCELLANEOUS SOLIDS—(Continued)		
Sulfur Monoclinic (to SO_2)	4 034	3 171
Rhombic (to SO_2)	3 998	3 142
		Hphr per Cord
WOOD		
General Average: Cordwood†	7 747	7 627
Cordwood		
Ash	7 669	7 550
Beech	7 679	7 560
Birch, yellow	7 667	7 548
Chestnut	7 867	7 745
Cottonwood	7 698	7 579
Elm, white	7 683	7 564
Hickory	7 691	7 572
Maple, sugar	7 677	7 558
Maple, red	7 690	7 571
Oak, red	7 691	7 572
Oak, white	7 683	7 564
Pine, yellow	8 025	7 901
Pine, white	8 044	7 919
Walnut, black	7 690	7 571
		Hphr per Ton
Nonresinous, Seasoned	6 300	4 950
Charcoal, Willow	13 530	10 655
Wood Waste		
Briquettes (sawdust), Douglas fir	8 130	6 390
California redwood	4 570	3 592
Douglas fir	5 800	4 559
Western hemlock	3 630	2 853
		Hphr per Ton
MISCELLANEOUS SOLID FUELS (from vegetation)		
Bagasse (residue of sugar refining)	8 000–9 000	6 288–7 074
Straw (depending on moisture content)	5 000–6 000	3 930–5 109
Tanbark (residue of tanning operations)	2 500–3 000	1 965–2 358

† Containing 12 percent moisture.

HEAT VALUE OF REPRESENTATIVE LIQUID FUELS

	Btu per lb	Btu per gal	Hphr per bbl
PETROLEUM PRODUCTS			
Liquefied petroleum gas (1948 sales)		95 500*	1 576
Natural gasoline			1 576
Aviation gasoline	20 440	120 200*	1 984
Motor gasoline	20 282	124 240*	2 051
Kerosene	19 900	135 000*	2 189
Distillates: *Weighted average*	19 200	138 700*	2 289
No. 1		136 000*	2 245
No. 2		138 500*	2 286
No. 4		145 000*	2 393
Residual fuel oil: *Average*		149 700*	2 471
No. 5		148 500*	2 451
No. 6		152 000*	2 509
Residuum		152 000	2 509
Acid sludge		107 000*	1 766
Crude petroleum: *Weighted average*		138 100*	2 279
Mexico		152 000	2 509
Oklahoma		141 000	2 327
Pennsylvania		132 200	2 182
Texas		142 000	2 344
Wyoming		141 500	2 336

	Btu per lb of Vapor	Hphr per bbl
PURE PARAFFIN HYDROCARBONS		
Gross Heat of Combustion		
Methane	23 920	
Ethane	22 350	1 137
Propane	21 690	1 507
Isobutane	21 290	1 639
n-Butane	21 340	1 700
Isopentane	21 060	1 794
n-Pentane	21 120	1 816
n-Hexane	20 970	1 896
n-Heptane	20 860	1 956
n-Octane	20 780	2 002
n-Nonane	20 710	2 038
n-Decane	20 660	2 068

* U.S. Bureau of Mines Official Conversion Factors adopted Jan. 3, 1950.

HEATS OF SOME LIQUIDS OCCASIONALLY USED FOR THEIR FUEL VALUE

	Btu per lb		Hphr per gal	
	Gross	Net	Gross	Net
ALCOHOLS				
Methanol	10 250	9 070	3.194	2.826
Ethanol	13 150	11 920	4.079	3.697
Isopropanol	14 243		4.396	
COAL TAR	16 000	15 000	6.050	5.660
Aromatic Chemicals				
Benzene	18 172	17 450	6.280	6.031
Naphthalene	17 328	16 734	7.797	7.530
Phenol	14 030		8.505	
Toluene	18 420	17 600	10.842	10.360
Xylene	18 610	17 720	10.971	10.446

	Btu per lb	Hphr per gal
FATTY OILS		
Butter	16 560	5.935
Cottonseed oil	17 100	6.163
Lard oil	16 740	6.012
Olive oil	16 920	6.097
Rape oil	17 100	6.149
Sperm oil	18 000	6.225

HEAT VALUES OF SOME GASES OCCASIONALLY USED FOR THEIR FUEL VALUE

	Btu per lb		Hphr per Mcf*	
	Gross	Net	Gross	Net
Acetylene	21 430	20 850	0.583	0.563
Ammonia	9 670	8 001	0.173	0.143
Butylene	20 830	19 480	1.213	1.136
Carbon monoxide	4 340	4 340	1.268	1.268
Ethylene	21 630	20 280	0.645	0.606
Hydrogen	60 960	51 570	1.275	1.079
Hydrogen sulfide	7 100	6 545	0.254	0.234
Propylene	21 030	19 680	0.925	0.866

* Gas at 60 degrees F and a pressure of 30 inches of mercury.

HEAT VALUE OF REPRESENTATIVE GASEOUS FUELS

	Btu per Mcf*		Hphr per Mcf*	
	Gross	Net	Gross	Net
NATURAL GAS				
General Average: *Natural Gas Wet*	1 075†		0.422	
General Average: *Natural Gas Dry*	1 050†		0.413	
West Virginia, Follansbee	2 220	1 970	0.872	0.774
Pennsylvania, McKean	1 482	1 350	0.582	0.426
Oklahoma, Washington	1 125	1 064	0.442	0.418
California, Los Angeles	1 123	1 053	0.441	0.414
Ohio, Sandusky	1 047	946	0.411	0.372
Texas, Nowata	1 044	988	0.410	0.388
Texas, Tarrant	738	698	0.290	0.274
MANUFACTURED GAS				
General Average: *Manufactured Gas*	540		0.212	
Blast-furnace gas	93	92	0.037	0.036
Blue water gas	310	285	0.122	0.112
Carbureted water gas	578	529	0.227	0.208
Coal gas	634	560	0.249	0.220
Coke-oven gas	536	476	0.2113	0.187
Oil gas (Pacific Coast)	516	461	0.20	0.181
Producer gas				
Buckwheat anthracite	143	133	0.056	0.052
Bituminous	163	153	0.064	0.060
Refinery gas	1 500		0.590	

* Gas at 60 degrees F and a pressure of 30 inches of mercury.
† U.S. Bureau of Mines Official Conversion Factors adopted Jan. 3, 1950.

HEAT, ENERGY, OR WORK EQUIVALENTS*

Ft-lb Foot-pound	Kwhr Kilowatt-hour	Hphr Horsepower-hour	Btu† British thermal unit	cal‡ calorie
1.00	3.766×10^{-7}	5.0505×10^{-7}	1.285×10^{-3}	3.241×10^{-1}
2.655×10^{6}	1.00	1.341	3 412.76	860 565
1.98×10^{6}	7.455×10^{-1}	1.00	2 545	641 615
778.16	2.93×10^{-4}	3.930×10^{-4}	1.00	252
3.086	1.16×10^{-6}	1.558×10^{-6}	3.97×10^{-3}	1.00

* Dr. Lewis V. Judson, National Bureau of Standards.
† 1 therm = 100 000 Btu.
‡ 1 Calorie = 1000 calories.

SOME WEIGHT-VOLUME RELATIONSHIPS OF WATER, TYPICAL PETROLEUM PRODUCTS, AND ALCOHOL

All Measurements at 60 Degrees F

	Specific Gravity	Degrees Baume	Degrees API	Lb per cu ft	Lb per gal	Lb per bbl	Bbl per short ton
H_2O	1.000	10.00	10.00	62.30	8.3283	349.78	5.72
Gasoline	0.700	70.00	70.64	43.59	5.8268	244.73	8.17
Diesel oil	0.835	37.66	37.96	52.01	6.9525	292.01	6.85
Residual fuel oil	0.965	15.08	15.13	60.12	8.0364	337.53	5.93
Alcohol (fuel)	0.820	30.63		49.40	6.8360	287.11	6.98

SOME WEIGHT-VOLUME-HEAT VALUE RELATIONSHIPS OF FUEL WOOD

Cordwood (12 percent moisture)	Cu Ft	Lb	Btu	Hphr
1 Cord	128	2 500	19.41×10^6	7 627
1 Ton	102.4	2 000	15.53×10^6	6 102

TEMPERATURE SCALE CONVERSION FACTORS

Fahrenheit (°F)	= (°C × $\frac{9}{5}$) + 32
Centigrade (°C)	= (°F − 32)$\frac{5}{9}$
Absolute or Kelvin (°K)	= 273.16 + °C
Rankine	= 459.72 + °F

POWER CONVERSIONS

1 horsepower = 746 watts = 33 000 foot-pounds per minute

1 watt = 1 joule per second = 10×10^6 ergs per second

TIME UNIT CONVERSIONS

1 year = 12 months = 365 days = 8 760 hours = 525 600 minutes = 31 536 000 seconds

VOLUME CONVERSIONS

Unit	Equivalent Value				
	U.S. Gallons	Imperial Gallons	Liters	U.S. Barrels	Cubic Meters
One U.S. gallon	1.0	0.833	3.7853	0.0238	0.0038
One Imperial gallon	1.201	1.0	4.546	0.0286	0.0045
One liter	0.264	0.220	1.0	0.0063	0.0010
One U.S. barrel	42.0	34.99	158.98	1.0	0.159
One cubic meter	264.1	220.0	1 000.0	6.29	1.0

WEIGHT CONVERSIONS

Unit	Equivalent Value			
	Pounds	Short Tons	Metric Tons	Long Tons
One pound	1.0	0.0005	0.00045	0.00044
One short ton	2 000.0	1.0	0.907	0.893
One metric ton	2 204.6	1.102	1.0	0.984
One long ton	2 240.0	1.120	1.016	1.0

APPENDIX 3:

Bibliography

The important role energy plays in our everyday living is exemplified by the enormous literature on all phases of the subject. An all-inclusive bibliography on energy would, in itself, be voluminous. It is evident, therefore, that this bibliography is not intended as a complete compilation of references concerning energy. Instead, an attempt has been made to present a representative cross section of recent literature relative to the various aspects of the energy problem discussed in this book. It is hoped that this bibliography will be useful to the reader who wishes to pursue further any particular aspect of the energy picture.

Table of Contents to Bibliography

I. ENERGY, GENERAL

A. General Sources and Utilization

1. Ayres, E.: "Major Sources of Energy," *Proceedings of the American Petroleum Institute*, Vol. 28, Part 3, p. 109, Nov. 8–11, 1948.
2. Ayres, E.: "The Fuel Problem," *Scientific American*, Vol. 181, p. 32, December, 1949.
3. Ayres, E.: "Look Ahead at Our Energy Sources and Resources," *Chemical Engineering*, Vol. 57, p. 110, May, 1950.
4. Dewhurst. J. F.: *America's Needs and Resources; A Twentieth Century Fund Survey Which Includes Estimates for 1950 and 1960*, Twentieth Century Fund, New York, 1947.
5. Earle, C. R.: "Where Will Ultrasonics Fit in the Power Field?" *Power Generation*, Vol. 52, p. 86, September, 1948.
6. Egerton, A. C. G.: "Power and Combustion" (The 27th Thomas Hawksley Lecture), *Journal and Proceedings of the Institution of Mechanical Engineers* (London), Vol. 144, Proc. 110, January, 1941.
7. Furnas, C. C.: "Future Sources of Power," *Westinghouse Engineer*, Vol. 3, p. 2, February, 1943.
8. Hartley, H.: "Man's Use of Energy," *Bulletin of the Atomic Scientists*, Vol. 6, p. 322, November, 1950.
9. Holaday, W. M., *et al.:* "Fuels, Their Present and Future Utilization," *Petroleum Processing*, Vol. 4, p. 1233, November, 1949.
10. Hubbert, M. K.: "Energy from Fossil Fuels," *Science*, Vol. 109, p. 103, Feb. 4, 1949.
11. Kettering, C. F.: "Age of Mechanical Power from Liquid Fuel," *The Oil Forum*, Vol. 3, p. 479, November, 1949.
12. Lahee, F. H.: "Our Oil and Gas Reserves; Their Meaning and Limitations," *Bulletin of the American Association of Petroleum Geologists*, Vol. 34, p. 1283, June, 1950.
13. Netherlands National Committee: "Energy Resources and Power Developments in the Netherlands," Preprint, Sec. A, Paper No. 23, Fourth World Power Conference, London, 1950.
14. Parker, A.: "World Energy Resources and Their Utilization" (The 36th Thomas Hawksley Lecture), *Journal and Proceedings of the Institution of Mechanical Engineers* (London), Vol. 160, Proc. 441, 1949.
15. Pigott, R. J. S.: "Fuel and Power Sources If and When Oil Fails," *Petroleum Refiner*, Vol. 28, p. 87, February, 1949.
16. United Nations: *Proceedings of the United Nations Scientific Conference on the Conservation and Utilization of Resources*, (Vols. 1–8: Vol. 1, *Plenary Meetings;* Vol. 2, *Mineral Resources;* Vol. 3, *Fuel and Energy Resources;* Vol. 4, *Water Resources;* Vol. 5, *Forest Resources;* Vol. 6, *Land Resources;* Vol. 7, *Wildlife and Fish Resources;* Vol. 8, *Index*), United Nations, Department of Economic Affairs, New York, 1950.
17. Whitman, W. G.: "Liquid Fuel Supplies and National Security," *Petroleum Processing*, Vol. 4, p. 1222, November, 1949.

B. Electric Power

1. Benedict, F. R.: "Future Electric Power Needs of American Industry," *Electrical Engineering*, Vol. 67, p. 477, May, 1948.
2. Mayott, C. W.: "Electric Power Supply and Load in the United States," *Edison Electric Institute Bulletin*, Vol. 16, p. 357, November, 1948.

3. Umansky, L. A., *et al.*: "Electric Power in Industry; Its Past, Present, and Future," *General Electric Review*, Vol. 51, p. 17, August, 1948.
4. Way, W. R.: "Electric Power Transmission and Distribution in Canada," Preprint, Sec. H1, Paper No. 11, Fourth World Power Conference, London, 1950.

C. Gas Turbines

1. Clarke, C. W. E.: "Present and Future of Thermal Prime Movers," *Edison Electric Institute Bulletin*, Vol. 17, p. 240, July, 1949.
2. Fiock, E. F.: *Bibliography of Books and Published Reports on Gas Turbines, Jet Propulsion, and Rocket Power Plants*, National Bureau of Standards Circular 482, U.S. Government Printing Office, Washington, D.C., 1949.
3. Johnson, P.: "Industrial Future of Gas Turbines," *Industry and Power*, Vol. 58, p. 98, February, 1950.
4. Meyer, A.: "Combustion Gas Turbine: Its History, Development, and Prospects," *Journal and Proceedings of the Institution of Mechanical Engineers* (London), Vol. 141, Proc. 197, May, 1939; Discussion, *Ibid.*, Proc. 212, May, 1939; *Ibid.*, Vol. 142, Proc. 393, February, 1940.
5. Yellott, J. I.: "Experimental Coal-Fired Gas Turbine Piles Up Hours," *Power*, Vol. 94, p. 80, May, 1950.

D. Statistics, General

1. Anon.: "Changing Patterns of Fuel Consumption," *Survey of Current Business*, Vol. 28, p. 7, July, 1948.
2. Brown, F.: *Statistical Year Book of the World Power Conference. Data on Resources and Annual Statistics for 1933–1946*, Vols. 1–4, The Central Office, World Power Conference, London, 1936–1948.
3. Grupp, G. W.: "Diesels in the Railroad Industry," *Diesel Power and Diesel Transportation*, Vol. 28, p. 40, September, 1950.
4. Guyol, N. B.: *Energy Resources of the World*, Department of State Publication 3428, U.S. Government Printing Office, Washington, D.C., June, 1949.
5. Matthews, A. F.: *Minerals Yearbook, 1948*, U.S. Government Printing Office, Washington, D.C., 1950.
6. Read, T. T.: "The World's Output of Work," *American Economic Review*, Vol. 23, p. 55, March, 1933.
7. United Nations: *Statistical Yearbook, 1948*, Prepared by the Statistical Office of the United Nations, New York, 1949.
8. U.S. Bureau of the Census: *Historical Statistics of the United States, 1789–1945* (a Supplement to the Statistical Abstracts of the United States), U.S. Government Printing Office, Washington, D.C., 1949.
9. U.S. Tariff Commission: *Synthetic Organic Chemicals, United States Production and Sales, 1949*, Report No. 169, Second Series, U.S. Government Printing Office, Washington, D.C., 1950.

E. Miscellaneous

1. Anon.: "Hydraulic Accumulators," *Fortune*, Vol. 38, p. 151, November, 1948.
2. Anon: "Direct Conversion of Chemical Energy Reported," *Chemical and Engineering News*, Vol. 27, p. 2490, Aug. 29, 1949.
3. Walker, C. L.: "Too Many People," *Harper's Magazine*, Vol. 196, p. 97, February, 1948.
4. Wilcox, O. W.: "Protein from Petroleum," *World Petroleum*, Vol. 21, p. 68, April, 1950.

II. CONTINUOUS SOURCES OF ENERGY

A. Solar Energy

1. Abbot, C. G.: "Solar Radiation as a Power Source," *Smithsonian Institution Annual Report 1942–1943*, Publication No. 3741, p. 99, 1944.
2. Anon.: "Algeria Uses Solar Energy in Nitric Acid Production," *Chemical and Engineering News*, Vol. 28, p. 259, Jan. 23, 1950.
3. Anon.: *Bibliography on Domestic and Industrial Applications of Solar Heating*, Bibliography No. 7, Engineering Societies Library, New York, 1950.
4. Ayres, E.: "Sunlight for Energy of the Future," *Carnegie Magazine*, Vol. 23, p. 42, July, 1949.
5. Ayres, E.: "Power from the Sun," *Scientific American*, Vol. 183, p. 16, August, 1950.
6. Daniels, F.: "Solar Energy," *Science*, Vol. 109, p. 51, Jan. 21, 1949.
7. Deutsch, A. J.: "Sun; Engine for Converting Matter into Radiation," *Scientific American*, Vol. 179, p. 26, November, 1948.
8. Hawkins, H. M.: *Solar Water Heating in Florida*, Bulletin No. 18, Florida Engineering and Industrial Experiment Station, September, 1947.
9. Hottel, H. C., and Woertz, B. B.: "The Performance of Flat-plate Solar-heat Collectors," *Transactions of the American Society of Mechanical Engineers*, Vol. 64, p. 91, February, 1942.
10. Lof, G. O. G., *et al.*: *Solar Energy Utilization for House Heating*, PB 25375, Office of Technical Services, Washington, D.C., 1946.
11. Parker, A.: "Man's Use of Solar Energy," *Engineer*, Vol. 190, p. 254, Sept. 8, 1950.
12. Telkes, M.: "Review of Solar House Heating," *Heating and Ventilating*, Vol. 46, p. 68, Sept. 1, 1949.
13. Telkes, M.: "Low-cost Solar Heated House," *Heating and Ventilating*, Vol. 47, p. 72, August, 1950.

B. Photosynthesis

1. Burk, D.: "Chemical Energy from Algae," *Chemistry*, Vol. 23, p. 1, January, 1950.
2. Calvin, M.: "Path of Carbon in Photosynthesis," *Journal of Chemical Education*, Vol. 26, p. 639, December, 1949.
3. Franck, J., and Loomis, W. E.: *Photosynthesis in Plants*, Iowa State College Press, Ames, Iowa, 1949.
4. Heidt, L. J., and Smith, M. E.: "Quantum Yields of the Photochemical Reduction of Ceric Ions by Water and Evidence for the Dimerization of Ceric Ions," *Journal of the American Chemical Society*, Vol. 70, p. 2476, July, 1948.
5. Manning, W. M., *et al.*: "Quantum Efficiency of Photosynthesis in Chlorella," *Journal of the American Chemical Society*, Vol. 60, p. 266, February, 1938.
6. Meier, R. L.: "Industrialization of Photosynthesis and Its Social Effects," *Chemical and Engineering News*, Vol. 27, p. 3112, Oct. 24, 1949.
7. Rabinowitch, E. I.: *Photosynthesis*, Vols. 1 and 2, Interscience Publishers, Inc., New York, 1945 and 1949.
8. Ryerson, C. G.: "Claim for High Efficiencies in Photosynthetic Activity," *Chemical and Engineering News*, Vol. 27, p. 3560, Nov. 28, 1949.

C. Agricultural Sources

1. Anon.: *Synthetic Liquid Fuels, Annual Report of the Secretary of the Interior for 1949, Part III, Liquid Fuels from Agricultural Residues*, U.S. Bureau of Mines Report of Investigations 4653, February, 1950.

2. Cain, S. A.: "Plants and Vegetation as Exhaustible Resources," *The Scientific Monthly*, Vol. 68, p. 321, May, 1949.
3. Clausen, H. E.: "The Problem of Efficient Burning and Utilization of Vegetable Wastes and Similar Fuels," Preprint, Sec. E4, Paper No. 6, Fourth World Power Conference, London, 1950.
4. Hilbert, G. E.: *Alcohol from Agricultural Sources as a Potential Motor Fuel*, Agricultural Research Administration, A.I.C. 233 (Rev.), U.S. Department of Agriculture, Washington, D.C., February, 1950.
5. Pleeth, S. J. W.: *Alcohol—A Fuel for Internal Combustion Engines*, Chapman & Hall, Ltd., London, 1949.
6. Wiebe, R., and Nowakowska, J.: *The Technical Literature of Agricultural Motor Fuels*, U.S. Department of Agriculture Bibliographical Bulletin No. 10, U.S. Government Printing Office, Washington, D.C., February, 1949.

D. Wood as Fuel

1. Anon.: *Forest Resources of the World*, United Nations Food and Agriculture Organization, New York, 1948.
2. Scarlott, C. A.: "Tree; More Wood, More Products," *Westinghouse Engineer*. Vol. 8, p. 130, September, 1948.
3. U.S. Forest Service: *Potential Requirements for Timber Products*, U.S. Department of Agriculture, Washington, D.C., 1946.

E. Peat Fuel

1. Bak, A. K.: "The Utilization of Brown Coal and Peat in Denmark," Preprint, Sec. E4, Paper No. 4, Fourth World Power Conference, London, 1950.
2. Linz, B. F.: "Liquid Fuel from Peat," *Oil and Gas Journal*, Vol. 48, p. 47, Apr. 6, 1950.
3. Maguire, M.: "The Winning and Utilization of Peat in Ireland," Preprint, Sec. B2, Paper No. 4, Fourth World Power Conference, London, 1950.
4. Uddgren, O., and Tonisberg, V.: "Production of Milled Peat and Briquettes in Sweden," Preprint, Sec. B2, Paper No. 5, Fourth World Power Conference, London, 1950.
5. Westh, H. C.: "Excavation, Processing, and Storage of Peat Fuel in Denmark," Preprint, Sec. B2, Paper No. 6, Fourth World Power Conference, London, 1950.

F. Tidal Power

1. Anon.: "Report of the International Passamaquoddy Engineering Board," March, 1950.
2. Halcrow, W.: "Tidal Power," *Engineer*, Vol. 179, p. 386, May 18, 1945.
3. Headland, H.: "Tidal Power and the Severn Barrage," *Proceedings of the Institution of Electrical Engineers*, Vol. 96, Part 2, p. 427, June, 1949; Discussion, *Ibid.*, p. 443, June, 1949; Vol. 96, Part 1, p. 201, July, 1949; Vol. 97, Part 1, p. 112, May, 1950; Vol. 97, Part 2, p. 389, June, 1950; *Engineer*, Vol. 187, p. 165, Feb. 11, 1949.
4. Richards, B. D.: "Tidal Power: Its Development and Utilization," *Journal of the Institution of Civil Engineers* (London), Vol. 30, p. 104, April, 1948.

G. Water Power and Water Supply

1. Anon.: "Water Problem; Chemical Engineering Report, July, 1949," *Chemical Engineering*, Vol. 56, p. 119, July, 1949.
2. Engineers Joint Council, Water Policy Panel: *National Water Policy—A Statement of Desirable Policy with Respect to the Conservation, Development and Use of the National Water*

Resources, Engineers Joint Council, American Society of Mechanical Engineers, New York, June, 1950.
3. Sayre, A. N.: "Ground Water," *Scientific American*, Vol. 183, p. 14, November, 1950.
4. Stoffel, P. A.: "Water Power and Layout of Industrial Plant in India," Preprint, Sec. H1, Paper No. 7, Fourth World Power Conference, London, 1950.
5. U.S. Geological Survey Information Circular: *Developed and Potential Water Power of the World*, U.S. Department of the Interior, Washington, D.C., 1948.
6. U.S. Geological Survey Information Circular: *Potential Water Power in the United States, 1949*, U.S. Department of the Interior, Washington, D.C., 1949.
7. Waring, G. A., and Meinzer, O. E.: *Bibliography and Index of Publications Relating to Ground Water*, U.S. Government Printing Office, Washington, D.C., 1947.

H. Rain and Rainfall

1. Abbot, C. G.: "Sun and Precipitation," *Journal of the American Water Works Association*, Vol. 40, p. 755, July, 1948.
2. Clawson, M.: "Range Forage Conditions in Relation to Annual Precipitation," *Land Economics*, Vol. 24, p. 264, August, 1948.
3. Fraselle, E.: "Precipitation Cycles," *Science*, Vol. 110, p. 148, Aug. 5, 1949.
4. U.S. Department of Agriculture: *Climate and Man—1941 Yearbook of Agriculture*, U.S. Government Printing Office, Washington, D.C., 1941.

I. Hydroelectric Power

1. Anon.: "Hydroelectric Resources of the Americas," *Engineering News-Record*, Vol. 135, p. 249, Aug. 23, 1945.
2. Anon.: "United States Department of the Interior, Bureau of Reclamation, Program of Power Development, Fiscal Years 1948–1957; Statistical Data by States," *Electrical World* (News ed.), Vol. 130, p. 16, Sept. 4, 1948.
3. DeLuccia, E. R., and Weaver, F. L.: "State of Hydro-electric Power Development in the United States," Preprint, Sec. H1, Paper No. 3, Fourth World Power Conference, London, 1950.
4. Gadkary, S. A., and Thacker, M. S.: "Projected Hydro-electric Power Development in India, and Studies from the Point of View of Economic Planning of Power Transmission and Interconnection of Power Systems in This Development," Preprint, Sec. H1, Paper No. 8, Fourth World Power Conference, London, 1950.
5. Giroux, C. H.: "Present Status of the Proposed Hydroelectric Development of the St. Lawrence River," *Midwest Power Conference Proceedings*, Vol. 9, p. 118, 1946.
6. Greene, B. H.: "Hydroelectric Power in the Missouri Basin," *Midwest Power Conference Proceedings*, Vol. 9, p. 123, 1946.
7. Holden, O.: "Generation of Hydro-electric Power in Canada," Preprint, Sec. H1, Paper No. 1, Fourth World Power Conference, London, 1950.
8. MacColl, E.: "Hydro-electric Developments in the Scottish Highlands," Preprint, Sec. H1, Paper No. 10, Fourth World Power Conference, London, 1950.
9. Woodward, S. M.: "Operation of the Multi-purpose Projects of the T.V.A.," *Midwest Power Conference Proceedings*, Vol. 4, p. 76, 1941.

J. Wind Power

1. Anon.: "Wind-power Studies Suggest Future Commercial Possibilities," *Power*, Vol. 89, p. 360, June, 1945.

2. Kloeffler, R. G., and Sitz, E. L.: "Electric Energy from Winds," *Kansas State College Engineering Experiment Station (Manhattan) Bulletin*, Vol. 52, p. 1, 1946.
3. Nettleton, A.: "Harnessing Britain's Gales; Wind Power Tests in the Orkneys," *Compressed Air Magazine*, Vol. 55, p. 70, March, 1950.
4. Putnam, P. C.: *Power from the Wind*, D. Van Nostrand Company, Inc., New York, 1948.
5. Thomas, P. H.: *Electric Power from the Wind*, Federal Power Commission, March, 1945.
6. Venters, J.: "Orkney Windmill and Wind Power in Scotland," *Engineer*, Vol. 189, p. 106, Jan. 27, 1950; Discussion, Watson, E. A.: *Ibid.*, p. 183, Feb. 10, 1950.
7. Warrilow, W. E.: "Problem of the Wind Dynamo," *Electrician*, Vol. 130, p. 643, June 25, 1943.
8. Wilbur, J. B.: "Smith-Putnam Wind Turbine Project," *Journal of the Boston Society of Civil Engineers*, Vol. 29, p. 211, July, 1942.

K. Volcanic Steam

1. Bodvarsson, G.: "Drilling for Heat in Iceland," *Oil and Gas Journal*, Vol. 48, p. 191, Sept. 22, 1949.
2. Day, A. L.: "Volcanoes, Geysers and Hot Springs," *Journal of the Franklin Institute*, Vol. 226, p. 341, September, 1938.
3. Pennycuick, J. A. C.: "Power without Fuel; Ethyl Chloride and Natural Steam Plants on Island of Ischia in Bay of Naples," *Electrician*, Vol. 140, p. 117, Jan. 9, 1948.
4. Verhoogen, J.: "Volcanic Heat," *American Journal of Science*, Vol. 244, p. 745, November, 1946.

L. Heat Pump

1. Anon.: "Literature of the Heat Pump; Bibliography and Abstracts of Articles Published in American and Foreign Periodicals in Past 25 Years," *Electrical World*, Vol. 122, p. 74, Sept. 30, 1944.
2. Anon.: "Progress Report on Heat Pump Research; Joint A.I.E.C.–E.E.I. Heat Pump Committee," *Edison Electric Institute Bulletin*, Vol. 17, p. 313, August, 1949.
3. Kemler, E. N., *et al.*: "Heat Pump; Past, Present, Future," *Refrigerating Engineering*, Vol. 53, p. 301, April, 1947.
4. Manchester, H.: "Fireless Heat for the Home," *Scientific American*, Vol. 176, p. 197, May, 1947.
5. Oldacre, M. S.: "Problems to be Solved in Applying Heat Pump," *Heating, Piping, and Air Conditioning*, Vol. 20, p. 84, May, 1948.
6. Penrod, E. B., *et al.*: "Earth Heat Pump Research," *Kentucky University Engineering Experiment Station Bulletin*, Vol. 14, p. 1, 1949.
7. Smith, U. G.: "Heat Pumps and Heat Sources," *Electrical West* Vol. 104, p. 70, March, 1950.
8. Thomas, T. F.: "Air Cycle Heat Pump," *Journal and Proceedings of the Institution of Mechanical Engineers* (London), Vol. 158, Proc. 30, June, 1948.

M. Air Engine

1. Anon.: "Compressed Air Used as Major Power Source in Building Conveyors," *Steel*, Vol. 122, p. 80, Jan. 19, 1948.
2. Anon.: "Tiny Jet Engine Builds a Fire," *Westinghouse Engineer*, Vol. 8, p. 82, May, 1948.
3. Anon.: "Berry Lightweight Rotary Air Motor," *Product Engineering*, Vol. 19, p. 98, July, 1948.
4. Engel, L.: "Philips Air Engine," *Scientific American*, Vol. 179, p. 52, July, 1948.

III. UNRENEWABLE SOURCES OF ENERGY

A. Atomic Energy

1. Atomic Energy Commission: *International Bibliography on Atomic Energy, Political, Economic, and Social Aspects*, Vol. 1 (Revised Edition), Atomic Energy Commission Group, United Nations, New York, 1948.
2. Ayres, E., and Thomas, C. A.: "What Are the Prospects for Industrial Nuclear Power?" *Nucleonics*, Vol. 7, p. 72, August, 1950.
3. Cockcroft, J. D.: "The Development and Future of Nuclear Energy," *Bulletin of the Atomic Scientists*, Vol. 6, p. 325, November, 1950.
4. Gustafson, J. K.: "Uranium Resources," *The Scientific Monthly*, Vol. 69, p. 115, August, 1949.
5. Hafstad, L. R.: "Reactor Program of Atomic Energy Commission; Current Status and Problems," *Chemical Engineering Progress*, Vol. 46, p. 109, February, 1950.
6. Hutcheson, J. A.: "Atomic Energy; Engineering Problems in Its Industrial Application," *Westinghouse Engineer*, Vol. 8, p. 37, March, 1948.
7. Kalitinsky, A.: "Atomic Power and Aircraft Propulsion," *Society of Automotive Engineers Quarterly Transactions*, Vol. 3, p. 1, January, 1949.
8. Kramer, A. W.: "Nuclear Power Engineering," *Atomics*, Vol. 6, p. 6, January, 1950; p. 17, March-April, 1950; p. 14, May-June, 1950.
9. Spedding, F. H.: "Chemical Aspects of the Atomic Energy Problem," *Bulletin of the Atomic Scientists*, Vol. 5, p. 48, February, 1949.
10. Sporn, P.: "Prospects in Industrial Application of Atomic Energy," *Bulletin of the Atomic Scientists*, Vol. 6, p. 303, October, 1950.

B. Coal, General

1. Bituminous Coal Institute: *Bituminous Coal Annual—1949 Facts and Figures*, The Bituminous Coal Institute, Washington, D.C., September, 1949.
2. Charles, I. M.: "Coal and Its Future," *Colorado School of Mines (Golden) Quarterly*, Vol. 45, p. 67, April, 1950.
3. Crichton, A. B.: "How Much Coal Do We Really Have? The Need for an Up-to-date Survey," *American Institute of Mechanical Engineers Technical Paper 2428*, 1948.
4. Fieldner, A. C.: *Coal for Coke Production*, U.S. Bureau of Mines Information Circular 7559, March, 1950.
5. Graham, J. P., *et al.*: "Metallurgical Coke (Preparation—Properties—Utilization)," Preprint, Sec. B3, Paper No. 1, Fourth World Power Conference, London, 1950.
6. Hoffert, W. H., and Claxton, G.: "The Recovery of Benzole at Gasworks and at Coke Ovens," Preprint, Sec. C2, Paper No. 6, Fourth World Power Conference, London, 1950.
7. Khan, N. M.: "A Survey of the Coal Resources of Pakistan," Preprint, Sec. A, Paper No. 26, Fourth World Power Conference, London, 1950.
8. McNeil, D.: "The Preparation and Utilization of Fuels from Coal Tar," Preprint, Sec. C2, Paper No. 5, Fourth World Power Conference, London, 1950.
9. Meyer, F. C.: "Preparation of Coals of High Ash Content," Preprint, Sec. B1, Paper No. 8, Fourth World Power Conference, London, 1950.
10. Popovich, B.: "Lignite: Its Processing and Utilization," Preprint, Sec. B2, Paper No. 3, Fourth World Power Conference, London, 1950.
11. Roberts, F. H.: "The Preparation and Utilization of Victorian Brown Coal," Preprint, Sec. B2, Paper No. 1, Fourth World Power Conference, London, 1950.

12. Roga, B.: "On the Improvement of the Quality of Coke in Poland," Preprint, Sec. B3, Paper No. 4, Fourth World Power Conference, London, 1950.
13. Scarlott, C. A.: "The Bright New Future of Coal," *Westinghouse Engineer*, Vol. 7, p. 143, September, 1947.
14. Searight, W. V.: "The Status of Coal Resources Studies," *Economic Geology*, Vol. 45, p. 324, June, 1950.
15. Simek, B. G., and Mejstrik, J.: "The Preparation and Utilization of Low-grade Fuels, I. Preparation and Improvement of Brown Coal and Lignite in Czechoslovakia. II. Utilization of Low-grade Fuels, in Particular Lignite, as a Source of Energy," Preprint, Sec. B2, Paper No. 2, Fourth World Power Conference, London, 1950.
16. Swartzman, E.: "Coal Preparation in Canada," Preprint, Sec. B1, Paper No. 1, Fourth World Power Conference, London, 1950.

C. Coal, Conversion to Liquid Fuels

1. Doherty, J. D.: "Synthetic Oil from Coal," *Colorado School of Mines (Golden) Quarterly*, Vol. 45, p. 77, April, 1950.
2. Fieldner, A. C.: "United States Fuel Reserves; Solid Fuels and Their Suitability for Production of Liquid and Gaseous Fuels," *Oil and Gas Journal*, Vol. 47, p. 138, Mar. 17, 1949.
3. Leonard, B. H., Jr., *et al.*: "Metallurgical and Fabrication Considerations in the Coal-hydrogenation Demonstration-plant Construction," *Transactions of the American Society of Mechanical Engineers*, Vol. 72, p. 379, May, 1950.
4. Lowry, H. H., and Rose, H. J.: *Pott-Broche Coal-extraction Process and Plant of Ruhrol G.m.b.H., Bottrop-Welheim, Germany*, U.S. Bureau of Mines Information Circular 7420, October, 1947.
5. Murphree, E. V., *et al.*: "Applications of the Fluid Solids Technique to Producing Synthetic Liquid Fuels," *Petroleum Processing*, Vol. 3, p. 358, April, 1948.
6. Odell, W. W.: *Gasification of Solid Fuels in Germany by the Lurgi, Winkler, and Leuna Slagging-type Gas Producer Processes*, U.S. Bureau of Mines Report of Investigations 7415, November, 1947.
7. Perry, H., *et al.*: "Continuous Gasification of Pulverized Coal with Oxygen and Steam by the Vortex Principle," *Transactions of the American Society of Mechanical Engineers* Vol. 72, p. 599, July, 1950.

D. Coal, Underground Gasification

1. Beniaminov, N.: "Underground Gasification of Coal in the U.S.S.R.," *Chemistry and Industry*, Vol. 60, p. 164, Mar. 8, 1941.
2. Dowd, J. J., *et al.*: *Experiment in Underground Gasification of Coal, Gorgas, Alabama*, U.S. Bureau of Mines Report of Investigations 4164, August, 1947.
3. Fies, M. H., and Elder, J. L.: "Experiments in Underground Gasification of Coal Continue at Gorgas," *American Gas Journal*, Vol. 173, p. 15, July, 1950.
4. King, J. G.: "World Power Conference; Section D2; Preparation of Gaseous Fuels; Gas from Solid Fuels; Underground Gasification," *Engineer*, Vol. 190, p. 46, July 14, 1950.
5. Lane, J. C., and Weil, B. H.: "Synthine Process; Underground Gasification of Coal," *Petroleum Refiner*, Vol. 25, p. 91, August, 1946.

E. Petroleum, General

1. American Petroleum Institute: *Facts About Oil*, The American Petroleum Institute, New York, 1950.

2. Anon.: "Report on the Long-term Availability of Petroleum," *Proceedings of the American Petroleum Institute*, Vol. 28, Part 1, p. 57, 1948.
3. Ayres, E.: "Chemicals, Their Production and Consumption by the Petroleum Industry," *Petroleum Processing*, Vol. 5, p. 726, July, 1950.
4. Carter, D. V.: "Petroleum Conservation and Conservation Laws," *Colorado School of Mines (Golden) Quarterly*, Vol. 45, p. 45, July, 1950.
5. Crookshank, H.: "The Search for Oil in Pakistan," Preprint, Sec. C1, Paper No. 6, Fourth World Power Conference, London, 1950.
6. Deegan, C. J.: "Reserves Are Up; Annual Joint A.P.I.–A.G.A. Report," *Oil and Gas Journal*, Vol. 48, p. 56, Mar. 16, 1950.
7. Derry, L. D., *et al.*: "Fuels for High-speed Diesel Engines," Preprint, Sec. C2, Paper No. 2, Fourth World Power Conference, London, 1950.
8. Dorsh, J. B.: "Will America Dig for Her Future Oil Supply?" *The Oil Forum*, Vol. 3, p. 377, September, 1949.
9. Eckhardt, E. A.: "World Geophysical Activity in 1948," *Oil and Gas Journal*, Vol. 47, p. 100, Mar. 17, 1949.
10. Egloff, G.: "Strategic Oil Supplies," *Oil and Gas Journal*, Vol. 49, p. 277, Nov. 16, 1950.
11. Fagin, K. M.: "How Economic Factors Govern Reserve Estimates," *Petroleum Engineer*, Vol. 21, p. B20, January, 1949.
12. Fanning, L. M.: *Our Oil Resources*, McGraw-Hill Book Company, Inc., New York, 1950.
13. Kaufmann, G. F.: "Modern Methods in Petroleum Exploration," *Colorado School of Mines (Golden) Quarterly*, Vol. 45, p. 39, January, 1950.
14. Kraus, E.: "Factors Used in the Allocation of Production among Pools and within Pools," *Proceedings of the American Petroleum Institute*, Vol. 28, Part 4, p. 35, 1948.
15. Murphree, E. V.: "Oil for the Future," *Institute of Petroleum Review*, Vol. 3, p. 307, October, 1949.
16. Struth, H. J.: *The Petroleum Data Book*, 2d ed., The Petroleum Engineer Publishing Company, Dallas, 1948.

F. Substitute Fuels, General

1. Ayres, E.: "The Synthine Process—A Composite of Research," *World Petroleum*, Vol. 15, p. 56, October, 1944.
2. Ayres, E., *et al.*: "Some Problems Associated with the Fischer-Tropsch Process," *Petroleum Refiner*, Vol. 27, p. 103, November, 1948.
3. Brown, B. K., and Gunness, R. C.: "Future Fuels, Liquid and Gaseous," *Mechanical Engineering*, Vol. 70, p. 421, May, 1948.
4. Egloff, G.: "Synthetic and Substitute Engine Fuels," *Industry and Power*, Vol. 52, p. 72, May, 1947.
5. Garfias, V. R., and Whetsel, R. V.: "World Production of Petroleum Substitutes," *Transactions of the American Institute of Mining and Metallurgical Engineers*, Technical Publication No. 1274, 1941.
6. Golumbic, N. R.: *Revised Bibliography of Bureau of Mines Investigations on the Production of Liquid Fuels from Oil Shale, Coal, Lignite, and Natural Gas (to 1949)*, U.S. Bureau of Mines Information Circular 7534, September, 1949.
7. Gunness, R. C.: "Future Liquid Fuels," *Chemical and Engineering News*, Vol. 26, p. 2123, July 19, 1948.
8. Lang, W. A.: "Fuel Investigations of the Research Council of Alberta (1919–1940)," *Transactions of the Canadian Institute of Mining and Metallurgy*, Vol. 45, p. 27, 1942.
9. Murphree, E. V., *et. al.*: "Liquid Fuels for Energy Supply," Paper before the American Institute of Chemical Engineers, Tulsa Regional Meeting, May 8–11, 1949.

10. Newman, L. L., *et al.*: "Manufacture of Fuel and Synthesis Gas in the United States," Preprint, Sec. D1, Paper No. 5, Fourth World Power Conference, London, 1950.
11. Osara, N. A.: "Substitution of Liquid Fuels by Other Materials in Finland during the Second World War," Preprint, Sec. C2, Paper No. 7, Fourth World Power Conference, London, 1950.
12. Powell, A. R., *et al.*: "Symposium on Production of Synthesis Gas," *Industrial and Engineering Chemistry*, Vol. 40, p. 558, April, 1948.
13. Russell, R. P.: "Fuels of the Future; Liquid Fuels in Improved Forms, Obtained from Crude Oil and Synthesized from Coal, Vegetable Matter, etc.," *Scientific American*, Vol. 177, p. 162, October, 1947.
14. Schroeder, W. C., and Fieldner, A. C.: "Synthetic Liquid Fuels," Preprint, Sec. C2, Paper No. 1, Fourth World Power Conference, London, 1950.
15. Solliday, A. L.: "Myth of Cheap Synthetic Oil Production," *The Oil Forum*, Vol. 4, p. 219, June, 1950.
16. Storch, H. H.: "Review of Development of Processes for Synthesis of Liquid Fuels by Hydrogenation of Carbon Monoxide," *Chemical Engineering Progress*, Vol. 44, p. 469, June, 1948.
17. Weil, B. H., and Lane, J. C.: *Synthetic Petroleum from the Synthine Process*, Remsen Press Division, Chemical Publishing Company, Inc., New York, 1948.
18. Wiley, J. L., and Anderson, H. C.: *Synthetic Liquid Fuels Abstracts* (New series, issued bimonthly), Vols. 1–3, U.S. Bureau of Mines, Pittsburgh, 1948–1950.

G. Natural and Manufactured Gas

1. American Gas Association, Bureau of Statistics: *Gas Facts—1948*, The American Gas Association, New York, 1949.
2. Baumel, J. K.: "Results of Conservation of Natural Gas in Texas," *Petroleum Processing*, Vol. 5, p. 871, August, 1950.
3. Dashiell, P. T.: "New Gas-production Processes; High B.t.u. Oil Gas and Catalytic Cracking Processes; Natural Gas Used," *Gas Age*, Vol. 105, p. 29, Apr. 13, 1950.
4. Falck, E.: "N.R.S.B. Estimates Total Gas Industry Supply and Requirements 1948–1952," Parts I and II, *Gas Age*, Vol. 103, p. 17, Mar. 17, 1949; p. 27, Mar. 31, 1949.
5. Gruy, H. J., and Critchton, J. A.: "Methods Used in the Estimation of Natural Gas Reserves," *Petroleum Engineer*, Vol. 20, p. 208, October, 1948.
6. Riesz, C. H., *et al.*: "Catalytic Reforming of Hydrocarbons (for Manufacturing Gas)," *American Gas Association Monthly*, Vol. 30, p. 17, 1948.
7. Smith, G. H.: "Transportation, Storage, and Peak Load Supply of Natural Gas," Preprint, Sec. D1, Paper No. 1, Fourth World Power Conference, London, 1950.

H. Natural Gas, Conversion to Liquid Fuels

1. Alden, R. C., and Clark, A.: "Liquid Fuels from Natural Gas," *Oil and Gas Journal*, Vol. 47, p. 111, Oct. 14, 1948.
2. Keith, P. C.: "The New Hydrocol Process," *National Petroleum News*, Vol. 38, Sec. 2, p. R506, July 3, 1946.
3. Roberts, G., Jr.: "Synthetic Liquid Fuels and Chemicals from Natural Gas," *Petroleum Processing*, Vol. 2, p. 905, December, 1947.
4. Ryan, P.: "The Synthol Process," *Oil and Gas Journal*, Vol. 43, p. 264, Mar. 31, 1945.

I. Oil Shale and Shale Oil

1. Anon.: *Synthetic Liquid Fuels; 1949 Annual Report of the Secretary of the Interior. Part II. Oil from Oil Shale*, U.S. Bureau of Mines Report of Investigations 4652, February, 1950.

2. Belser, C.: "Oil Shale Resources of Colorado, Utah, and Wyoming," *Petroleum Technology*, Vol. 11, p. TP 2358, May, 1948.
3. Blanding, F. H., and Roetheli, B. E.: "Retorting Oil Shale by the Fluidized Solids Technique," *Oil and Gas Journal*, Vol. 45, p. 84, Feb. 15, 1947.
4. Cadman, W. H.: "Oil Shale Deposits of the World and Recent Developments in Their Exploitation and Utilization, Reviewed to May, 1947," *Journal of the Institute of Petroleum*, Vol. 34, p. 109, February, 1948.
5. Gunness, R. C.: "Shale Oil: Fact versus Fancy," *Chemical Processing*, Vol. 13, p. 4, August, 1950.
6. Johansson, A., and Hedback, T. J.: "Recent Possibilities for Development by Means of Modern Retorts for Oil Shale and Modern Boilers for Shale Coke," Preprint, Sec. C2, Paper No. 4, Fourth World Power Conference, London, 1950.
7. Klosky, S.: "An Index of Oil-shale Patents," *U.S. Bureau of Mines Bulletin, 468*, 1949.
8. McAllister, S. H.: "Shale Oil as a Future Source of Energy in Western States," *Petroleum Processing*, Vol. 5, p. 1076, October, 1950.
9. Odell, W. W., and Baldeschwieler, E. L.: *European Shale-treating Practice*, U.S. Bureau of Mines Information Circular 7348, May, 1946.
10. Stelling, A. R., and Robertson, G. G.: "The Occurrence and Exploitation of Oil Shales in South Africa," Preprint, Sec. C2, Paper No. 3, Fourth World Power Conference, London, 1950.

J. Bituminous Sands

1. Adkins, W. E.: "Novel Separation Process Unlocking Canada's Oil Sands," *Chemical Engineering*, Vol. 57, p. 103, March, 1950.
2. Ball, M.W.: "Development of the Athabaska Oil Sands," *Transactions of the Canadian Institute of Mining and Metallurgy*, Vol. 44, p. 59, 1941.
3. Barb, C. F., and Ball, J. O.: "Hydrocarbons of the Uinta Basin of Utah and Colorado," *Colorado School of Mines (Golden) Quarterly*, Vol. 39, p. 1, January, 1944.
4. Clark, K. A.: "Athabaska Tar Sands," *Scientific American*, Vol. 180, p. 52, May, 1949.
5. Shea, G. B., and Higgins, R. V.: *Laboratory Study of the Hot-water Process for Separating Hydrocarbons from Surface Deposits of Bituminous Sandstones near Edna, California*, U.S. Bureau of Mines Report of Investigations 4246, October, 1948.

INDEX